The Althouse Press
Faculty of Education, The University of Western Ontario/
Environmental Challenges: Learning for Tomorrow's World
Edited by Paul F. Wilkinson and Miriam Wyman

Environmental Challenges: Learning for Tomorrow's World

edited by

PAUL F. WILKINSON
York University

and

MIRIAM WYMAN
York University

THE ALTHOUSE PRESS
London, Ontario, Canada

Published by The Althouse Press, Faculty of Education
The University of Western Ontario, 1137 Western Road,
London, Ontario, Canada N6G 1G7

Copyright © 1986 by The University of Western Ontario, London, Ontario,
Canada, No part of this publication may be reproduced, stored in a retrieval
system, or transmitted in any form or by any means, electronic, photocopy-
ing, mechanical or otherwise, without the prior permission of the publishers.

First Printing: February 1986

Editorial Assistants: K. Grebenc, J. Murray, B. Nelson, and D. Webber

Cover Design: Bothwell Graphics

Canadian Cataloguing in Publication Data

Main entry under titles:
Environmental challenges: learning for tomorrow's world

Some of the papers presented at the Man-Environment
Impact Conference, held in Hamilton, Ont., Oct. 20-23, 1982.
ISBN 0-920354-15-7

1. Environmental education - Congresses. 2. Human ecology -
Study and teaching - Congresses. I. Wilkinson, Paul F.,
1948 -   II. Wyman, Miriam. III. Man-Environment Impact
Conference (1982: Hamilton, Ont.)

TD172.5.E52 1986 363.7'007 C85-099899-9

Printed and bound in Canada by The Aylmer Express Limited,
17-23 King Street, Aylmer, Ontario, Canada N5H 1Z9

Contents

Foreword

The idea of a Man-Environment Impact Conference was originally conceived some years ago by four professional teacher organizations involved in the improvement of programmes in environmental education and in the professional development of educators, the Science Teachers' Association of Ontario (STAO), Ontario Association for Geographic and Environmental Education (OAGEE), Environmental Science Teachers' Association of Ontario (ESTAO) and the Council of Outdoor Educators of Ontario (COEO), who later invited the Ontario Horticulture Teachers' Association to join them. These groups envisaged a jointly sponsored educational conference to assist in the development of environmental awareness by fostering the teaching and learning of positive environmental attitudes. Their planning led to the first—very successful—Man-Environment Impact Conference, held in Toronto in November, 1976.

Having found that conferences are an important way to heighten the awareness of educators and stimulate a desire to improve their programmes, the four original sponsoring associations decided to hold another Man-Environment Impact Conference in the fall of 1982. The conference theme "Learning For Tomorrow's World" was chosen to indicate what was seen to be a significant direction for educators in the next decade.

The conference was conceived, from the outset, as an international conference on education and the environment which would bring together participants from around the world so that they might contribute to each other's professional development in matters relating to education and the environment. It was hoped that through such sharing, educators could improve their programmes and better prepare our youth to cope with the problems they will face.

The participants were drawn from all levels of education and from the many government and non-government organizations from around the world which share a concern for the human environment, as well as from the general public, including the school-age population. To meet the needs of all the delegates who attended, the programme was planned with a clearly defined objective. The goal was a conference with related events which would:

1. contribute to the quality of environmental education throughout Ontario, across Canada and around the world;
2. enhance environmental awareness and globally increase our understanding of one another's problems through a wide variety of conference sessions provided at all levels;
3. improve liaison among all groups concerned with the environment.

A three-component programme was developed to maintain an environmental focus and at the same time meet the varied needs of the delegates in both a disciplinary and an interdisciplinary sense. The International Environmental Education Leadership Forum attracted 100 delegates from countries around the world. The Educators' Conference with the keynote address by Richard

Underwood, plenary sessions by Albert Baez, Joseph MacInnis, David Suzuki and Captain Jacques-Yves Cousteau, and more than 200 concurrent sessions including 34 featured speakers offered all delegates an interesting and varied programme from which to choose. The Cousteau Society Festival held on the final day was open to the public. A giant step was taken during the conference toward establishing strong international relationships among environmentalists and environmental educators.

The papers that appear in this book constitute only a small proportion of the total number presented. They are, nonetheless, broadly representative of the variety of topics discussed and the background and experience of the people who attended. It is my expectation that this book, based on the conference programme, will not only provide useful information concerning the environment and environmental education to all interested persons but also provide contacts in the field which will facilitate the dissemination of information and result in an improved communication network around the world.

H. Dene Webber
Conference Chairperson

Preface

What is environmental education? What does it do? Where does it happen? Why do we need it? These are some of the questions addressed in this book. The papers presented here have been selected from the many presentations made at the 1982 Man-Environment Impact Conference held in Hamilton, Ontario, the theme of which was "Learning for Tomorrow's World." The conference was a major and influential educational event. It began with an International Symposium which drew environmental educators from 28 countries around the world. The Educators' Conference was a four-day symposium presenting hundreds of seminars, lectures, demonstrations and films directed toward educating educators in order that they might better understand (and thus be better able to convey to their students) the current environmental situation around the world. The last day was devoted to the Cousteau Society Festival, a one-day event open to the public featuring Captain Jacques-Yves Cousteau and numerous displays, music and workshops—all on environmental themes. The conference drew more than 2000 people and may well have been the largest environmental event of the 1980s.

Throughout human history, people have been expressing concern about the impact of human activities on the environment. However, most formal programs of environmental education are very recent; many trace their history to either the United Nations Conference on the Human Environment in Stockholm (1972) or the International Conference on Environmental Education in Tbilisi, Georgia (USSR) in 1977. The wide range of environmental concerns that is so apparent today—pollution, environmental health, energy, deforestation, acid rain, population, food, etc.—provides overwhelming evidence that this last part of the twentieth century is a crucial period in history for all countries, both developed and developing. It is also clear that every country has much to offer to and much to learn from every other. People throughout the world have become increasingly conscious of the enormous impact of technology on human as well as natural systems—its many benefits may well not be balanced by its many problems. People are increasingly concerned about the well-being of both human and non-human environments—the former cannot exist without the latter. If we are very careful and very wise (and very lucky!), we can create opportunities to choose the best and reject the worst that contemporary civilizations offer.

The term "environment" has been used to mean so many different things that we no longer know what it is or is not—and in coming to mean everything, there is a danger that it may actually mean nothing. A number of substitutes have been suggested. "Context" rightly indicates that environment is not a piece of our lives, or even a backdrop for human events, but rather the entire complex of social, cultural, and bio-physical features that characterize a people or a region or a nation. *Umwelt* is a German word loosely translated as "surround" which also attempts to convey the totality of the world in which we and all other living and non-living things co-exist; "lifeworld" is a term derived from phenomenology, a twentieth-century philosophic tradition (European in origin though increasingly prominent in North America) that also intends to convey the complexity of living as well as the interconnectedness of humans and other occupants of this world. However, the term "environment" has become deeply entrenched in our vocabulary and we are likely to continue to use it. Therefore, it is important for each of us to remember both how much and how little the word means and how essential it is to convey just what we mean when we use it. For the purposes of this book, "environment" refers to all of the interacting factors and circumstances that surround, influence, and direct the growth and behaviour of individual beings, groups, species, and communities. Environments evolve and change; what does not change is interconnectedness.

The same confusion might justifiably describe the word "education." Education is a life-long learning process, which occurs in formal, non-formal, and informal settings. School is only one of many places where learning takes place, and often the relative importance of school is over-emphasized. Even within the formal school system, in addition to whatever "environmental" curricula there may be, there are countless tacit agendas which have posed, and continue to pose, environmental problems. Many people, however, believe that the most powerful and lasting education has little to do with formal institutions, but has much more to do with experience: direct contact with and understanding of those environments in which we are so enmeshed.

Learning about environments is a life-long process; it occurs at home, at school, at work, in fields, in forests, in cities, towns and villages—wherever people live. It is our hope that the papers in this volume represent many views of environment and many perspectives on education. The educational models presented here attest to the creativity, flexibility, concern, and practicality of their founders, directors, and staff. On the basis of these models, environmental education programs can be adapted, created and offered in virtually any situation in any part of the world.

The environmental problems described here are not abstract or beyond the understanding of lay people; they are concrete problems and affect each of us every day. No universal solutions are proposed; indeed, one of the few things we have truly learned is that such solutions do not exist. Whatever there is to be done to solve environmental problems will depend on the particular and total situation; in ecological terms, both the problems and their solutions are site-specific. The roots of the problem, however, are more abstract, deep and complex. They are based on long-standing, unquestioned attitudes toward the non-human environment that are difficult to unravel and even more difficult to change. There is a critical need for constant work at problem definition and analysis alongside widespread development and evaluation of plans of action. Given the massive and widespread nature of the problems, and the frustration that inevitably comes with knowing how much time, effort, and commitment are required to even begin to redress them, it is painfully difficult to hold on to the necessary understanding that change is incremental and relies on individuals—whether they be local farmers, kids doing field studies or powerful decision makers.

There has literally been an explosion of interest around the world in environmental education. The excitement in the air at the Man-Environment Impact Conference 1982 was palpable, and none of us wanted to lose it. This volume is a reflection of that ongoing excitement. It does not represent the "proceedings" of the conference, but rather a careful selection of the most significant of the 170 papers which were submitted to us for consideration. The range of topics is broad and was designed to reflect the diversity of environmental concerns and approaches to environmental problems that was so evident at the conference. Similarly, the nationalities, disciplines, professions, and politics of the authors reflect the diversity and complexity of the issues involved.

The papers focus on two basic themes. First, they deal with a variety of current environmental issues that should be of concern to both educators and the general public, both in Canada and other parts of the world. Second, they explore a variety of formal and informal educational approaches which are being used throughout the world to teach people about these issues and about possible ways of addressing present and future environmental problems.

A note on language is in order. It was of some concern to us that this conference was called *Man*-Environment Impact. Many of the papers presented here, as well, used "man" to refer to all people. It can be argued, especially in the light of current eco-feminist literature, that environmental problems are indeed "man's" creations—man's alone; women would never have allowed such things to happen. These cogent and credible arguments deserve our attention, if only to highlight how limited our perspective on the ways of the world has been. In spite of some inclination to place the problems of accumulated human impact on the world squarely with the men to whom they probably belong, we have chosen to take a more generous interpretation—that "man" was in fact intended to represent all people. Thus, the language of all the submissions has been adjusted accordingly.

Finally, we would like to extend our thanks to a large number of people who were instrumental in the development of this volume: Dene Webber and Craig Copland of the Conference Committee; the 170 conference participants who submitted papers; Helen Gross for her word-processing skills; and Melanie, Chris, Doh, Jessica, Jonathan, Jennifer, and Roel for their patience throughout this somewhat lengthy process.

Paul Wilkinson
Miriam Wyman
York University

Part 1:

An Environmental Dilemma

This Part addresses an environmental dilemma: humans are part of the global ecosystem and yet that system cannot continue to support many of the common characteristics of human society—economic development, resource exploitation, population growth, increased economic consumption—without the threat of serious and irreversible environmental disruption. While this dilemma could be illustrated by many examples, the papers in this Part present three very different types of environmental problems. Ehrlich, an internationally-known biologist, explores the impact of the extinction of various species of flora and fauna on natural systems and on humans and presents an array of arguments as to why humans should try to prevent such extinctions. Building on his many years of oceanographic research and public media presentations, Cousteau describes the potentially disastrous implications of economic development in the Amazon Basin, the world's last great "undeveloped" area, and the impact of the disruption of the world's largest freshwater system on the oceans. Finally, Lappé (author of *Diet for a Small Planet*) demonstrates the interaction between environmental constraints and political systems which create a continuing pattern of starvation and hunger for large numbers of people throughout the world. These papers illustrate that, because all of the problems are so interconnected, it is impossible to try to solve any one of them without considering the others. In other words, there are no simple solutions, because there are no simple problems.

1
Why We Should Worry About the Extinction of Other Species

Paul R. Ehrlich
Bing Professor of Population Studies
Department of Biological Sciences, Stanford University
Stanford, California

The Effects of Species Extinction—Why Does it Matter?

Charles Darwin did more than make respectable the idea that new species originated from pre-existing ones—he also brought the necessity of extinction to the attention of the world. Before Darwin, the prevailing view was that living things had been created once and for all by God in a sequence of increasing complexity. There was no more room for the disappearance of existing species from the sequence than there was for the appearance of new ones. Darwin, once he had worked out his scheme of evolution by natural selection, recognized the inevitability of extinction: ". . . as new forms are continually and slowly being produced, unless we believe that the number of specific forms goes on perpetually and almost indefinitely increasing, numbers inevitably must become extinct." (*Origin of Species*, first edition, p. 109.)

Ironically, Darwin's view, which is shared by all modern biologists, is now used as an excuse by the ignorant for the wholesale destruction of the products of Darwin's marvelous evolutionary process. For instance, the *New York Times* gave *op. ed.* space to no less an expert than Sam Witchell, a "financial and corporate public relations consultant," to opine that there is no reason to be concerned at the disappearance of species. Witchell stated, in a piece entitled *Give Me the Old-Time Darwin*, "The Darwin people tell us that species come and go, that this is nature's way of experimenting with life. The successful experiments survive for a time; the failures disappear to no one's detriment."

There unfortunately is part of the "Darwin people's" story that Witchell and his ilk seem not to have heard: that in recent times the "going" of species has been accelerating at an alarming rate, while if anything, the "coming" has slowed down. Witchell is like a man watching water spurting through an ever-widening crack in the face of a giant dam, who says to the folks downstream, "Don't worry—water has always come over the spillway anyway."

It is difficult to estimate the magnitude of the rate problem, but it appears that between 1600 and 1975, the rate of extinction of species of birds and mammals was on the order of five to 50 times the average rate for the last 50 million years or so. Of even greater concern is that the rate of extinction for the period

1975-2000 is projected to accelerate to some 40 to 400 times "normal." By the end of the century, perhaps 15 to 20% of the world's present complement of species will have been lost, and the rate of extinction will still be accelerating unless firm action is taken to retard it.

Should we be concerned about this loss of organic diversity? After all, as the Witchell-minded are fond of pointing out, the dinosaurs went extinct and "nobody misses them." That statement is incorrect on a number of levels (e.g., they did not all go extinct; some people miss those that did). But the most important point is that dinosaurs are not much mourned because other organisms evolved to replace them. The extinction of most dinosaurs occurred when the mechanism for generating diversity was fully capable of functioning—and function it did, as the existence of ourselves and of some 4000 other species of mammals attests.

Extinctions that are occurring today and that can be expected in the future are likely to have far more serious consequences than those of the distant past. First of all, unless action is taken, contemporary extinctions seem certain to delete a far greater proportion of Earth's biotic diversity than did earlier extinctions. Furthermore, the same human activities that are causing extinctions today are beginning to shut down the process of *allopatric speciation*, by which diversity could be regenerated.

The ranges of organisms are being progressively reduced and environments made increasingly homogeneous. In addition, large mammals are more and more being restricted to reserves and zoos, among which transfers of individuals will be increasingly necessary to reduce the effects of inbreeding and to avoid stochastic extinctions. All of these factors tend to reduce the isolation of populations and the differential selection pressures that are the major mechanisms of speciation. Therefore, entire new groups of organisms are unlikely to evolve as replacements for those lost if Earth's flora and fauna are decimated now.

But what does it matter if no new species evolve to replace those lost? Why should people care if enormous numbers of plants and animals disappear from the planet? There are four basic reasons why everyone should care.

Esthetics

The first two arguments are from esthetics and ethics. They are basically that other species are beautiful and interesting, and have a right to exist. The beauty of many organisms—birds, butterflies, flowers—is widely recognized. But biologists know that many other organisms have great, if unexpected, beauty when examined microscopically—the delicate scaling on the wings of malarial mosquitos, for example. And all organisms have a beauty of intricacy and design. At a meeting I once attended, the great French anthropologist Claude Lévi-Strauss correctly stated that "any species of bug that people spray with insecticides is an irreplaceable marvel, equal to the works of art which we religiously preserve in museums."

Indeed it is sad that in the developed world, where so much effort goes into providing "entertainment" for bored human beings, these attributes are relatively unrecognized. The insects alone can supply precisely the kind of variety and esthetic values that captivate gun nuts; airplane, train and car buffs; stamp collectors; sci-fi and computer freaks; bibliophiles; and so on.

Ethics

But in my view, more important than these human-oriented values of other species are the ethical reasons for not driving our fellow passengers on Spaceship Earth to extinction. David Ehrenfeld put the argument very well in his provocative book, *The Arrogance of Humanism*. He enunciated the "Noah Principle," named after the best-known historical practitioner of conservation. According to the Noah Principle, species and communities should be conserved

> . . . *because they exist and because this existence is itself but the present expression of a continuing historical process of immense antiquity and majesty. Long-standing existence in Nature is deemed to carry with it the unimpeachable right to continued existence.*

This is essentially a religious argument. There is no way to "prove" scientifically that non-human organisms (or for that matter, human organisms) have a right to exist. It is clear, however, that there has been a trend in human cultural evolution to extend rights beyond the boundaries of *Homo sapiens*. A century or so ago, it was permissible for an owner to beat a horse to death. It no longer is. Indeed, compassion for other species has been a major factor in helping to preserve some of them. The whales are an excellent case in point. A grass-roots international movement has greatly reduced the assault on those magnificent mammals, and some human beings have even risked their own lives to protect whales from pirate whalers.

The esthetic-ethical arguments are to me, and to many others, among the strongest for the preservation of Earth's biota. But most people find homocentric arguments more persuasive. The third and fourth arguments are, therefore, focused on the needs of people rather than those of other species.

Economic values

The third argument is that other species should be preserved because they are a potential source of great direct economic benefit to humanity. Few people truly appreciate the enormous bounty our species has already received from nature. For example, a large fraction of the thousands of medicines employed by humanity are derived from the chemicals that plants have evolved to poison herbivores. In 1979 the sales of a single such compound, the anti-cancer agent vincristine (derived from a Madagascar periwinkle plant), amounted to some $35 million worldwide.

Human beings, of course, derive all of their food from other organisms, domesticated or wild. And an enormous array of other products are harvested from the same source: timber, rubber, leather, a wide variety of oils, waxes, furs, spices, fibers, preservatives, and insecticides, to name just a few. The important thing, though, is that great as the bounty from nature has been, it represents a mere scratching of the surface. The benefits that potentially could be extracted from other species are obviously vastly greater than those already gained. For example, according to one estimate, only about 5000 plant species, about 2% of the total, have ever been screened for alkaloids, one medically important group of plant chemicals. Moreover, the screening that has been done has certainly not been adequate to uncover all the potentially useful compounds. It is well known that the presence and composition of plant biochemicals varies from time to time in the same part of the plant, from part to part, from plant to plant, and from population to population in the same species.

To my knowledge, no single plant species has yet been adequately screened for all possible useful biochemicals. The same is true of animals—especially marine species, which seem to have high potential as sources of useful drugs. This is one potent reason for not restricting conservation efforts to the preservation of species, but to include the preservation of the unique populations that make up species of sexually reproducing organisms and the genetic variability within those populations.

Human utilization of plants as food sources has also been surprisingly limited. Only about 150 species of crops have been grown commercially, and only 3000 or so (about 10% of the total plant species) have ever been used as food. Today human nutrition rests on a narrow base of some 20 major crops, of which three species of grasses—rice, wheat, and corn—are by far the most important.

Enough is known about the food potential of plants now commercially grown to make it clear that humanity has a great deal to gain nutritionally by not wiping out plant populations and species. As a single example, the Seri Indians of the west coast of Mexico have long made flour from seeds of one of the 18 species of eel grasses that grow in the sea. Here is a potential crop that would need no fresh water, pesticides, or fertilizers; a crop that might prove an enormous bonanza in many hungry nations.

It is important to note, however, that successfully developing new crops and maintaining established ones both depend on the preservation of genetic variability for plant breeders to work with. For instance, the average useful life of a new cultivated wheat variety in the northwestern United States is about five years. Then rusts adapt to the strain, and a new resistant one must be developed. Without a reservoir of genetic diversity for artificial selection to operate on, such development is impossible.

Especially since the development of high yielding, fertilizer-sensitive crop varieties (HYVs) and their dissemination around the world, the reservoirs of genetic diversity of major crops have been rapidly dwindling. One or two HYVs have replaced hundreds of indigenous strains, greatly constricting the genetic base of such crops as rice and wheat. Furthermore, an additional source of germ plasm for crop maintenance—populations of wild relatives of the cultivated plants—is being exterminated in many parts of the globe.

Therefore, although plant species now supply humanity with much of its food directly (and the remainder indirectly), both the ability to maintain production of current crops and to develop new crops are in jeopardy because of extinctions. Potentially useful species are disappearing, and the loss of genetic variability is lessening the chances of successfully domesticating many others.

The situation with respect to animal food sources is similar. Relatively few animals have been domesticated and some wild ones have high potential for domestication. For example, cultivation of mixed herds of antelope species seems capable of outproducing cattle in certain parts of Africa, while doing much less environmental damage. But, of course, the *sine qua non* of developing such polycultures is the preservation of the antelope species themselves.

The potential for extracting new non-food products from other organisms, especially plants, is also very large. It is possible that certain plants of the family *Euphorbiaceae* might be genetically improved to give a high yield of petroleum-like hydrocarbons. "Gasoline farming" is not out of the question in the future if the appropriate species and populations are preserved.

Thus nature is, in essence, a vast "genetic library" from which humanity has just begun to withdraw useful items. Unhappily, though, all too few people are aware of the existence of the library or of its importance. As a result, *Homo sapiens* is on the verge of burning it down.

Life-Support Services of Ecosystems

Indispensable as are the direct benefits humanity receives from other species, they are only part of the story. Equally important are the indirect benefits supplied through ecosystem services. The ecological systems of Earth, the planet's living organisms interacting with each other and with their physical environment, provide free public-service functions on which civilization depends utterly. These services include maintenance of the quality of the atmosphere, control of the climate, operation of the hydrological cycle, generation and maintenance of soils, disposal of wastes and recycling of nutrients essential to life (including agriculture), control of over 95% of potential crop pests and carriers of disease, provision of food from the sea, and maintenance of the genetic library just discussed.

Breakdowns of these services on a local scale have often been observed. For example, in the Cañete Valley of Peru, farmers sprayed large quantities of DDT and other persistent pesticides beginning in 1948. At first they obtained good control of cotton pests—so good in fact that they increased the spraying. By the mid-1950s the results were utter disaster. Yields dropped well below the levels obtained before spraying had been initiated. Cotton pests quickly became resistant to the pesticides, and, more importantly from our point of view, brand-new insect pests appeared. These insects were "promoted" to pest status because they were less susceptible to the pesticides than were the insect predators that normally controlled them. The killing of those predators disrupted the ecosystem's pest-control function and "released" new plagues.

It is important to remember that populations of other species are vital working components of ecosystems and that they are usually not interchangeable.

The predators that were decimated in the Cañete Valley, if driven to extinction, could not be replaced with just any predator. The replacement predators would have to fit the physical and biological requirements of the niche vacated by the extinct predators, and in most cases a sufficiently close fit would be impossible.

Deforestation provides another example of the consequences of disrupting ecosystem services. Floods occur in river valleys below denuded watersheds; nutrients are lost from soil and the soils themselves are often washed away; and local climates become more severe. In areas of limited rainfall, deforestation may be the first step toward desertification. If deforestation is sufficiently extensive around the world—and it is proceeding rapidly—at least regional, if not global, climate changes are likely to ensue due to changes in the Earth's reflectivity. Deforestation may also contribute to the increasing concentration of carbon dioxide in the atmosphere, and that, too, is sooner or later likely to have profound effects on worldwide climate.

These are but two examples of the consequences to society of disrupting or destroying ecological systems. Because the organisms within an ecosystem are its functioning components, the loss of any population is at least potentially disruptive of that system. In addition, the accelerating disappearance of population after population around the world is indicative of the damage people are inflicting on ecosystems everywhere—damage we inflict at our own peril, since those ecosystems support our lives as well. Thus, it is their role in supplying ecosystem services that I believe provides the most compelling argument against deliberately exterminating *any* population or species that does not present a clear and present danger to *Homo sapiens.*

We can illustrate the argument with a simple analogy. Suppose you are about to board an airliner, and you notice a man on a ladder busily popping rivets out of the wing. Curious, you approach him and ask what he's doing.

"I'm taking these rivets out of the wing," he replies.

"Why?"

"Growthmania Airlines, which owns the plane, sells them for $1.00 each, and I get $.50 from them for each one I pop."

"Are you crazy? The wing will be weakened and sooner or later it'll fall off!"

"Don't worry, there's a lot of redundancy built into the wing—I've popped out a lot of rivets, and nothing has happened yet. Besides, I'm going to ride on this same flight, so you can be sure it's safe."

At this point, you would doubtless return to the terminal, report the man and Growthmania Airlines to the Federal Aviation Administration (FAA), and book a flight on a different airline—hoping the Growthmania aircraft did not encounter any servere turbulence before the FAA grounded it.

The assault that humanity is mounting on Earth's ecosystem is in many ways parallel to popping the rivets out of an airliner's wing. The ecosystems and airliners have built-in redundancy. The precise role of each population in an ecosystem is usually unknown, just as is the precise role of each rivet in an aircraft's wing. Equally, the results of popping a single rivet or deleting a single population cannot be predicted with great precision, especially since future stresses on the system are unpredictable in detail. But what *is* known with precision is the end result of either continuing to pop the rivets or to exterminate populations or species. Both will inevitably lead to a failure: of the wing in the first case; of the ecosystem in the second.

Failure of the ecosystem services would be fully as disastrous for the passengers on Spaceship Earth as the failure of a wing would be for those on an airliner. For instance, it is possible that the destruction of the forests of the Amazon and the rich complex of species they contain could trigger rapid changes in global climatic patterns. Agriculture remains heavily dependent on stable climate, and human beings remain heavily dependent on food. By the end of the century, the destruction of the forest in the Amazon Basin—including the extinction of perhaps a million species—could entrain famines in which a billion human beings perished. And, if our species were very unlucky, the famines might lead to a thermonuclear war, which could extinguish civilization.

At best, humanity is capable of only partially substituting for natural ecosystem services. And many services, such as the climate-regulating function of the Amazon forest and the waste-disposal and nutrient-cycling functions, society could not begin to replace. Even if we knew how, the magnitude of the effort would be beyond our capabilities. Humanity is already paying the price of ecosystem disruption in many parts of the world. The alarming rate of desertification is one clear example. The need to install flood-control works in many areas and to resort to irrigation in others (or, as is often the case, in the *same* areas) is usually the result of deforestation or other ecosystem degradation. And such degradation is virtually always accompanied by losses of populations and species.

The Forces of Extinction

There are two basic ways by which humanity pushes populations and species over the brink of extinction. One is by direct endangering—primarily by overexploitation; harvesting individuals of a population more rapidly than they can reproduce themselves. The other is by indirect endangering through the destruction of habitats.

Overexploitation is a tried-and-true method, dating back at least to Pleistocene times when hunting pressure from human beings helped erase a whole spectrum of large mammal species. The extermination in historic times of the dodo, great auk, passenger pigeon, and most populations of American bison followed the same tradition. Today, direct endangering threatens, among many others, several species of whales and rhinos and numerous populations of wild cats, elephants, reptiles, and cacti. Some endangered species are hunted for food, but most are at risk because of other products: rhino horn (with reputed aphrodisiac properties), ivory, fur, tortoise shell, and so on. A surprising number of species of birds, reptiles, and plants are threatened because their rarity or beauty makes them the target of collectors. And depredations carried out by zoos or in the name of medical research are helping to decimate the already far reduced populations of gorillas, chimpanzees, and other primates.

But serious as this direct endangering of populations and species is, it is a relatively minor cause of extinctions in comparison with the alteration and destruction of habitats—the ecosystems of which species are components. Such indirect endangering has been in the past, and will be in the future, the principal way in which *Homo sapiens* erodes organic diversity.

Habitat Destruction—Paving Over

In urban areas one major source of loss is the paving over or other development of habitat. For the past 20 years, our group has been studying the ecology and population genetics of checkerspot butterflies. The array of populations under investigation is now probably the best-known group of natural populations, and the most intensively studied population is an ecotype that is restricted to "islands" of serpentine grassland in the San Francisco Bay region. Populations of that ecotype are subject to periodic natural extinctions (we have observed several) and eventual recolonization from other islands. Gradually, however, development has been removing islands from the mosaic. In 1979, a crucial colony at Woodside that we had been working with for two decades disappeared under a housing development. Enough islands have now been destroyed that the ecotype as a whole is in danger of extinction.

The destruction of the Woodside checkerspot population is only the latest known butterfly extinction caused by urbanization of the Bay area. As long ago as 1880, the sthenele brown disappeared under the spreading city of San Francisco, and in 1943 the last individual of the Xerces butterfly was taken. Then it, too, went extinct as San Francisco spread over the Xerces' sand-dune habitat. And the San Francisco story is being repeated all over the world as urban areas expand. The butterflies, of course, are only prominent representatives of the multitudes of populations of unsung organisms—inconspicuous plants, small mammals, reptiles, amphibians, and invertebrates—that succumb to urban sprawl and other forms of development (airports, highways, etc.).

Plowing Under

As serious as habitat destruction through urbanization is, it is minor compared to that accompanying the spread of agriculture. Entire ecosystems are converted into stands of one or a few plant species and heroic efforts are made to exclude all herbivores. Other ecosystems are dramatically modified by the introduction of exotic herbivores—cattle, sheep, and especially goats. Since agricultural areas are vastly greater than urban areas, the extinctions caused by agriculture are proportionately greater.

The first victims of agriculture are native plants, which are either plowed under or devoured by grazers. For example, most of the Mediterranean basin is already a "goatscape," long since largely stripped of its native vegetation by deforestation and overgrazing. In the midwestern United States, the few remaining relatively undisturbed native prairie plant communities occupy only tiny threatened enclaves; and, in the overgrazed hills of California's Inner Coast Range east of Oakland, almost all the visible plants are introduced weeds. Indeed, California's flora was so completely changed by the grazing of cattle and by competition from Mediterranean species introduced by the Spanish that botanists are not sure what the original flora really was like. China's native flora was already so reduced by agricultural development 50 years ago that, when famed entomologist Gordon Floyd Ferris searched for scale insects on their native hosts, his labours were virtually confined to temple courtyards where a few stragglers of once-abundant plant species persisted.

When humanity embarked on the agricultural revolution 10 000 years ago, it also embarked upon a slaughter of Earth's natural flora that continues to this day. Undocumented billions of plant populations and numerous plant species have been exterminated. The seriousness of this loss of plant diversity is greatly multiplied because of the foundation position of plants in food chains. Peter H. Raven, Director of the Missouri Botanical Garden and a leading plant scientist, has estimated that, because of the specialized feeding habits of most organisms that attack plants, every plant species that goes extinct takes an average of 10 to 30 species of other organisms with it. As he wrote:

> . . . the diversity of plants is the underlying factor controlling the diversity of other organisms and thus the stability of the world ecosystem. On these grounds alone, the conservation of the plant world is ultimately a matter of survival for the human race. (In J.B. Simmons et al., Conservation of Threatened Plants, Plenum, New York, 1978.)

Agricultural destruction of habitat has also had dramatic effects on larger animals, from the recently discovered Iriomote cat of Japan to many of Africa's spectacular game animals. Indeed, animals that require large unbroken stretches of habitat to maintain their populations are threatened over most of the world by the continuing conversion of natural ecosystems into farms and grazing land.

Activities associated with agriculture, moreover, can lead to extinctions far from the farms themselves. Diversion of water for irrigation always alters and often destroys the aquatic habitats at the source, and the organisms, terrestrial and aquatic, that depend on them.

Poisoning

Pesticides intended for farms often find their way into other habitats and have severe impacts on non-target organisms. Predatory birds are the most famous victims of persistent pesticides, which wiped out peregrine falcons in the eastern United States and were implicated in the decline of the bald eagle. But from the standpoint of ecosystem functioning, the impact of pesticides on predatory insects, pollinators, and soil organisms may well be more significant. Unhappily, the impacts of insecticides on ecosystems have rarely been documented in detail; still less is known of the effects of massive applications of herbicides. But there is little question that both are significant factors in causing extinctions.

Many of the toxic substances implicated in extinctions are not sprayed purposely in the course of agriculture, but are released inadvertently. These include such chemicals as PCBs (which are structurally similar to persistent pesticides of the DDT family), heavy metals, radioactive materials, and many others.

Spewing

Among the most important substances spewed into the environment by industrial civilization are oxides of sulphur and nitrogen. In the atmosphere these are converted into sulphuric and nitric acids—and as a result rains over many parts of North America and Europe are 100 to 1000 times as acid as rains from unpolluted skies.

Acid rains have already destroyed all the fish populations in 300 Adirondack lakes, are helping to destroy the spawning rivers of Atlantic salmon, and have made breeding impossible for spotted salamanders in upper New York State. Their impact on soil organisms (and thus on the nitrogen cycle, among others) and on forest trees are still a matter of dispute, but only the most dedicated Pollyanna would find the prognosis anything but grim. Recently, for example, a German scientist has concluded that acid rains may have already irreversibly doomed Europe's forests.

Mobilizing Energy

Humanity's search for minerals and energy also has wide-ranging deleterious effects on habitats. Strip mining for coal totally destroys large areas, and many mine wastes contain toxins that find their way into bodies of fresh water and kill all or part of the organisms present. Tailings ponds of vast extent are often required by modern mining operations. They destroy the ecosystems where they are sited as thoroughly as would paving them over; and they often have far-flung impacts because of the fugitive dust and water pollution they generate. And strip-mining is possibly the most biologically destructive human activity outside of tropical deforestation. More than 4000 square miles had been strip-mined for coal in the United Stated by 1980, and the natural ecosystems that once occupied those square miles are irretrievably gone. Projected destruction in the Rocky Mountain states under current plans to turn them into an energy colony for the two coasts will dwarf what has already been done in eastern states such as Kentucky.

Oil spills are another inadvertent assault on habitat associated with humanity's attempts to mobilize energy. Their impacts seem to vary a great deal from spill to spill, depending on the kind of oil, physical conditions, and the ecosystem affected. But they are clearly putting pressure on some marine birds such as the South African blackfooted penguin and have deleterious effects on a wide variety of smaller marine organisms, including several of commercial value.

Damming

In the United States, dam building is perhaps the most notorious energy-related activity on the extinction front. This is because two dam projects—both outrageous boondogles—have recently threatened two obscure organisms. One is the relative of the snapdragon, the Furbish Lousewort, populations of which are threatened by the Army Corps of Engineers' Dickey-Lincoln Dam in northern Maine. The other, more famous case was that of the snail darter, an obscure species of fish, the only known population of which was endangered by the Tellico Dam in Tennessee.

The confrontation of the snail darter and the dam is a classic case of pork-barrel politics. The Tellico Dam was acknowledged to be an ill-conceived and destructive project by a long series of governmental reviewers. More was clearly to be gained by not completing it than by completing it—even if its completion would not exterminate the snail darter. Nonetheless, completion of the dam was finally forced through Congress by legislative guile, presumably in order to enrich a few contractors in Tennessee. It is the first known instance of *Bakerism*—the deliberate extermination of another species for economic gain. (The act was named in honour of former senator Howard Baker who holds much of the responsibility for the attempt to assassinate the snail darter. Whether transplanted populations will survive is not known at this writing.)

Tropical Deforestation

The human activity that seems certain to cause by far the greatest number of extinctions in the next few decades is the destruction of tropical rain forests. Rain forests are the greatest reservoir of organic diversity on Earth. Their destruction will impoverish our planet more than the loss of any other habitat type, because perhaps 40% of Earth's species occur in rain forests.

Rain forests are now under an escalating, multipronged attack; they are being destroyed by expansion of farming, lumbering, ranching, and to a lesser extent, cutting for firewood. One major assault comes from farmers attempting to wrest a living from the poor soils of the tropical forests. Exploding populations of these farmers, growing either crops for their own subsistence or cash crops for local or foreign markets, are quickly converting vast tracts from sustainable slash-and-burn rotation patterns to permanently destructive clearing.

More and more, the world is looking toward tropical forests as a source not only of solid lumber but of wood pulp to be used in producing newspapers, books, cartons for Japanese radios and television sets, and the like. Recent technological advances have made it possible to convert the diverse tropical forests to pulp, hardwoods and all. This has greatly escalated the attack on southeast Asia's forests as Japan, hungry for pulp, has turned in that direction to meet its needs. The outlook for those forests and their inhabitants, from the orangutan and the Sumatran rhino on down, is dismal indeed.

In the Western Hemisphere, an important force in the destruction of rain forests is the demand for beef in rich countries. This is causing the conversion of large areas of forests to rangeland for the grazing of cattle. In twelve years ending in 1978, 30 000 square miles of Brazilian Amazonia were cleared to make room for 336 ranches running six million head of cattle. In Central America, the area for rangeland more than doubled between 1950 and 1975, and almost all of the increase was gained by clearing virgin forests.

Transporting

A form of habitat alteration that has already caused many extinctions has been the transporting of organisms. Moving plants and animals from the ecosystem in which they evolved into ecosystems where other plants and animals have no evolutionary experience with them has often had catastrophic effects on the recipient community. These effects have been especially severe on islands, where plants and animals normally have to contend with fewer predators and competitors than do their mainland relatives. When exotic organisms—rats, mongooses, goats, weeds—are introduced to islands, they often make quick work of the native species. Under the impact of exotic organisms, more plants and animals are known to have gone extinct in Hawaii than in all of North America.

Although the most dramatic effects of transporting can be seen on small islands, the impacts of imported organisms are also obvious on larger land masses. The native floras and faunas of New Zealand and Australia have been ravaged by imported plants and herbivores. The beautiful eastern bluebird of North America has gone into serious decline in the past 50 years because of heavy competition for nesting holes from two introduced birds, the starling and the house sparrow. A fungus, the chestnut blight, accidentally imported into the United States from Asia on nursery plants, has virtually exterminated American chestnut trees.

The Total Impact

In this partial recitation of the sources of habitat destruction, each individual assault may seem relatively minor. Import goats here, pave a little there, release some more oxides of sulphur and nitrogen some other place. In a sense, ecosystems are being nickel-and-dimed to death. Each of us constantly contributes to their destruction in the course of our everyday activities—buying food grown in the agricultural system, using energy, purchasing an enormous variety of goods that have diverse environmental impacts tracing all the way back to the extraction of the original resources from which they were created. Just as the seemingly trivial act of throwing a gumwrapper away can, if done by enough individuals, convert a lovely scene into a rubbish-strewn mess, so seemingly minor actions on the part of all human beings can in the aggregate destroy the ecosystems of our planet by eliminating their working parts.

The results of habitat destruction are written in the historic record for those willing to read it. Past civilizations—the farmers of the Tigris and Euphrates valleys, the Khmers, the Mayans, the Greeks, the Romans—all paid the price of being insensitive to the long-term ecological effects of their activities. What is so horrifying now, in the light of past localized ecocatastrophes, is the specter of a global civilization traveling precisely the same route, equipped with destructive tools unimaginable to past civilizations which, in spite of their lack of technological capacity, still managed to ruin their life-support systems thoroughly.

What Can Be Done?

The fundamental solution to the problem of the ongoing impoverishment of Earth's biota is to create a massive system of ecosystem reserves, which must be kept as undisturbed as possible, and to manage the rest of Earth's surface in a manner that makes it relatively hospitable to other organisms. While zoos, botanic gardens and captive-breeding programs may help to save a few prominent organisms for a time, there simply is no substitute for preserving entire ecosystems and abating planet-wide threats such as pesticide pollution and acid rains. Only in that way can a substantial fraction of Earth's original biological diversity be preserved and enabled to continue evolving. And only by preserving entire ecosystems can civilization continue to receive benefits from them—both useful products and essential life-support services.

What needs to be done, then, is perfectly clear: the tactics for conserving Earth's biota can be outlined in a few sentences. The strategy for accomplishing this is quite another matter. It means, of course, mobilizing the resources of society to control human population growth as rapidly as possible, since resources co-opted by *Homo sapiens* in most cases are not available to support other species. It means moving to a sustainable, steady-state economic system with equal alacrity, for it is not just the number of people that generate impacts on ecosystems, it is how the people behave. Thus, facing up to a substantial redistribution of wealth between the rich and poor of the planet will be essential, because the poor cannot be frozen in poverty as the transition to a sustainable society is made. Sharing the wealth is also necessary because many of the biological reserves will have to be established in poor tropical nations, where the principal reservoirs of diversity are.

It will not be easy. The strategy will require a virtual end to further development in rich nations—indeed, in some ways a regression in development, a retreat to *lower levels* of energy use and material throughput (which fortunately can be accomplished with a *rise* in the quality of life). It will also require very different development goals, what I have called "grass-roots development," in poor nations. It means a revolution in the attitudes of most of humanity about our species' relationship with the entire planet, and especially with the other life-forms with which we share it.

But there is an encouraging side of the picture, too; the signs of change are already upon us. Most people now recognize the need to halt population growth quickly. Those who are not yet alerted are mostly unalertable. The smarter economists are starting to look at steady-state economic systems and to appreciate the physical and biological constraints within which the systems must operate. And many people among the "haves" seem to understand that sharing with the "have-nots" is becoming a matter of survival. Whether the job will be done in time is problematical, but at least there is hope that "practical men" can be awakened from their dreamworlds in time to change the lethal course they are now steering for civilization. If they do not awaken, our fellow passengers on Spaceship Earth will be decimated, and the handful of human beings that survive the resultant collapse may, if they are lucky, be able to eke out a livelihood hunting and gathering. For make no mistake about it—the bell that tolls for the snail darter and the mountain gorilla tolls also for *Homo sapiens*.

2
The Amazon Basin:
Our Last Area of Freedom

Capt. Jacques-Yves Cousteau
President, Cousteau Foundation, New York

The Relationship Between the Oceans and Freshwater Systems

Amazonia is a huge area, larger than Europe, that encompasses much of Brazil and part of Venezuela, Colombia, and Peru. It is entirely dependent ecologically on the rivers of the Amazon system. After 52 oceanographic expeditions since 1950 in the Mediterranean Sea, Red Sea, Black Sea, Indian Ocean, the Arctic and Antarctic Oceans, the Atlantic and Pacific Oceans, and the Sea of Cortez which focused mainly on marine biology and occasionally geology, the Cousteau Foundation has come to realize that more emphasis must be given to freshwater systems.

Since 1959, various environmental indicators have alerted us to the decreasing vitality of the sea. It has become clear that the most productive area of the sea—the coastal waters of the continental shelves, the upper or surface layers of the oceans, and the bottoms of the oceans—are also the three most vulnerable zones and those most devastated by the carelessness of land-based human activities. Two of these areas—the continental shelves and the surfaces of the sea—are directly affected by evaporation and rain, on the one hand, and by running waters of teluric (land-based) origin, on the other hand. That is, fresh liquid water (rain, lakes, rivers, groundwater, which amount to only 0.7% of the water supply of Spaceship Earth) plays a crucial role in the tragedy of the sea. Not only is freshwater the fluid of the Earth's thermodynamic machine powered by the Sun, not only is it responsible for the Earth's climate, not only is it responsible for the harvests that feed the world's people, but it is also washing down to Earth the industrial pollutants released in the atmosphere—what is termed "acid rain." Subsequently all this garbage is washed to the sea, which has come to be considered the ultimate sewer system. Rivers that used to fertilize the sea with nutrients—like the breasts of Mother Earth—have been turned into kidneys, soiling the sea with the toxic residues of our over-populated and short-sighted modern world.

Human life is heavily influenced by the sea and by the intricate life systems that thrive in its salty waters, but freshwater is even more important for the very survival of most forms of life on the land and in the air. Freshwater is constantly moving from sea to air, from air to land, and from land to sea. Each gram of seawater turned into vapour extracts 22.7 kilojoules of solar heat from the sea, stowing that energy in the clouds, and releasing it in both beneficial and destructive forms: rains to fertilize the fields, but also hurricanes and storms. The study of the ocean/atmosphere interface, now the subject of intensive study the world over, has to be complemented by the study of two other interfaces: atmosphere/land and freshwater/saltwater. When the freshwater of a river mixes with the saltwater of the oceans, it releases a substantial part of the energy that it has extracted from the sea in the evaporation process. The energy released then is about the same as the energy released by a waterfall almost 200 metres high. Imagine all of the waters of the Amazon falling from an altitude of 200 metres and the amount of energy that would be released. Modern technology can be used today to transfer 25% of this energy directly into electricity. There is at the mouth of most rivers, including the Amazon, a formidable promise of clean, renewable energy that could be partially tapped, with no ecological damage.

We understand now that rivers, born from the ocean and ending in the ocean, are the bloodstream of Planet Earth. Convinced that we cannot obtain a vital understanding of our global water system without carrying out parallel studies of the oceans and the rivers, lakes and polar caps, the Cousteau Foundation has launched, along with oceanographic surveys, expeditions to Lake Titicaca, Lake Tanganyika, the Bering Strait, Antarctica, the Nile River and the St. Lawrence River. The Amazon was always on our list, but it was only in 1982 that we were able to gather the financial resources necessary for the most important and complicated of all freshwater surveys. After the Amazon, we have three other freshwater projects: the Yang Tze in China, the Danube in Europe, and Lake Baikal in Siberia.

The Amazon Expedition

Through our studies of the Amazon Basin, we hope to contribute to the understanding of how its enormous water resource—almost one-quarter of the Earth's freshwater—can be best and most harmoniously exploited. The population pressures on the southern borders of the forests and on the hills of Peru make the development of Amazonia inevitable. In the Brazilian part of Amazonia, there are only seven million people in an area the size of Europe; beyond the southern border of Amazonia, there are almost 120 million Brazilians. This pressure means that it is neither realistic nor possible to keep the vast forests untouched.

We have undertaken an array of naval and airborne expeditions in Brazil, Peru, Colombia, and Venezuela, in cooperation with these countries. The Research Vessel *Calypso*, the headquarters of the expeditions, is well-equipped with the latest electronic instruments and can store many samples for further analysis. Teams of Brazilian and Peruvian scientists are working on board *Calypso* at the moment; all data are donated, without exception, to the countries concerned. We are using a variety of other equipment: speed launches; a hovercraft; a helicopter; a river boat, the *Anaconda*, which drafts only 0.6 metres and is able to go much further up the tributary rivers than the *Calypso*; an amphibious seaplane; a very large inflatable boat; kayaks; and two trucks (one a 16-tonne, six wheel drive truck with a cabin accommodating up to nine people, a two-tonne crane, a 20-tonne winch, an air-conditioned container, two refrigerators, a five kilowatt generator; and the other a revolutionary amphibious truck, with four-wheel drive, capable of 100 km/h on a good road and propelled by hydro-jets on the water where it moves easily at 10-12 km/h).

On the way down the Amazon, we will be concentrating more on the animals of the forest that depend entirely on the water system, and on the local human populations who depend almost entirely on the water system. For example, we have been studying the subsistence methods of various local Indian groups. We have also made recordings of dolphin sounds. We have shot 20 000 metres of film and taken thousands of pictures above and below water. We also visited experimental stations working on aquaculture, reforestation, and monoculture. At the end of *Calypso's* trip downriver, we will study the influence of the Amazon's waters on the Atlantic Ocean.

In addition to the *Calypso* voyage, another expedition in southern Peru, led by my son Jean-Michel, travelled to the very headwaters of the Apurimac River. They started from the Mismi Mountains at 5600 metres, the source of the Amazon. This survey collected a considerable number of water, sediment and plankton samples and has made valuable observations. For example, samples taken at the confluence of the Apurimac, descending from high mountains to Cailloma, and samples taken from a tributary coming from the silver mines of Cailloma show that the mine waters were 100 times more polluted than upstream waters. The Apurimac was very rich in plankton, while the mine waters appeared devoid of all life. Farther down, by the confluence of the Apurimac and Jolloc Rivers, the Apurimac was 10 times more turbid than the Jolloc. The Jolloc was clean and had much aquatic vegetation, arthropods, and fish. The only life detectable in the Apurimac at that point was grey-green scum along the shorelines. Just when the Apurimac had cleaned itself again at the entrance to the canyon area, it received the effluent of another mine and once again became turbid and poor. Such spread of pollution from development serves as a warning for the future. I met recently with the Minister of Energy of Peru; he told me that he was perfectly aware of the problem and that he knew what needed to be done to solve the pollution problem, but that he had neither the money nor the political clout to act accordingly. That indicates the complexity of the problem, a problem that is not, however, limited to the Third World.

We also sent an expedition to the Planalto in the southern part of the Amazon Basin in Mato Grosso, consisting of two trucks and a jeep travelling from Manaus on a 4800-kilometre expedition. We are trying to examine the area south of Cuiaba where the very source of the Tapajos River, a tributary of the Amazon, connects underground with the high waters of the Parana Basin. The fish in the two rivers are exactly the same, which suggests that the rivers must join underground. Another independent expedition was sent on the riverboat *Anaconda* to the Pacaya Park, which Peru has recently declared a two-million hectare wildlife reserve. This area is now protected from any human activity—except oil exploration. Indeed, oil drilling has already begun there.

In 1983, other expeditions will be sent to Colombia and Venezuela. There are obvious limitations to these flying expedition teams, but they had succeeded in gathering an important amount of data that, after careful analysis, will extend the picture of the water quality of the Amazon based on *Calypso* measurements.

Results From the Expeditions

It is obviously presumptuous to draw any final conclusions at this stage in our research. Preliminary results, however, are as follows:

1. The chlorophyll content of the Amazon River and of its tributaries is roughly equivalent to the levels found on the continental shelf 5-50 km offshore the southeast United States.
2. Both the Amazon and its tributaries were found to be well-mixed, both vertically and horizontally from surface to bottom.
3. The photic zone—the zone in which all primary production takes place and which is defined as the zone illuminated by at least 1% of the surface light—is extremely shallow, typically less than 1-1.5 m. In other words, 99% of the light striking the surface of the water is either reflected or absorbed in the 1-1.5 metres of the water column. This is in contrast to the oceanic photic zone, which varies from 50-100 m in depth. Light is obviously blocked and scattered by the heavy load of sediments in the "white waters" (the white waters of the Amazon and many of its tributaries are in fact not white, but chocolate) and absorbed by the humic acid in the "black waters," which are not black, but red.
4. The low light levels combined with the high rate of mixing in the horizontal and vertical axes present the phytoplankton with an interesting physiological problem related to light penetration. This plankton, which needs light to develop through photosynthesis, may be likened to a diver using a snorkel. The turbulence brings phytoplankton briefly to the surface, where it has the opportunity to grab a breath of light; then it is rapidly mixed downwards into the dark waters, and periodically brought back to moments of photosynthesis.
5. The lack of sunlight has also resulted in the development of highly-developed acoustic behaviour in fishes and dolphins. The river dolphins proliferate in the Amazon by the millions, even in the shallow waters of the tributaries. Hydrophone recordings reveal an acoustic environment not unlike a forest filled with sound-producing insects and birds. It is an underwater cacophony. We were able to hear and record the noise of a fish grabbing a nut and cracking it in its powerful jaws. Other fish made sounds which became more and more rapid as we heard the whistles of approaching dolphins. The message was clear; the fish were frightened by the approach of dolphins and rightly so, because dolphins eat a lot of fish.

6. The extraordinary proliferation of fish life wherever the rivers have not been overfished or polluted is incompatible with the low level of primary production for the phytoplankton and clearly demonstrates that organic materials are being drained from the forests to the rivers. The forest feeds the river and the river, when it floods, feeds the land in return. In effect, photosynthesis occurs above water level in the trees to feed aquatic creatures; that is a very, very striking feature of the Amazon.

7. Because algal blooms occur on the black side of the white-black confluence of rivers, fish, dolphins, and fishermen abound in those areas and major towns have been built there for obvious reasons. Obviously, humans are following the same pattern as animals.

8. The Amazon and its tributaries are acidic from Belem to Letecia, but are increasingly alkaline above Letecia, all the way to the Maranon River.

These results lead to a very important conclusion which is directly related to the implications of economic development of Amazonia. The more time we spend in this fascinating Amazonian world, the more we come to compare the forest to a land-based coral reef. The complexity of both is comparable. Both forest and coral reef are fed by surrounding waters; both at the same time feed the surrounding waters. Both are astonishingly fragile; both are difficult to exploit. Scientists of the stature of Howard Odum and Carl Jordan emphasize these difficulties; they have, however, proposed solutions to the potential negative environmental impact of development, which are based on a perfected understanding of the complex systems involved. Many of their recommendations have striking similarities with methods used for 6000 years by local Indians, for example, a 15-year rotating agricultural system. The problem is that if we want both to keep the forest and to exploit it we will have to simplify the forest ecosystem to some extent. It has been commonplace to say that the more complex an ecosystem is, the more stable it is. The comparison is frequently made with a pyramid: the wider the base, the more stable it is, while the narrower the base, the more fragile it is. However, the stability theory has recently been questioned. Ramon Margolef has advanced the view that many relatively simple ecosystems have proven less vulnerable than other more complex communities; the ESS (ecologically stable systems) theory calls for more important factors than complexity. Unfortunately, once long-lasting methods of rational exploitation are defined (if they can be defined at all), the real problem is in implementing them. The settlers are often a wild, uneducated crowd, eager for short-sighted benefits. How can we tame them?

There is, however, another more important aspect of Amazonian development. If we can accept a certain simplification in exploited areas, how can we ensure that not one single species of plant, insect, animal, or fish would be completely eradicated? We must study in depth all threatened species, for we have even less knowledge than the Indians of how useful to mankind the most insignificant species could prove to be in future years or centuries. We have no right to take those options away from future generations. This means that all exploitation schemes must include the creation of immense and wisely-chosen wilderness reserves. In fact, the only way that such areas can be effective is to be large enough, to be characteristic of each ecological area, and to be off-limits to all humans, including oil companies. A working group in the Foundation is busy defining a new doctrine—"Ecotech"—whereby teams of economists, ecologists, and technicians will cooperate in combining scientific, social, and political inputs along with their own specialties in attempts to outline the most efficient, the least destructive, and the most far-sighted solutions to the development problems that the global community must solve urgently. It is an ambitious task. The elaboration of an Ecotech doctrine concerning the extremely complex Amazonia is a formidable and fascinating challenge. We would like to implement in a few universities throughout the world "Chairs of Ecotech." Such chairs would have three professors—one ecologist, one economist, and one technician—working and teaching together about the rational exploitation of areas such as the Amazon.

Conclusion

Our general recommendation when we have finished the Amazon project will almost certainly be rational exploitation combined with radically-protected wilderness areas. The Nile River of antiquity is now a catastrophe. The Danube and the St. Lawrence Rivers of modern industrial areas have been irretrievably damaged. The Amazon—still practically untouched—is the river of the future and its future is at our mercy.

This detailed description of the Amazon has been necessary because it is the most striking example of our last area of freedom. There we can do good or evil at will. If we let the short-sighted decisions of eager governments or industries take place, this area will be destroyed. If we accept that it has to be exploited to a certain degree, with precautions that can save its essentials, then we will have served the future of humankind. It is not, however, through advancing total preservation that we will save it. It is too big, it is too tempting, and it is being submitted to too much pressure to be left intact. It would be unrealistic to hope for that. So, we as educators have a very delicate task to transmit to future generations sound ideas about realistic protection of the environment. Progress can either be inspired by short-sighted profit or it can be organized in a long-range program of rational exploitation. There is obviously a need for progress, especially in the Third World. People have to eat and they have to have a minimum of comfort in order to develop their minds; the Third World has not yet reached that level. The responsibility of the developed countries is enormous.

It is difficult for us—we who have destroyed the planet—to teach our children not to do the same. We have given them a bad example. How we are going to explain this to them is up to each of you. It will be very, very difficult.

3
World Hunger and Personal Power

Frances Moore Lappé

Co-Founder, Institute for Food and Development Policy, San Francisco

Introduction

I would like to begin by going back 20 years and describing how my life came to be focused on the issue of world hunger.

I often describe myself as a classic child of the 1960s. I graduated from a small Midwestern American college during the height of the anguish over the war in Vietnam. As many of us were, I was a very desperate young person. I felt we had to transform our country very fundamentally and rapidly or all would be lost. With this sense of terrible urgency, I did what people like Tom Hayden suggested—I went to work in the ghettoes where I felt people were suffering the most under our current economic structures. I ended up in Philadelphia, working with people on welfare, trying to ensure that they got the help to which they were entitled under the United States' welfare laws.

But instead of becoming *less* desperate, I became *more* desperate because I could not see how what I was doing each day really addressed the root causes of this, so evident, suffering. However, like so many of us, I went on doing what I was doing because I did not know what else to do. I entered a graduate program in California doing the same kind of work—until 1969. It was in that year that I made the most important decision of my life: I vowed to myself that I would not again "change the world" until I understood how my work related to the underlying forces that were creating such suffering.

I was terrified at the prospect of dropping out of school and beginning to explore on my own. I had no identity—no label. I was afraid that people would ask me what I was doing and I would have no answer for them. So I stayed at home a lot, perhaps to avoid such questions, and I began reading on my own. For the first time, I discovered questions generated from inside me, rather than from a professor. Soon, I began to focus on the question of food. I was influenced by books like Paul Ehrlich's *The Population Bomb* and *Famine* and by newspaper headlines suggesting we had reached the Earth's limits to feed people, that nature could no longer provide for humans. I felt that, if I could just understand why people are hungry in the world, I could penetrate the seemingly overwhelming complexity of international, economic, and political structures.

So, I set out to find out how close we were to the Earth's limits to feed people. Then one day, in the agricultural research library at the University of California, I made a discovery that changed my life. I learned that *half* of the harvested acreage in the United States goes to feed livestock, while only a tiny fraction of the nutrients fed into the livestock return to us in the form of meat on our dinner plates. Thus, while the "real experts" were telling us that the Earth's limits to feed people had been reached, I learned that we in fact were living in a world of sufficiency. The economic and political structures—the forces that determined what would happen to that tremendous abundance—were denying the hungry access to food.

This realization, and the ensuing research, led to the book *Diet for a Small Planet*, which was published in 1971. Overnight, I became a media celebrity, appearing on television talk shows throughout North America, stirring the beans and rice and trying to get across my message about the political and economic roots of hunger. That period of my life ended, thank goodness, in 1974. That year I attended the World Food Conference in Rome: the meeting of government and corporate leaders that signified that the world food crisis had truly hit the international "marquee." I attended, thinking I would rub elbows with the real experts on food—obviously the process of demystification of the experts had not ended for me with the writing of *Diet for a Small Planet*.

But something unexpected happened to me. I realized that these global experts—government leaders and corporate executives—were locked into a false diagnosis of the problem of world hunger that I had penetrated in my own modest study. They were saying that hunger can be solved by increased production using the chemicals and seeds and equipment that, of course, they were selling. However, I had learned that a narrow focus on increasing production could actually contribute to greater and greater hunger, because it ignores the issue of who controls the productive resources. I knew that there could be more food and yet more hunger.

Returning home, I had shed critical layers of self doubt. I knew I could not look to the government leaders to solve these great problems. Their narrow training and institutional commitments had locked them into this false diagnosis that is perpetuating and in fact worsening hunger. I realized more fully than ever, therefore, that the answer must lie with the rest of us, those with less vested interest in the status quo. This realization led me back to a renewed commitment to take my own work more seriously than ever before. I undertook a more indepth study which led my colleagues and me to write *Food First: Beyond the Myth of Scarcity*, and to establish an educational centre we call the Institute for Food and Development Policy, nicknamed "Food First".

I sense there is a deep fear blocking people's search for solutions to the problem of hunger—it is the fear that the economic models that we have believed in have failed us and that perhaps there *are* no other alternatives—that there are no answers. I want to address that feeling that our models of capitalism and communism have failed us. How can we acknowledge that failure without despair?

To do so will take tremendous courage. One way to find that courage is to truly internalize the depth of the deprivation that is increasing throughout the world today and, with that understanding, to develop a sense of outrage—an outrage that is not immobilizing, but that is empowering. Since I believe that rage can be a source of great courage, I would like to speak to sources of outrage.

The Facts

The first step in fuelling outrage is to get the facts straight. There are all sorts of false messages. For example, we are told that if we can just get out of this recession, soon everything will be fine; or, as A.W. Clausen, the head of the World Bank has said, that India represents a model of development success. Such messages are intended to lull us back to sleep, to quiet our sense of outrage. Poverty did not begin in the United States with Ronald Reagan; it did not come about as a result of a recession; even in the booming years of the 1950s, more than 20% of our people lived below the poverty line. Our welfare programs have never eliminated poverty. Welfare and food stamp programs do not even bring people to the poverty line. Today, there are 31 million Americans below the poverty line; that is more than the entire population of Central America. One out of every five children and one out of three black people live in poverty today in the United States.

Facts are not enough, however. We must carry with us human images of what it really means to be poor and hungry in order to keep alive the outrage we need to gain the courage we require to risk change. Each of us must have his or her own personal images of the problem. Let me give you one of mine. I was in Los Angeles in May, 1982, talking with the people who operate the local "Hunger Hotline," the service that answers calls from desperate people who are without food. While I was there, a call came in from a daycare teacher who said that she could no longer provide lunches for the children and that their parents could not afford to send lunches with them. At lunchtime, the children were running out into a nearby parking lot and fighting for food out of the garbage cans. This is what it really means to be poor and hungry in Los Angeles, located in a country with the greatest food abundance in the history of the world.

Now let's turn to the deepening crisis of hunger and poverty globally. Today, in both absolute terms and in terms of the percentage of the world's population, hunger is deepening. More and more people go hungry; 3000 calories (12.6 kJ) are produced daily for every man, woman, and child on Earth *just in grains alone*. Why hunger amidst plenty? We have uncovered a consistent pattern: in country after country agriculture has become a growth industry for those who already have equity in the land, have access to credit, indeed have everything needed to make the land produce. But they are a small minority. In 70 countries studied by the World Bank, less than 5% of the land-holders controlled more than three-quarters of the land. As this minority increases its production, it expands its holdings, often at the expense of the small farmer and share cropper. Thus, the numbers of landless people increase faster than the population growth rate. In fact, today in 20 countries in the Third World, 50% or more of the people are effectively landless. As a result of this increasing disenfranchisement, the majority of people are less and less able to make effective demands in the marketplace for the basic food—grains and beans—they need for survival. As a result, those who control the land shift production away from the production of these basic foods towards more lucrative crops which the local elite and foreign consumers will purchase.

In the last 15 years in Central America, it has been estimated that between one-half and three-fourths of the forests have been destroyed to create pasture land for cattle for export, largely to hamburger restaurant chains in North America. More meat is being produced in Central America—three or four times more—than 15 years ago and yet the average meat consumption of Central Americans is declining. Similarly, in India, the Green Revolution's "success" has made it possible to greatly increase production; yet the caloric intake of the lower half of the rural population has declined since the 1960s.

This process of cutting the poor out of control of productive resources and therefore out of consumption is often accelerated by government-to-government aid. Our study of aid to the Philippines for example, has led us to conclude that government-to-government aid is only as good as the recipient government. During the last decade, $3 billion in multi- and bilateral foreign assistance has been granted or loaned to the Marcos government. Yet, during this period, the welfare of the poorer Filipinos has declined so much that the World Health Organization now suggests that the average caloric intake of the Filipinos is among the lowest of any group in Asia. As foreign aid reinforces the power of the dominant groups, the wealthiest 20% of the population has doubled its share of national income. The case of foreign aid to the Philippines teaches that one can not channel support through the powerful and expect to reach the powerless.

The Meaning of Hunger and Poverty

But statistics outlining these critical patterns can still leave us cold, failing to ignite a sense of appropriate outrage. Therefore, I will take you a step further and suggest that we also need a very *personal* understanding of what it means to be hungry and poor in the Third World. There are at least four ways to describe what it means to be hungry and poor, I believe, and many could apply to North America as well as the Third World.

First, being both hungry and poor in the Third World means watching people you love die. When I was in Nicaragua in February, 1982, I talked to a woman who told me she had had five still-births; she had watched six of her children die before the age of five. To her hunger and poverty meant watching her children die.

Second, hunger and poverty in the Third World mean making choices that no one should be forced to make. In Guatemala today, for example, poor families often send their young sons to join the army, even though they know—and we know, according to Amnesty International—that the Guatemalan government killed over 2000 people in the first four months of 1982. Yet, poor Guatemalan peasants have had to send their sons to join the army because it is the only way to earn some income to buy food and keep the other children in the family alive. Being poor and hungry means having to make impossible choices.

Third, hunger and poverty in the Third World means living in humiliation—the feeling that you are to blame for the terrible circumstances of your life. If you walk into a home in the rural Philippines, the first thing you are likely to hear is an apology, expressing a feeling of shame that their home is so primitive.

Fourth, hunger and poverty in the Third World increasingly mean living in fear for your life. When I was in Guatemala in 1977, for example, I met two people who were working with their neighbours to improve agricultural techniques so that they could grow higher yielding corn on the steep slopes to which they had been pushed by the big plantation owners. Two years later, reports from friends in the Guatemalan highlands reached us: of the two people we had met, one had been killed and the other had been forced underground. Their "crime" was teaching their neighbours better agricultural techniques. That, in and of itself, is considered a threat to the powers that be in a country like Guatemala.

These points are my attempt to personalize and internalize what it means to live in hunger and poverty. It is not simply a denial of the creature comforts that we in North America take for granted. It is not simply the hunger pangs that people without enough to eat obviously feel. It is also watching people you love die, making choices you do not want to make, and living in humiliation and in fear.

Rigid Ideological Models as False Gods

I have suggested that these insights can be sources of outrage to give us the courage to let go of the rigid ideological models of development into which we are now locked. I hope that you do not find it offensive if I suggest that we have made capitalism and communism into false gods which we place above our basic democratic values. I am not suggesting, of course, that communism and capitalism have nothing to teach, but that we have made ourselves slaves to them; that is our sin.

Since most readers in North America would be able to strongly critique the communist "religion," I will focus on the capitalist "religion." I will emphasize what I believe are three of the tenets which, if followed dogmatically and blindly, lead to the deprivation and degradation that I have been describing in the area of food resources: the market, private property, and the absolute distinction between the rights of ownership and work.

1. *The Market*

When we make ourselves slaves to the market rather than making of it a useful distribution technique to meet human needs, we become blind to three of its serious pitfalls.

Since the beginning of the 1970s, 60 000 new food items have been introduced into the United States market—items such as reconstituted potato flakes, breakfast bars, and the latest human need: "juice treat," a drink for dogs! The lesson is that the market responds not to need, but to money. This fact is so obvious that it is often overlooked. It is why we have a proliferation of new food items while, at the same time, doctors who are working in ghettoes in the United States estimate that 20% of American children who live below the poverty line suffer from malnutrition and that more than 10% are actually physically stunted by malnutrition. This unspeakable deprivation is the consequence of our being slaves to the market, rather than using the market.

Let me turn to the global picture. When I first started writing *Diet for a Small Planet*, about one-third of the world's grain went to feed livestock; today, the figure has risen to almost one-half. We are told greater grain-fed meat consumption reflects upgrading of the diets of those in the Third World; rather it reflects that a small but growing stratum of better-off people throughout the Third World can afford to make a demand in the market for grain-fed meat while the majority in these countries go without the basic staple grains they need. And two-thirds of American agricultural exports go to feed livestock for this growing but narrow stratum in the Third World. This group acts as a siphon, pulling grain—the basic food of most of the world's people—into the production of livestock. That almost one-half of the world's grain is used to feed livestock is the most dramatic example of what it means to follow the market, slavishly allowing it to determine what happens to our agricultural resources.

Secondly, the market misleads us because it cannot report back the true costs of production. In the United States, the market tells us that our agricultural exports are booming and that this boom is a bonanza for all of us. It tells us that we are exporting over $40 billion in agricultural commodities that then pay for needed oil imports. But what does the market *not* tell us? The market fails to report the actual fuel costs of those agricultural exports. We are not told by the market that for every dollar we earn exporting grain, we must spend 29 cents on energy to produce those exports and this figure is increasing as United States agriculture becomes more energy-intensive. Neither does the market tell us that we are exporting our soil to pay for oil at such a rate that the productivity of American farmland is threatened. Only chemical fertilizers hide the resulting loss of fertility.

Nor does the market tell us about the groundwater—much of which is virtually irretrievable—that we are pulling out of the earth. In a large area of the Midwestern United States, groundwater that is presently supporting the agricultural boom is renewed at such a very slow rate that we should think of it as a fossil resource, now being mined. For example, in much of North Texas today, it is already uneconomical to use groundwater because the water table has dropped so low. We are jeopardizing our long-term food security because the market tells us only that exports are a great bonanza.

Nor does the market report back the *human* costs of production. With the great market expansion for export over the last decade, the production treadmill on which farmers are trapped has sped up. The result is the bankruptcy of many efficient farmers because the market lies to farmers: it tells farmers that the market rewards hard work and good management and greater production, but, in truth, the market *forces* farmers to produce ever greater quantities. As their profit per acre slides, they must grow more and more. The market does not reward production; it rewards only those who can expand. And who are they? The minority who already have considerable equity in their land and access to credit.

We are moving toward a landed aristocracy in the United States. Precisely because of the market's rewarding wealth and size, we are moving toward the type of landed aristocracy that we document as lying at the root of so much needless suffering throughout the Third World. United States Department of Agriculture statistics indicate that over one-half of the food produced today is on farms larger than can be justified on grounds of efficiency. In the United States today, 6000 farmers at the top earn an average of $80 000 per year, while the majority of farmers—if they tried to survive on their farm incomes alone—would be below the poverty line. Clearly, the market does not report back the true human costs in the transformation of ownership, the driving out of agriculture of farm families whose lives and livelihoods depend on it.

An equally dramatic example that demonstrates the painful, human costs of the market is the proliferation of hazardous pesticides throughout the world, again justified on the grounds of feeding the hungry world. In 1981, we published a book, *Circle of Poison*, in which we pointed out that approximately 20% of pesticides exported from the United States were either restricted or hazardous or were totally banned in the United States; yet, these pesticides were being exported at increasing rates to the Third World, where they are not used to help feed hungry people, but are used primarily by the larger landholders who have no concern at all for their workers' safety. In Mexico for example, people bathe in the irrigation ditches receiving runoff from the pesticide-laden fields and wash their babies using the empty pesticide cannisters. I am suggesting that the increasing number of pesticide deaths throughout the world can be directly linked to the slavish notion that where the market leads, we should go. The market leads to the increasing export of goods which are extremely hazardous to the environment even in our own countries of the United States and Canada where people can read warning labels and where government regulations provide some protection—goods totally inappropriate in the Third World where farm workers have no protection. In the Philippines, pesticides have deliberately been used as weapons against workers by plantation owners who have sprayed them to deter them from organizing unions.

Thirdly, if left to its own devices, the market inevitably leads to the concentration of economic power, which I believe is a direct threat to political democracy. In my lifetime, half of all the food manufacturing firms in the United States have been lost. Many of these were efficient economic operations, but they were undercut by those who were somewhat larger and who had more economic power. According to economists, "shared monopolies" now exist in almost every food line, resulting in an estimated $20 billion in overcharges to United States consumers directly related to this concentration of economic power.

Economic power directly threatens our political democracy: Louis Brandeis warned that we can have democracy in the United States or we can have wealth concentrated in a few hands, but we cannot have both. I believe this very firmly, especially when I see that corporations not only break laws that are not in their favour, but also help to make laws that are in their favour. In California, for example, large corporate farming operations have, for most of this century, broken the law requiring that the tax-subsidized water so necessary to California agriculture go only to the small family farmers. Then, after years of lobbying against those trying to enforce the law, in 1982 they were able to so change the law that they are no longer breaking it.

2. Private Property

Now let us turn from the market to the second tenet of the "capitalist religion": private property. In the capitalist religion, it stands above all else—above the meeting of human need and above justice. What is the consequence of making private property an absolute; of following it instead of using the concept to serve human need? According to the World Bank, we have reached the point where 3% of the landholders in 80 countries control almost three-quarters of the land, while increasingly the majority go hungry for want of any land at all. Even in the United States the concentration of land ownership is such that about 5% of landowners control half the land while many would-be farm families cannot afford farmland.

3. Ownership and Work

Finally, the "capitalist religion" dictates that ownership and work shall be separate and distinct and that owners have all the prerogatives of decision-making power. The consequences of this tenet touch every aspect of our lives. I'll mention only one example. In 1981, $50 billion of the United States economy was tied up in corporate mergers and acquisitions, thus diverting needed capital from job creating investments. This enormous lock-up of capital made credit scarce elsewhere—for more housing, more credit for small businesses, etc.—and helped push inflation upward, hurting most Americans.

A Return to Democratic Human Values

The above examination of three central tenets of the "capitalist religion" suggests the inevitable consequences of following them slavishly: the proliferation of nonessentials while people starve, the mining of resources, and the distortion of investment away from needed priorities of the majority. Now, I am not suggesting that we look for a new model, a third model, better than communism or capitalism. Rather, I am calling on us to give up such a false search and to return to our basic human values—which I call "democratic values" but which others may call Judaeo-Christian or other religious values—and then base economic policies and political decisions on how they contribute or do not contribute to those values.

I suggest that democratic values are grounded in the assumption that society's purpose is to protect the right of every individual to fulfill his or her potential. That means first the *right to life and livelihood* which must include the right to work—and the right to be cared for if necessary (because in every society there will be those who cannot care for themselves), as well as the right to health care and education. Second, democratic values must include the right to take on responsibility in the workplace, in our communities, and in the polity in which our communities operate. For how can anyone fulfill their human potential unless allowed to take on responsibility?

Why do I call these democratic values? I use this term because it is only through this understanding of society that democracy can thrive, because unless society defines its purpose as I have defined it, in terms of the ability of each of us to fulfill our potential, then people will be insecure, and I believe that democracy cannot exist in a society where people are insecure. When people are insecure, fear, violence, and depression spread; as a result, people do not want democracy, they want fascism. Insecurity is increasing in the United States and Canada, because more and more people cannot afford even to meet their basic food needs. In the United States, for example, it is possible to work full-time at the minimum wage and still go hungry if you have a family to care for.

What would it mean to start with our democratic values and then look critically at the above-mentioned three tenets of the capitalist model? Let us look at the market, private property, and the separation of ownership and work.

First is the market. Do we have to be a slave to it or can we tame it to serve our democratic values? Our Institute has examined the process of agrarian reform in Nicaragua over the last three years and learned that the Nicaraguans are attempting not to follow slavishly any foreign model. (Fidel Castro, for example, told them not to follow the Cuban model which tried to do away with the market.) The Nicaraguan government has attempted not to do away with the market, but to tame it in order to protect the most vulnerable. It has opened government food outlets in the poorest barrios, not because it wants to drive out the private food sellers, but because its goal is to keep the private system honest.

In every underdeveloped country there are periodic shortages, even when no absolute scarcity exists, due to inadequate transportation and hoarding. Those who control the food often gouge their neighbours in such times. Such hoarding and speculation in food prices is what creates famine, not absolute scarcity. Therefore, the government of Nicaragua, rather than doing away with the market, intervenes on behalf of the poor and keeps prices down even in times of shortage through their government outlets. Another example is health. Because it is basic to life itself, health care has been taken out of the marketplace in virtually every Western industrial country; we have not yet made that step in the United States.

Second is private property. The idea of private property is quite important to the concept of security and yet, if followed blindly, it undercuts the security of a majority of people, as for example, the ownership of land becomes increasingly concentrated. What is the alternative? Is it possible to protect the right to private property yet prevent the concentration of economic power? Sweden has a very simple rule in the transfer of farmland: you have to be a farmer to own farmland. In the United States today, by contrast, almost half of the farmland is controlled by people who do not directly work it themselves. Sweden, also a capitalist country, has avoided the wild speculation in land that has occurred in the United States. Is it possible to protect the right to private property yet attach to it an obligation to serve the needs of society? Nicaragua is attempting this path. It has decided to protect the right of private property; its moderate and flexible agrarian reform process places no ceiling on the amount of land anyone can own. But the law says that if a land owner is not using the land productively the government will redistribute it to those who need it.

Third is the separation of ownership and work—capitalism's idea that labour and ownership are distinct and that ownership carries all of the prerogatives and decision-making powers. Is this structure the only way that economic enterprises can be efficient?

In September, 1982, I visited in Spain perhaps the largest, most successful worker-owned and -managed network of industries in the capitalist world. There are 83 enterprises employing almost 20 000 people in which every employee is an owner of this industrial network. These worker-owner enterprises have been more successful than most of their capitalist counterparts. And during an era of 15% unemployment in Spain as a whole, this industrial network has not laid off a single person. Perhaps, there does not have to be an absolute distinction between owners and workers in order to achieve efficiency and viability. In Sweden, the newly-elected government has been studying and promoting a plan through which worker and employer contributions to decentralized funds would, over several decades, give the citizens of Sweden majority ownership in major corporations in the country. Rejecting state ownership and individual ownership, the Swedes have arrived at a truly creative alternative.

Conclusion

People throughout the world are attempting to break free of rigid ideological models, to look creatively, to learn lessons, and to apply them, rather than looking for some third model. But let's return to the most basic question. Why should we make the effort to give up our desperate clinging to the false gods of capitalism and communism? As an American, it is very clear to me that, by making capitalism our god, we are at great risk. Our government has, in the name of that religion, supported dictators around the world—and continues to do so—who are a direct threat not only to their own people, but also to ourselves. This occurred in Iran where, in an attempt to fend off the communist religion, we made profound enemies. More to the point today is Central America, where, because we have juxtaposed the communist religion with the capitalist religion, our policy makers simply label

Nicaragua a Marxist-Leninist puppet of the USSR. As a consequence, we misinterpret and fundamentally misunderstand. We contribute to brutal conflict by arming Nicaragua's neighbours. The United States gives so much military and economic aid to El Salvador, for example, that it has become the third largest recipient of such aid in absolute terms in the world and the largest in per capita terms. So, the stakes are extremely high: we are headed toward an all-out war in Central America. But the stakes are even higher than that. By following false gods, we have already paid a heavy price: starvation throughout the world and wars that are needless. But because we have still not given up our false gods, the ultimate stake today is the very survival of life on Earth.

The challenge is clear—we must break free of false models. That means having the courage to talk about things which make other people uncomfortable. Most importantly, it requires *believing* very fundamentally that *change is possible*. There is only one way to achieve such a belief: *we have to change ourselves*. I do not believe that we will believe that change of a positive nature is possible in a country like Nicaragua or the Phillippines, unless we experience ourselves changing. And the only way that we can change is by taking risks and learning that we can rise to the challenge. I am convinced that change in the world comes about through committed minorities, including educators who have the capacity to communicate with others and to show where our real values lie.

Paraphrasing William Hastie: Democracy is a process, not a static condition; it is becoming, not being. It can be easily lost, but never finally won. The essence of democracy is eternal struggle.

It is to that struggle that I challenge each of us.

References

Paul Ehrlich. 1971. *The Population Bomb*. New York: Ballantine Books, 2nd edition.

Frances Moore Lappé. 1982. *Diet for a Small Planet*. New York: Ballantine Books.

Frances Moore Lappé. 1979. *Food First: Beyond the Myth of Scarcity*. New York: Ballantine Books.

Frances Moore Lappé, Joseph Collins and David Kinley. 1980. *Aid as Obstacle: Twenty Questions on Our Foreign Aid and the Hungry*. San Francisco, California, Institute for Food and Development Policy.

W. Paddock and P. Paddock. 1975. *Famine*. Boston: Little, Brown and Co.

Part 2:

Approaches to the Dilemma

This Part argues that the lack of knowledge about environmental problems presents a major barrier to coping with the environmental dilemma and that increased attention must be paid to environmental education, in both formal and informal settings, before a meaningful search for solutions can begin. One approach, discussed by Kirk and Baez, is the "World Conservation Strategy," an education program initiated by the International Union for the Conservation of Nature and Natural Resources which is being adopted throughout the world as a strategy to explore and make better known the environmental issues which face various countries. Positive environmental action, however, is based on people placing a value (in the non-monetary sense) on the environment and creating a personal set of ethics that will guide action. Following Paehlke's discussion of environmental values, Timmerman explores the difficulties involved in teaching environmental ethics. Suzuki, however, argues that even though more people may develop positive values toward the environment they will be at the mercy of a scientific and technological explosion in the 1980s, the environmental consequences of which they are not capable of understanding. Indeed, science and technology contribute to the very problems which they purport to solve. Thus, he argues that improved scientific and technological education must be an integral part of any environmental education program.

4
The World Conservation Strategy: The Key to Survival and the Nucleus for Environmental Education

John J. Kirk
Director, School of Conservation
Montclair State College, Branchville, New Jersey

The Origins of the World Conservation Strategy

The World Conservation Strategy was commissioned by the United Nations Environment Programme which, in cooperation with the World Wildlife Fund, provided the necessary finances for the preparation and development of the basic theme and structure of the project. The International Union for the Conservation of Nature with headquarters in Gland, Switzerland, was given the responsibility of conducting the research and drafting the final document. No other organization in the world is better equipped than IUCN to assume the awesome responsibility for such a project. There are more than 450 government agencies and conservation organizations in over 100 countries that work very closely with IUCN. Over 700 scientists and other environmental experts shared their talent and concern in drafting the World Conservation Strategy, which speaks to threatened species, protected areas, environmental planning, environmental policy, law, government administration, and environmental education. If the governments of the world will accept and implement the suggestions in the Strategy then there is yet hope for the survival of the human race and other species on this planet.

The seeds which ultimately germinated into the Strategy were actually planted in 1972 at the first United Nations Conference on Human Environment held in Stockholm. Then, in 1975, the United Nations Conference on Environmental Education in Belgrade, Yugoslavia, which had as its focus the development of a master plan for environmental education, further demonstrated the need for cooperation among the various people of the world in safeguarding and preserving all of our life support systems. In 1977, the Intergovernmental Conference on Environmental Education held in Tbilisi of the Soviet State of Georgia, added additional support to the need for a global assessment of our natural resources. On March 5, 1980, the World Conservation Strategy was launched at centers in 34 countries throughout the world. Presidents, prime ministers, kings, and leading government officials enthusiastically received the document and pledged their support in exploring ways to implement the plan of action suggested.

What is the World Conservation Strategy?

The aim or purpose of the Strategy is to help the governments and people of the world to place in motion a plan of action that will guarantee sustainable development through the conservation of living resources. At the present time, there are many inequities related to resource use. Currently, 25% of the world's population is consuming over 60% of the world's resources, driven on by the desire for greater profits and what seems to be a better way of life. They are oblivious to the desecration and potential disaster to which their demands on resources are contributing. Tragically, 50% of the remaining people living today are destroying the natural world around them because of the stark poverty in which they find themselves in their desperate struggle to stay alive. For example, in some countries people are forced to take animal dung, which should be used to fertilize the barren fields, and burn it as fuel to heat their homes, because nothing else is available. Virtually everywhere on Earth, renewable resources are being exploited beyond recovery and these unfortunate circumstances seriously threaten the future status of life on the planet. To make the situation even worse, the world's population is soaring and consumption demands are therefore increasing.

The World Conservation Strategy attempts to stimulate a more controlled approach to living resource management and to provide guidance on how a workable solution may be implemented. It focuses upon the main problems generated by human use and misuse of the Earth's resources. The Strategy also identifies the actions and techniques which must be implemented to improve the conservation of natural resources and emphasizes the need for conservation with necessary future development. This is the hallmark of the plan.

Target Groups

The Strategy is therefore designed principally for three different groups. First, as has been stated, it is a guide for the development of government policy. The majority of governments throughout the world lack the financial and technical resources to research and evaluate all the complex problems related to the conservation of natural resources. Therefore, it is advantageous for government leaders to have such information made available to them in order that they may establish workable priorities. The Strategy identifies the action which must be taken to overcome the main obstacles to conservation and further suggests what actions should be given primary consideration. The data contained in the Strategy can be used by any level of government—local, regional, or national—which has responsibilities for the management and utilization of land.

The second target group is the industrial and business complex and the labour movements within the various countries of the world. In looking at the Strategy, labour, industry, and commerce will discover the reality that only through better management of resources will development be enhanced and more jobs be created. Furthermore, the Strategy also identifies those specific areas where conservation interests and the interests of the developer are most likely to coincide. A working relationship established to implement the priorities identified by the Strategy would be mutually beneficial.

The third target group is the conservationists, environmentalists, and educators of the world. In my judgement, it is the responsibility of this third group to interpret the significance and importance of the Strategy to all the people in every nation of the world. In order to achieve this, all educators must closely examine programs within both the formal and non-formal sectors of education. Teachers responsible for guiding the development of young minds must have curriculum materials available which focus upon the problems identified within the Strategy. They must also utilize all the subjects in the curriculum to help the students examine these problems. They must then explore techniques for the implementation of the suggested solutions or develop other solutions which appear more workable. For college and university professors, it is necessary to include—not only in the teacher training programs but also in all college concentrations—experiences to help their students discover their role and their responsibility in altering present environmentally-destructive courses of action.

For conservationists and environmentalists working in private agencies, government agencies, the national parks and forests of the world, and in museums and nature centers, it is necessary to formulate and develop programs and activities that will interest and excite all those countless millions of people outside the formal stream of education. Only through such a massive educational endeavor will the attitudes and values of the world's citizens be sufficiently altered so that they will become aware of the seriousness of the problems which threaten their very existence and of their responsibility to work cooperatively to solve these problems.

The Issues

The Strategy identifies a number of significant issues: diminishing food supplies; loss of forest lands; disruption of marine environments; and reduction in genetic diversity. Environmental educators must adapt school curricula to highlight the seriousness of these issues in the minds of students and stimulate their intellectual curiosity in seeking solutions.

1. Food Supply

The first problem area discussed in the Strategy is that of diminishing food supplies. Throughout the world today less than 10% of the land surface is suitable for agriculture and approximately 20% of the Earth's land surface is available for the grazing of farm animals. Throughout the world, cropland is being lost at an alarming rate. In Canada between 1961 and 1971, more than two million acres of prime farmland were lost to urbanization. In Japan, during the same time frame, more than 7% of the agricultural land was lost to construction of roads and buildings. In the United States during the 1970s, over three million acres of prime agricultural land were lost to parking lots, high-rise apartments, and shopping centers. In addition, both the development of cropland and poor farming practices world-wide are causing the loss of top-soil at a great rate. If these poor farming practices are continued, between now and the turn of the century, one-third of the world's cropland will be destroyed. Soil is absolutely necessary as a life support system since most of all food production depends upon it. Soil erosion is a natural process; in most cases, soil is regenerated at approximately the same rate it is lost. However, if soil and vegetation are not in balance, and they are not in most cases, the process of erosion is seriously accelerated. Under ideal conditions, it takes approximately 400 years for one-third of an inch of top soil to be formed. It is, therefore, safe to say that once serious soil erosion has taken place, the land will never again serve agricultural purposes.

The productivity of farmland also depends on retaining the habitat for beneficial insects and other animals. Crop pollinators and the predators of parasites and pests are essential in order to achieve optimum yield. The overuse of insecticides and pesticides has destroyed the habitat of many of the natural enemies of the pests and parasites which feed upon crops. This practice has also turned formerly harmless species into pests which contaminate and destroy the potential food supply.

Unfortunately, the mismanagement of grazing lands has also reduced the available meat supply throughout the world. Overstocking has had serious negative effects throughout Africa, the Mediterranean, and the Near East. Such mismanagement has contributed significantly to the phenomenon known as desertification, which is the conversion of grazing and farmland into desert land worthless in terms of agricultural production.

In order to correct these deficiencies, educational programs must be initiated both in the formal and non-formal sectors. Children and college students must be taught the importance for farmlands. Local, regional, and national units of government must enact legislation to prevent the loss of farmland to the developer. Farmers must be provided with the technical assistance that will give them the knowledge, attitudes, and values necessary to initiate programs of soil and water conservation, the recycling of nutrients, and the protection of habitats for insects and animals beneficial to agriculture. For every three million acres of farmland lost, the capability of feeding one million additional people is lost. With expanding populations in many parts of the world, this is a most frightening statistic. We cannot allow farmland and grazing land throughout the world to be further damaged if we are to provide adequate nourishment for all people.

2. Forest Lands

The second problem area identified by the Strategy relates to the frightening loss of forest lands throughout the world. During the last 25 years, half of all forest lands on this planet have been destroyed. Robert Allen, in his excellent text, *How to Save the World*, points out that forest lands of the world contribute heavily to human welfare by serving as environmental buffers. Forests tend to influence local and regional climates, generally serving to moderate the temperatures. They provide a continuous flow of clean water by serving as filters and, in some cases, they increase the availability of water by intercepting moisture from the clouds. This latter condition is particularly important when considering the tropical cloud forests.

In Southeast Asia, excessive clearing of forests has caused a fluctuation in river flow that has seriously lowered the yield of rice. In Argentina, approximately $10 million a year is spent to dredge the silt from the estuary in order that ships can reach Buenos Aires. In many countries, watershed forests are being cleared with the idea that agriculture might be a profitable substitute. Overzealous logging operations and stripping forests for fuel also present serious problems in some countries. Sedimentation as a result of improper management of watershed forests is also very damaging, both to the economic life of a country and also to reservoirs, hydro-electric facilities, and irrigation systems. When examining such data, it becomes quite apparent that such practices cannot continue.

Teachers must provide students with learning experiences in science and in social studies that point out and illustrate the significant role that forest lands play in their lives. I like to point out to my students that forests are like giant factories which provide oxygen in the air that we breathe and to destroy a forest is like closing an oxygen factory and thus threatening life as we know it.

In Bulgaria, there is a very fine environmental education program that attempts to unite youth and their teachers and also utilizes the mass media to develop an environmental awareness and sensitivity among the general public. The Green and Blue Patrols involve thousands of elementary and secondary school children. The activities conducted by these youngsters relate to the preservation and improvement of forest lands and water resources. During the spring months, there are many special campaigns involving the Green Patrols which improve the quality of forest lands in Bulgaria. Such activities as tree planting, forest clean-up and lake clean-up help the students to develop an understanding and appreciation of what they should do to protect and enhance the life-giving qualities of forest lands and woodlands. April has become "the month of the forest" in which the mass media, press, radio, and television schedule environmental education programs in coordination with the nature and conservation activities that are being conducted by the schools. While in the classroom, the students are exposed to the environmental dimensions of such traditional subjects as history, literature and art, as well as geography, economics and industrial technology. The town or the village becomes the laboratory for the younger children to develop the attitudes and values relating to environmental conservation and the preservation of forest land.

In Japan, the Japanese Broadcasting Corporation produced a series of twenty programs, entitled *The Green Earth*. Parents are encouraged to watch these presentations with their children in order to stimulate conversation in the home about the problems of environmental degradation in their country. The Japan Environment Association has produced several films relating to the preservation of forest lands and the Japan Economic Education Center has also produced such films as *This Beautiful Earth* and *Precious Earth*. Both of these organizations distribute these films at no charge to the boards of education throughout Japan.

It is this type of activity, which involves the children in the schools and their parents in the community, that must be initiated. For too many years, forest lands and woodlands have been taken for granted. In some segments of society, forest lands are considered an impediment to industrial and commercial development. If we, as a people, are to continue living on the planet, such attitudes must be eliminated. The importance and significance of forest lands must become an integral part of our universal values system. As we discuss forest land preservation, it is essential to develop in the minds of all students the understanding that the forests of the world are part of a global commons which must be preserved at all costs. I like to point out to the students visiting the New Jersey School of Conservation that it is not only the forest lands of New Jersey and the United States that are critical to our survival, but also forest lands everywhere. I illustrate this point with the story of the tropical rain forests of South America which are being destroyed because of certain business interests. If this practice continues in South America, then the wheat fields of Kansas and Nebraska—sometimes called the bread basket of the world—will no longer be capable of producing the food products that now enable the United States to feed over 300 million people in our country and elsewhere in the world. The clouds which carry the moisture northward and nourish the croplands of Kansas and Nebraska originate over the rain forests of South America. If the forests are gone, then the life-giving rain will no longer be available for our crops and they will wither and die. The lush wheat fields of Kansas will be turned into a worthless desert. Thus, it is necessary for all the countries of the world to work cooperatively because it is mutually advantageous to retain the forest lands and the woodlands of the world. These connections must appear more frequently in the learning experiences teachers provide for their students in all countries throughout the world.

3. Marine Resources

The next critical area identified in the Strategy is the misuse of marine resources. The first problem area identified is the damage to and destruction of wetlands throughout the world. Wetlands (sometimes described as bogs, mires, marshes, mud flats, and mangroves and called worthless swamps by some) are one of the most valuable links in the planet's chain of genetic diversity. Wetlands contain the greatest variety and richest collection of animal and plant species to be found anywhere on Earth. Two-thirds of the world's fisheries are dependent upon the unique fertility which is found in these environments.

Desecration and destruction of wetlands in the United States caused by industrial and agricultural pollution amounts to a loss of $86 million per year, a terrible economic waste that could easily be corrected. The wetlands are important not only as habitat for water fowl, spawning fish, and many other species of plants and animals, but also as buffer zones between the land and the sea which serve as barriers to serious erosion.

In educational programs, a sensitivity and awareness that international treaties are necessary and vital in order to guarantee protection of the wetlands of the world must be developed. Under the provisions of the Ramsar Convention held in Iran some 12 years ago, 216 wetland sites have been identified for their international importance. The total area that these wetlands represent would be equivalent to a combined land mass equal to Belgium and Holland. The importance of Ramsar was confirmed in 1980 at the Wetlands Conference in Cagliani, Sardinia. Many delegates reported that the wetlands set aside in their respective countries were saved from exploitation as a result of the Ramsar Agreement. At present, our knowledge is seriously limited concerning the wetlands of South America, southern Asia, and Africa south of the Sahara. Ironically, these are the last great pristine wetlands of the world and much research is needed to discover their unique features. More education is needed in order to convince government leaders to provide the necessary funds to conduct research projects of this type.

The oceans, which cover seven-tenths of the earth's surface, present many examples of mismanagement. Overfishing has seriously diminished the annual world catch. At the present time, the annual world catch is approximately 20 million tons less than what it would have been if overkill had not occurred in previous years. This represents a loss of approximately 24% of a valuable food source in an already starving world. At the present time, 25 of the world's most valuable fisheries are seriously depleted. Although there is local overfishing in all the regions of the world, overexploitation is generally more evident in those areas of the world dominated by the fishing fleets of the developed countries. Greed and ignorance distort the visions of those in the fishing industry and they become satisfied with short-term gains that will soon be converted into long-term losses. The desire for profit is perhaps best illustrated in the accidental killing of non-targeted species. For example, with every ton of shrimp caught, at least three tons of other fish species are thrown away dead. In 1976, the world catch of shrimp was 1.3 million tons and it is safe to assume that with this catch, 6.5 million tons of fish were destroyed—a tragic loss of food and protein. This travesty coincides with World Bank estimates that 500 million people throughout the world are malnourished. Through the educational process, pressure must be placed on government leaders and members of the fishing industry to refine their harvesting techniques to prevent the unnecessary killing of non-targeted species or perhaps, better yet, develop techniques for using those less desirable species as a source of food for the starving millions of the world which some scientists claim is the most serious environmental problem facing mankind.

One of the most serious problems facing inland waters is that of acid rain. In the province of Ontario, the fish in over 140 lakes are sterile; this has seriously reduced the freshwater fish catch and the sports fishing industry which represents millions of dollars to the local economy. The salmon industry in Canada has also been adversely affected as a result of acid rains. Two sources of the problem are the burning of coal in the industrial complex in the midwestern United States which causes the emission of sulfur oxides into the atmosphere and the nitrogen oxides of automobile emissions. Tragically, we have the technical expertise to correct the problem, but it goes ignored because industry does not wish to cut into its profits and government pretends it is doing all it can to correct the problem.

4. Genetic Diversity

The next problem is the preservation of genetic diversity. The basic concept of genetic diversity is that all life, and all living things, are important and although their importance may not be immediately or readily observable we should not knowingly cause the extinction of any species. Although it is true that mankind lacks the knowledge to control the biosphere, unfortunately we do have the power to change it radically. We are, however, morally and ethically obligated to those generations of living things yet unborn to act prudently and wisely as we attempt to manage the land and all that lives on it.

The continued preservation of the wild and the primitive variety of the world's plants is our only insurance against diseases that attack the more cultivated and economically valuable plants and animals. The classic example cited in the Strategy, raised by Olmo (1976), is the problem of the European grapevine and the insect which, in the 1860s, fed on the root systems and threatened the destruction of every vineyard on the continent of Europe. Fortunately, it was discovered that a native North American vine is tolerant of the insect, phylloxera. The European wine industry was saved as a result of grafting European vines onto North American root stocks, a practice that is still continued. We have become far too smug and self-satisfied because we have been fortunate enough to find a few species that seem to meet the majority of our needs. For example, only four varieties of wheat produce 75% of the crop grown on the Canadian prairie and more than half the prairie wheatlands are devoted to a single variety. In the United States, 72% of the potato production depends on only four varieties and just two varieties supply all of the United States pea production. In Brazil, every coffee tree descends from a single plant. The United States soybean industry is derived from a mere six varieties which grow in one location in Asia. Should any type of insect or disease attack these species, the food supply of the world would be irreparably damaged. A rapid search of the wild and uncultivated varieties that might be grafted to the cultivated type, might avoid such a disaster.

The problem is not limited to plant life. In Europe, 115 of the 145 indigenous cattle breeds are threatened with extinction. In North America, when the early settlers slaughtered bison at random and cut the herds from an estimated 60 million to less than 600, not only did they destroy one of the most picturesque animals on the face of the earth, but also lost an opportunity to provide meat and meat products for countless millions around the world.

Another reason for being concerned with genetic diversity relates to the production of prescription drugs. In the United States, more then 40% of the prescriptions filled each year contain a substance of a natural origin, derived either from higher plants, microbes or from animals. If and when these species are lost it will be impossible to produce the various medications which are saving thousands of lives annually. Only through the preservation of these species and those species related to them which appear to have no economic value can we mitigate the possibility of these dangerous conditions becoming a reality.

Two of the most serious threats to the preservation of genetic diversity are overexploitation and the introduction of exotic species. The introduction of exotic species places a tremendous burden on native species because they may compete for space, food, predation, habitat destruction and the transmission of diseases and parasites. In the United States, the introduction of rainbow trout and bass are threatening many native species of fish and animals that have no defenses against them. In the islands of the Pacific and Indian Oceans, the introduction of goats and rabbits are threatening the existence of indigenous plants, birds, and reptiles.

Science programs for school children must somehow provide experiences that illustrate the importance and significance of all life. We must try to formulate in the minds of our students a reverence for life and a land ethic. We humans are merely the temporary stewards having the responsibility and moral obligation to protect and nurture all living things.

Additional Problems

These are the four major areas of concern upon which the World Conservation Strategy has been formulated. No one can minimize their importance and the need to solve these life-threatening problems. It will certainly strain the collective minds of all responsible people throughout the world in attempting to implement the possible solutions. Yet, there are two other major problems which the Strategy did not address and which must be included in any global strategy intended to preserve the existence of the human race on the planet: overpopulation and nuclear disarmament.

Overpopulation

Overpopulation is mentioned a few times in the Strategy, but no solutions were explored or offered. I realize the question of population control raises moral and ethical questions that some government officials and church leaders choose to ignore. However, the problem has reached such gigantic proportions that it can no longer be ignored. In the *Global Two Thousand* study, the need for some type of population management was based on the following projection of population. From the year 1975 to the year 2000, more people will be born than were born in the last 2000 years. What makes this statistic even more staggering and frightening is that 90% of this population increase will take place in Third World Countries where hunger and disease are already ravaging the people. Insufficient food, inadequate housing, and lack of proper medical care are causing such untold agony that it defies human comprehension and signals the need for some plan of action. There are some who will state that it is immoral and even sinful to suggest any type of population control. I would like to ask those who hold this position which is more immoral:

to allow a child to be born where conditions are such that there is a 60% chance the child will die of starvation or disease during the first or second year of life, or to initiate some form of population control? I hasten to add that I do not agree with those pseudo-sophisticates who practice birth control only because they do not wish to be inconvenienced with the responsibility of raising a family. I find this hedonistic philosophy totally repulsive, even though the result is a reduction of population. Nor could I ever condone abortion as a means of regulating population. The destruction of life is not the same issue as suggesting some means of preventing conception.

I do not offer any answers or solutions to this perplexing problem. However, I would strongly urge that all of us work to bring the government officials and church leaders together. After examining the facts concerning the proliferation of life combined with the diminishing food supply, some program must be initiated world-wide that would provide hope of survival for these children of the world where now there is no hope. A problem of this magnitude deserves discussion, thoughtful reflection and a reasonable plan of action. No conservation strategy for the world can be complete without facing the problem of population control.

Nuclear Disarmament

The last issue is one that makes all of the other problems seem somewhat insignificant by comparison: the threat of a nuclear holocaust. As the super powers continue to engage in sabre rattling with the proliferation of nuclear weapons, the world trembles in fear. There is now a call in the United States for a nuclear freeze and, were it to be enacted tomorrow, it would not be enough for there are far too many nuclear weapons already strategically located which could bring total destruction to the world.

In August of 1945, the cities of Hiroshima and Nagasaki were reduced to rubble. In Nagasaki, 40 000 lives were lost in a flash, and that figure climbed to nearly 75 000 by the year's end. Similar figures of horror also exist for Hiroshima. Of the 370 000 known survivors of the bombings in Hiroshima and Nagasaki, many carry genetic defects which have been passed on to their children. In 1979, Sivard in her work, *World Military and Social Expenditures*, stated that in the United States, there are over 2055 missiles and planes that can launch 9200 nuclear weapons, each of which are many times more powerful than the bombs dropped on Hiroshima and Nagasaki. Since 1979, those figures have increased considerably; in the Soviet Union, the arsenal of atomic weapons at least matches that of the United States.

The fear of a nuclear holocaust, which has hung heavily over all of us in the world for nearly two generations, has taken a heavy toll on human sensibility and rationality. Some psychiatrists tell us on the basis of psychological research that a combination of cynicism and fear born as a result of the nuclear age may be having an impact on the structure of personality itself. Our children find themselves adrift in a world racing toward ultimate destruction. The capacity for long range planning shrivels under the ever present fear of nuclear war and mass death. In February of 1981, Pope John Paul II, on the occasion of his visit to Japan, told the world that, "to remember Hiroshima is to take responsibility for the future."

All of us who call ourselves educators must use all means at our disposal to develop in our students and in our government leaders the understanding and the realization that nuclear weapons must never be permitted in warfare. We must not have a nuclear freeze, but a total nuclear disarmament. Let us urge the super powers to re-evaluate the positions they now hold. Only through a mass effort including the total community of nations will such a goal ever be achieved. If we are to conserve life and preserve life on this planet, we must all make certain that there will never, never be another Hiroshima or Nagasaki. Nuclear disarmament is essential for the success of any World Conservation Strategy and for the preservation of life. This may be our last chance.

Conclusion

In this paper, I have tried to review the major threats to the continuation of life on this planet: the breakdown of agricultural systems; the loss of forest resources; the destruction and misuse of coastal, freshwater, and saltwater systems; the indifference to preserving genetic diversity. These are the problems so clearly and frighteningly stated in the World Conservation Strategy. In addition, there are two extremely serious threats to life not addressed in the Strategy: overpopulation and the chilling spectre of a nuclear holocaust. Hopefully, your interest and concern have been aroused and you will undertake a more detailed examination not only of the problems, but also of solutions which will prove to be applicable in your corner of the world. It is also my hope that you will use all of your talents and skills to convey the seriousness of these threats to life to your friends, to your colleagues, and, above all, to your students.

If this planet is to be saved and if life is to continue, it will take a commitment and a sense of determination on the part of countless millions throughout the world. All of us must work to this end. The World Wildlife Fund, the United Nations Environmental Programme, and the International Union for the Conservation of Nature, through their joint efforts have provided us with the factual material, the awesome statistics and possible solutions. It is now our strategy to implement; it is also our destiny!

References

Robert Allen. 1980. *How to Save the World: Strategy for World Conservation.* Scarborough, Ont.: Prentice-Hall.

Council on Environmental Quality. 1980. *Global Two Thousand.* New York: Pergamon Press.

H.P. Olmo. 1976. "Grapes." In N.W. Simmonds (ed.) *Evolution of Crop Plants.* London: Longman.

Ruth Sivard. 1978. *World Military and Social Expenditures.* Leesburg, Virginia: WMSE Publications.

5
The Educational Challenge of the World Conservation Strategy

Albert V. Baez

Chairman, Commission on Education
International Union for Conservation of Nature
and Natural Resources, Greenbrae, California

A Turning Point

The World Conservation Strategy is a document which states clearly and forcefully how conservation and sustainable development can, and indeed must, work hand in hand to avoid the destruction of the living resources which sustain life. It presents an educational challenge because it will never be implemented unless a majority of people understand the problems of living resources and are motivated to conserve them. It requires a basic environmental education whose scope is broader than conservation education alone.

Some progress *has* been made through environmental education. On my way to the north-easterly tip of Australia, I stopped at Cairns for a rest before boarding the small plane that would fly us over the Great Barrier Reef. The leader of the expedition, Graham Kelleher, and I were walking along the shore and facing the Pacific Ocean. We were talking about the importance of raising the level of public awareness of environmental issues when a large pelican swooped down gently and started to walk gracefully at the water's edge. As it did several people, including some children, stopped to look at this extraordinary bird. No one disturbed it. All seemed to enjoy just watching this elegant creature who obviously belonged there.

Kelleher said:

You know, I think we have made some progress. If this bird had landed here just twenty years ago a boy might have thrown a stone at it just for fun. It wasn't cruelty. He didn't mean any harm. In those days it was just considered sport to try to hit a moving target. Birds were considered much lower on the scale of living things than people. There were lots of them. They were expendable and it was our right to deal with these lower forms of life as if they had no feelings and didn't matter very much anyway. I think people have different feelings towards the earth and its inhabitants today. They seem to have a greater respect for living things whether they be plants or animals. I sense a new respect for life. There also seems to be a new appreciation for the beauty of living things.

It is good to note that some progress has been made toward conservation and environmental sanity otherwise we might be overwhelmed by gloom as we consider the global trends. *The Global 2000 Report to the President* (Barney, 1979) says "If present trends continue, the world in 2000 will be more crowded, more polluted, less stable ecologically, and more vulnerable to disruption than the world we live in now." Other documents, including *North-South: A Program for Survival, Limits to Growth, 100 Pages for the Future* and *Down to Earth*, document the destructive impact of man on the environment and the degradation of the biosphere.

Other books, like *Extinction* (Ehrlich and Ehrlich, 1981) and *Fate of the Earth* (Schell, 1982), develop the theme, with alarming statistics, that not only humanity but all life on earth is doomed either to an accelerated destruction of nature and natural resources or the sudden destruction of all forms of life on earth if a holocaust results from a full scale exchange between the two superpowers.

The key phrase, however, is "if present trends continue." People everywhere, and especially those who have the slightest grain of optimism, should now dedicate themselves to ensuring that present trends do *not* continue. The adage "if you are not part of the solution you are part of the problem" was seldom more appropriate.

The World and Its Resources are Finite

Until very recently all curves of consumption of fossil fuels, for example, continued to rise exponentially, but it is clear that, because the earth and its resources are finite, they cannot continue to do so forever. At the present rate of consumption known oil reserves will be depleted in two or three decades and there is no solace in hoping that a huge new source equivalent to the sum of all previous oil consumption will be found because even if it were *it would last only about a decade*. This is the conclusion one reaches from the law of exponential growth with a doubling time of ten years—the present figure applicable to global oil consumption.

Population growth follows a similar curve with an average doubling time of 35 years. A slow down of birth rates will cause the curve to slope downward but the significant fact is that the increment alone in the world population will be 4000 million, if not in 35 years then in 40 or 50 years. In other words, there is no escaping the fact that we are headed toward a world population of 8000 million somewhere between 2017 AD and 2032 AD at a time when your grandchildren and mine will still be alive.

If we don't make an effort to turn things around in a controlled way they will turn around in disastrous ways simply because the world and its resources are finite. In the process the quality of life will decrease and life will become unbearable for some people.

Thinkers in different fields are expressing the thought that we are at a crucial turning point in history. Some point to inevitable trends and others are, perhaps, expressing a hope that through our own active participation we can effect changes for the better. Capra, *The Turning Point* (1982), expresses it in the language of Yin and Yang and gives arguments that stem from modern physics. In *Person/Planet* (1979), Roszak, speaks of "the creative disintegration of industrialized society" which will bring about the transition from an industrial to an ecological society. Bybee (1979) notes that the change will require a shift from competition to cooperation; whereas aggressiveness was adequate for a society in which resources seemed to be unlimited and were, apparently, there to be exploited for gain, he points out that in a world where all resources are known to be limited a willingness to share might be more conducive to survival.

Whether a trend exists or not there is certainly a need to change from habits of waste to those of conservation of resources. Conservation, therefore, has an important role to play in bringing about and living in the new era. The World Conservation Strategy, whose education implications I wish to explore, is a document that gives us hope for implementing conservation while at the same time permitting economic development to take place.

The World Conservation Strategy

In order to describe the educational challenge of the World Conservation Strategy, it is necessary to briefly summarize the content of the Strategy. This is not an easy task because it deals with subtle and difficult concepts from the physical and social sciences and economics in an integrated way. Ecology, the study of the interrelationships of all living things, is at the heart of it.

The World Conservation Strategy is a guide for living and surviving on the planet. It shows the way for nations to conserve their portion of the earth even as they go forward with much needed developments. It also points the way to greater cooperation among nations to protect the great commons of the Earth: the oceans and the seas, the atmosphere, international river systems, migratory wildlife and Antarctica. Representing the combined ideas of hundreds of scientists and other thinkers associated with three international organizations—The International Union for Conservation of Nature and Natural Resources, The United Nations Environment Programme and the World Wildlife Fund—it describes what must be done if we are to create a planet which we, in good conscience, can pass on to the next generations.

The Strategy reconciles the human need to develop the Earth *in order to live* with the human need to conserve the Earth *in order to survive*. It argues that conservation and development can be mutually re-enforcing, and sets the scene for conservation-minded people and development-minded people to come together in a common effort toward survival.

The World Conservation Strategy is a long-term plan to ensure that the Earth remains habitable. It is a guide for the use of the earth's living resources based firmly on the logic of conservation. We have to face the fact that the biosphere that sustains us—the Earth's thin layer of air, water, soil and living things—is deteriorating rapidly because of the burden our species puts on it. If the deterioration due to our impact on the environment continues, we face a dismal future.

The Strategy identifies the most urgent environment problems the world faces. It then goes on to describe in detail how governments and other organizations can solve these problems. The Strategy is a guide by which each nation can prepare a conservation strategy applicable to its own particular needs. The goal of the Strategy is a *sustainable world society*. It calls for a community of nations, each maintaining its own part of the Earth, all cooperating to protect the biosphere that sustains life.

It is not intended to save a particular species nor to remake the human character. It is intended to convince people in government, commerce, industry, labour unions and the professions that conservation must be in the forefront of our endeavours if the human enterprise is to be successful.

The first priority, according to the Strategy, is *to see that the essential ecological processes and life-support systems of the earth are in good functioning order*. Examples of essential ecological processes include: the regeneration of soils helped along by micro-organisms, the recycling of nutrients such as carbon and nitrogen in plants, the purification of air and water by forests and the pollination of flowering plants by insects. Such processes are essential because all life depends on them.

Examples of *life-support systems* include the agricultural and forest systems, the coastal wetlands and the fresh water systems. Because of the widespread destruction and pollution of these systems, they are losing their productivity at ever-increasing rates. The Strategy outlines management programs to stop such destruction.

The second priority for keeping the Earth habitable is the *preservation of genetic diversity*. That means managing our use of living resources so that the maximum number of different species of plants and animals are allowed to remain alive. The Strategy describes methods for the preservation of genetic diversity. It lays out a program for the sound management of land and water uses and the preservation of habitats. It describes procedures, for example, to prevent over-fishing and over-hunting, to stop the illegal trade in wild plants and animals, to prevent the introduction of exotic species into habitats where they will, in all probability, devastate the native species. And because the Earth's gene pool is a common heritage of all mankind, it calls for cooperation among all nations to protect all species before it is too late to do so.

There are, of course, other reasons for preserving the species. Simple human compassion is one. The extraordinary beauty of natural forms is another. Perhaps most important, we are morally obliged to our descendants not to leave the Earth less alive, less interesting and less wondrous because we have been here.

The Strategy's third main objective is the *sustainable utilization of species and ecosystems*. In simplest terms this means setting aside portions of the Earth as untouched reserves and using the remainder wisely so that it remains forever productive. Sustainable utilization is somewhat analogous to spending the interest while keeping the capital intact. To those ends, the Strategy provides a guide for managing living resources that is applicable everywhere. The Strategy's ultimate goal, a sustainable world society, would benefit everyone. Conservation and increased yields might, to cite just one example that applies in some parts of the world, "put fish back on the working man's table."

This summary of the World Conservation Strategy cannot do justice to a densely packed 70-page document, which represents the combined ideas of hundreds of people and includes sections on national and international action, but it is enough to provide a basis for outlining its educational implications.

Because of the devastating impact of the human species on the environment, Russell Peterson, President of the National Audubon Society, notes that sufficient emphasis is not given in the Strategy to the overwhelming impact of the problem of human overpopulation and its relentless growth. My own list of major global concerns—the four P's—population, pollution, poverty and proliferation of nuclear weapons has always put population first. There is no question but that humans have had the most devastating impact on the biosphere of any species and that this will continue to get worse as long as population growth continues to outstrip all indicators of economic growth and development.

Educational Problems Posed by the Strategy

The greatest educational challenge of the World Conservation Strategy is to produce clear and succinct reading materials and programs based upon the Strategy in a language which is understandable to the target group for whom it was written, namely policy makers in government and industry. The purpose of this action is to raise their level of awareness of the seriousness of the problems of conservation and to convince them of their responsibility to bring about changes that will reverse present ecologically destructive trends. It is an educational task, all right, but an impossible one unless educators are willing to analyze what characterizes this particular target audience carefully before embarking on a special program for them.

The magnitude of the educational task posed by the Strategy can be gauged at once if we consider the totality of the target groups that must be addressed. Here is a partial list taken from the Strategy itself, except for the last three items, which I have added:

- legislators and administrators,
- development practitioners in industry, commerce and trade unions,
- professional bodies and special interest groups,
- communities most affected by conservation projects,
- school children and students,
- teachers and teacher trainers,
- youth group leaders,
- the general public.

The first educational problem, therefore, stems from the fact that so many target groups must be served.

The second problem is how to apply our modern ideas of learning to a task that is so demanding both in terms of new knowledge and in terms of profound changes in the ways we look at and think about the world.

In order to assess the magnitude of the education task ahead, let us review the essence of the teaching-learning process. First, what do we mean by teaching and learning? Here are some statements which I believe are in accord with modern learning theory.

- To teach is to create situations where learning can take place.
- Learning manifests itself in behavioural changes.

There is a lot of information packed into those two statements. The first implies that learners can make discoveries for themselves. The second implies that if you have really learned something you are capable of generating *self-induced* behavioural changes. If learning does not take place teaching has been futile.

Since we are trying to induce changes of attitude and behaviour the materials must do more than inform. They must, essentially, teach. Even if they are used outside the classroom, as they must be for policy makers, they *are* educational materials. Although the role of the teacher is both to inform and to motivate, motivation is by far the most difficult and more important task. It is a human aspect of teaching that cannot be replaced by mechanical devices.

Here, then is a brief review of the steps necessary to induce learning. Naturally, the choice of the target group is at the top of the list.

Steps necessary to induce learning:
- Specify and characterize your target group.
- Specify your objectives (in behavioural terms if possible).
- Choose the subject matter (content) and arrange it in some sequence that takes logic and psychology into account.
- Specify how and when you will evaluate learning based upon the objectives.
- Choose the appropriate combination of approaches and media.
- Teach—in other words, create the learning situations.
- Make a final evaluation of learning based upon previous evaluations.

These seven steps to learning deal with what and how to teach but they omit the very important why? Here is what the Strategy says about that:

Lack of awareness of the benefits of conservation and its relevance to everyday concerns prevents policy makers, development practitioners and the general public from seeing the urgent need to achieve conservation objectives. Ultimately, ecosystems and species are being destroyed because people do not see that it is in their interests not to destroy them. The benefits from natural ecosystems and their component plants and animals are regarded by all but a few as trivial and dispensable compared with the benefits from those activities that entail their destruction or degradation.

The behavioural changes proposed in the Strategy are so sweeping that they amount to a new environmental ethic. It says:

Ultimately the behaviour of entire societies towards the biosphere must be transformed if the achievement of conservation objectives is to be assured. A new ethic, embracing plants and animals as well as people, is required for human societies to live in harmony with the natural world on which they depend for survival and well being. The long-term task of en-

vironmental education is to foster or reinforce attitudes and behaviour compatible with this new ethic.

The element of time is an important consideration. To stop the destruction of some endangered species, for example, requires immediate action. Administrators and decision makers in government and industry could possibly do something about this. Raising the level of public awareness and creating an environmental ethic, on the other hand, are long range goals for which the target group includes the general public as well as pupils and students in schools and universities.

The educational problems posed by the Strategy center on the following:
1. It is a policy document without an educational strategy.
2. It is a technical document, full of concepts and words, many of them scientific, which are not known to the general public.
3. Its concepts demand educational objectives in the cognitive domain but the long-term implementation of its goal demands the generation of an environmental ethic whose objectives are strongly in the affective domain.
4. It was written for a single, highly specialized target group—policy makers in government and industry—but its message has to reach a vast array of target groups.
5. The number of target groups is vast. Yet teaching materials and programs must be generated for each group. They should exemplify the best of what is known about the teaching-learning process.
6. Although it specifies what needs to be done about conservation for development it does not spell out what needs to be done in education, nor who should do it, nor who will fund educational projects.

Toward a World Environmental Education Strategy

Several strategies are needed to solve the global crisis: a strategy for peace and a strategy for population control, as well as a strategy for conservation. I think the time has also come to consider the need for a world environmental education strategy.

Since the Strategy poses but does not solve its educational problems and leaves it to the reader to invent solutions, I have approached the problem from two points of view: personal and institutional. I shall first give personal reflections about some aspects of environmental education which merit special attention and then I shall consider what actions the Commission on Education might be able to take considering its special role in the World Conservation Organization—the International Union for Conservation of Nature and Natural Resources (IUCN).

The Case for Individual Efforts

Individuals can act in at least three ways which may have positive results. They can *make decisions*, they can *pass judgments*, and they can *exercise an influence by example.*

Before considering a global strategy, therefore, I would like to make two recommendations involving individual action.

First, recognizing that the greatest possible environmental devastation, including the extinction of many species, would occur in a nuclear holocaust it behooves all environmentalists and lovers of life on this earth to participate in activities which would minimize the probability that such a holocaust will occur. Men and women of good will everywhere *should act in such a way as to reduce the probability that a nuclear exchange takes place.* Proliferation of nuclear weapons is, in my estimation, "a holocaust looking for a place to happen."

If you are not already doing so, I suggest you start to live your daily life following an environmental ethic *as presently conceived by you.* This would include taking steps to conserve natural resources and to minimize the extinction of plant and animal species. Band together with other like-minded people to reinforce one another and to learn more. In particular, I would urge you to obtain, read and discuss the World Conservation Strategy. Hold seminars, reflection groups, and study sessions based upon it in order to develop your own personal educational strategy. Try to expand the boundaries of your environmental thinking so that they broaden daily to the point where you are, indeed, thinking about the global implications of what you once conceived as merely local environmental problems. By sharing your thoughts the basis of a world environmental education strategy may be created.

Compassion as a Basis for Conservation and an Environmental Ethic

I have written elsewhere that to improve the quality of life, education must generate curiosity, creativity, competence and compassion—the four Cs. As time goes on the importance of compassion has, in my judgment, increased. It is needed more than ever to effect change at this turning point in history. When I first wrote about the role of compassion in education, I had only fellow-feeling and social responsibility in mind. I now believe that a feeling of compassion, and even affection, must be extended to all living things—plants and animals—and to the entire biosphere which teems with life, if we are to animate an environmental ethic. The fifth C—conservation—can be a direct consequence of compassion.

The Role of Science in Environmental Education

A special plea should be made for the role of science in environmental education. Although the generation of humane attitudes toward living things is of utmost importance, these attitudes must rest on accurate knowledge—the firm foundation of ecology. The subject of ecology upon which many of the arguments of the Strategy are based leans heavily on biology, chemistry and physics. The concepts of ecosystems, species and genetic diversity, for example, require a thorough understanding of genetics. The concept of the biosphere which links the laws of thermodynamics with the requirements of living things also illustrates the interdisciplinary nature of the knowledge base which underlies environmental studies.

Since both ecology and environmental education are interdisciplinary activities, it is only natural that the environment has already been chosen as the integrating concept in many integrated science courses. This was recognized a decade or so ago in the science education sector of Unesco even before a formal environmental education program was started there. Throughout the 1970s many integrated science courses were generated round the world using the environment as the integrating factor. We need to strengthen the integrative and scientific aspects of environmental education.

The International Level

Instead of attempting the impossible task of cataloguing in detail the different levels of action from individual through community action, local governmental action, national programs, regional programs and finally international programs, I will jump directly to the international program in which I am involved, namely that of IUCN.

The mechanisms which I propose to use as Chairman of the IUCN Commission of Education are (1) the network of individuals and committees which have some intimate link with the Commission and, (2) the program of the Commission.

The network of the Commission consists in the first place of over 250 members of the Commission in 77 countries. This gives us access to information on educational needs as perceived by the people on the spot. We also have two regional committees: the North West Europe Committee and the East Europe Committee. These have been functioning for several years. Recently some national committees of the Commission have been formed with the hope that at a future date some of them might combine to form new regional committees. At present national committees of the Commission exist in ten countries: Australia, Canada, China, Costa Rica, Czechoslovakia, India, Ireland, Mexico, Nepal and Pakistan. The network also includes some of the national organizations of the World Wildlife Fund and some sub-regional groups in the vicinities of Boston, Washington D.C., and San Francisco.

Space does not permit a review of the Commission's program here but I would like to inform you about two projects which are in progress and in which I have a particular interest. One is beamed at the general public including policy makers, and the other at school children, possibly in out-of-school situations.

Noting the need to have the existence of IUCN and the World Conservation Strategy known to a wider audience, we have commissioned the production of a photographically illustrated introduction to the Strategy. It has been written by Stan Croner in non-technical language understandable to the general public including, we hope, policy makers in government and industry. The illustrations are of the highest dramatic and photographic quality. Ansel Adams and several other photographers of note have given us the right to use some of their photographs. Our aim was to make it attractive enough to demand attention and clear enough in its message to lay the groundwork for future involvement.

Another project currently underway is the production of a Handbook on Environmental Education Activities. The inspiration for this book came from the Unesco Source Book in Science Teaching which has sold over a million copies and has been translated into over 25 languages. Annette Greenall of Australia is the author. She has received contributions from both developing and industrial countries.

The Commission on Education proposes to spark global activity for the improvement of environmental education world-wide. We also welcome collaboration with other groups interested in working on global environmental education issues.

In response to a request for ideas on the educational challenge of the World Conservation Strategy I received 43 replies from members of the Commission. Some of this information was used in the writing of this paper. I plan to use more of it in a guide for reflection seminars on the subject of a world environmental education strategy.

One particular response which dealt with what needs to be done before a global educational strategy can be formulated came from John Smyth of the North West Europe Committee. He feels that any educational response to the World Conservation Strategy must deal with the following matters, among others:

- Identify the deficiencies in the general public concept of people's relation with the environment which lead to failure of support for conservation measures.
- Identify the characteristics of the educational system which perpetuate these conceptual deficiencies in the general public.
- Define the aims and objectives of a re-oriented education strategy. It is at this point that the task becomes one of incipient revolution since whole attitudes are involved and no element of education is left unaffected.
- Define the nature of environmental education in its more formal education context. There have been, of course, many attempts at this, but no agreed solution. *A high-powered effort is needed, to be as definitive in the eyes of society as the World Conservation Strategy appears to be.*
- Define carefully the connections within human/environment systems which it is necessary to understand in order to undertake the practical measures needed to achieve World Conservation Strategy objectives and, by extension, environmental education objectives world-wide.
- Now return to a more detailed statement of behavioural objectives and deploy them among different kinds of target groups and different channels by which they can be approached. Assess gaps, both in contacts and materials.
- Since formal school education is often the pace-setter in these matters, try to devise more specific sets of objectives covering desired knowledge of facts and concepts, desired skills to be attained, desired attitudes to be fostered.

- Examine carefully by discussions with relevant groups the contributions which can be made at any level of education by associated interests—artists, planners, engineers, lawyers, public health workers, psychologists, psychiatrists, anthropologists, sociologists, economists, politicians and so on. As far as possible build these into the conceptual framework of environmental education.

If members of the Commission on Education network hold reflection seminars to read the World Conservation Strategy and give careful consideration to the response by Smyth, we will have laid the foundations of a world environmental education strategy.

A Turning Point?

To temper the optimism which I voiced in citing the pelican incident at the beginning of this paper I must now read you part of a story that appeared in the *Wall Street Journal* for October 8, 1982:

"Why Turkeys Tend to Dislike Yelville: It's a Real Downer, Throwing Birds from Planes is a Big Arkansas Event: Cruelty or Just Plain Fun?

YELVILLE, Ark.—It's all set. The turkeys should start dropping into town this afternoon despite the efforts of a few spoilsports.
Most of the 1,031 citizens of this Ozark Mountain village, along with twice as many outsiders will be down at the square, necks craned skyward, to witness Yelville's claim to fame: It's time for the 37th Annual Turkey Drop.
Once today and four more times tomorrow, a small low flying airplane will make several swoops along the bed of Crooked Creek. On each swoop, a turkey will be tossed out to the cheers of the multitudes below. The ungainly birds, 17 in all, will plummet a hundred feet or so and then, if all systems are go, spread their wings and glide gracefully to whatever roosting place they can find, most likely one of the trees that are just beginning to turn color. Spectators will then try to catch a bird to bring home for dinner."

The article continues with many more details. It is clear that the environmental ethic has not permeated Yelville—and no doubt many other places as well.

Conclusion

In conclusion let us consider why human impact on the environment is the key educational issue of the 1980s.

People pride themselves on being the only intelligent animals on the Earth. Yet they are the only ones that have caused such vast devastation on the biosphere.

In less than a thousand years, the blink of an eye in geologic time, we have consumed most of the fossil fuels which took nature millions of years to produce. The air we breathe is full of noxious fumes and radioactive particles of our making.

We have placed millions of tons of concrete and cement on roads and cities where there were once forests and wildlife. At least 3000 square kilometres of prime farm land are disappearing each year under buildings and roads in developing countries alone.

Thousands of millions of tons of soil are being lost each year as a result of deforestation and poor land management.

Hundreds of millions of rural people in developing countries are forced to strip their land of vegetation in order to find wood for cooking and heat.

Each year 4000 million tons of dung and crop residues which could otherwise regenerate soils are burned for fuel.

And now we have the capability of generating a nuclear holocaust which could devastate the biosphere and extinguish life on Earth.

A new sense of humility must be born in humankind. We should realize that if human beings were removed from the Earth, the Earth could probably heal itself and become once again a planet where the oceans were clean, the air pure and the forests green and filled with wildlife. The Earth, its plants and animals can survive without us *but we cannot survive without them!*

There are those who believe that a world environmental education strategy is too grandiose a scheme. But what, short of that, is going to reverse the trends that are driving us to damage the planet even further?

I believe humans are intelligent enough to generate an environmental ethic, through education, which can point the way to achievement of the goals of the World Conservation Strategy, and I look to each of you for further ideas and for support of the development of a world environmental education strategy.

References

Baez, Albert V. 1980. "Curiosity, Creativity, Competence and Compassion: Guidelines for Science Education in the Year 2000." In Charles P. McFadden (ed.), *World Trends in Science Education*, Halifax: Atlantic Institute of Education.

Baez, Albert V. 1976. *Innovation in Science Education—World-wide.* Paris: The Unesco Press.

Barney, G.V. (ed.) 1979. *The Global 2000 Report to the President, Vol. 1. A report prepared by the Council on Environmental Quality and the Department of State*, Washington, DC: US Government Printing Office.

Brandt Commission Report. 1980. *North South: A Program for Survival.* Cambridge, Mass.: MIT Press.

Bybee, Rodger W. 1979. "Science Education and the Emerging Ecological Society," *Science Education*, Vol. 63, January, pp. 95-109.

Capra, Fritjof. 1982. *The Turning Point.* New York: Simon & Schuster.

Eckholm, Erik P. 1982. *Down to Earth.* New York: W.W. Norton & Company.

Ehrlich, Paul and Anne Ehrlich. 1981. *Extinction.* New York: Random House.

International Union for Conservation of Nature and Natural Resources. 1980. *World Conservation Strategy.* Gland, Switzerland: IUCN.

Meadows, Donella H.; Dennis Meadows; Jorgen Randers; William W. Behrens III. 1972. *The Limits to Growth.* New York: New America Library.

Peccei, Aurelio. 1981. *100 Pages for the Future.* New York: Pergamon.

Roszak, Theodore. 1979. *Person/Planet.* New York: Anchor Press/Double-day.

Schell, Jonathan. 1982. *The Fate of the Earth.* New York: Alfred A. Knopf.

6
Communicating Environmental Values

Robert Paehlke

Professor, Environmental and Resource Studies Program
Trent University, Peterborough, Ontario

Introduction

Environmentalism must seem to many of those who are outside its organizations and perspective to be little but an embodiment of pessimism and paranoia. Environmentalists deliver the news that pollution is poisoning our rivers and lakes, and even the oceans. Environmentalists tell us what air pollution does to our lungs, buildings, forests and crops. Environmentalists warn of the imminent extinction of species, of the overheating of the planet through the "greenhouse effect" and of the potential for various hideous disasters associated with nuclear power. Our food, we learn, will cause cancer if our crops don't fail, our minerals and energy are almost gone, and the rain is turning to acid. Environmentalism, some might argue, could be defined as an undue emphasis on bad news.[1]

This view can, however, be rebutted in several ways. First, one can argue that most of what environmentalism has said, however bleak, has later come to be accepted as reality.[2] Ignoring reality is clearly more unhealthy than facing it and changing it. In imagining and seeking a better world, this rebuttal continues, environmentalism is deeply optimistic. Another form of rebuttal might argue that change within modern liberal democracies comes either through the holding of economic power or through the gaining of the public eye. And since the media rarely report "good news," one must paint a dismal scenario to get attention in a busy world. A third reply simply says that there is more to a complex phenomenon like environmentalism than pessimism or optimism. Environmentalism, as I will set out shortly below, has also articulated a wide range of positive values.

Another point is worth making here as well. Books like the *Limits to Growth* and *The Population Bomb* and many others indeed envision bleak future prospects for humanity.[3] But David Brooks and Alma Norman, Canadian environmentalists *par excellence*, in 1974 put such views in perspective.[4] It is not the case, they made clear, that we will automatically and inevitably run out of, for example, minerals. Rather we *should* come to *prefer* a world with less emphasis on mineral extraction and more emphasis on the protection of the quality of our air and water. That is a very different way to see the situation. The Brooks/Norman view explicitly rejects any escape into prophecies of doom. It argues that we should face up to the value choices which are before us. In this light one can see environmentalism itself as a set of values and value priorities.

It has been argued also that environmentalism is anti-technology, perhaps even anti-science.[5] Environmentalists generally oppose nuclear power, they oppose large scale hydroelectric projects; in Canada they oppose many Northern pipelines, some even have their doubts about the automobile. They seem, again some would have it, to wish us back to burning wood, eating nothing but home grown grains and vegetables and washing our clothes down at the creek. This is I think a misperception of the views of most environmentalists. Note the care with which Lovins and others have argued that in Canada and elsewhere we can produce with minimal environmental damage all the energy we need to do all that we do now.[6] Environmentalism, then, does not involve "going back," it involves going forward in a different direction.

The misperception here occurs in overlooking a fundamental distinction: that between being anti-technology and being selective of one's technologies. Environmentalists reject the technological imperative, but they have not on the whole rejected technology.[7] Some in fact enthuse about the potential environmental *benefits* of such new high technologies as telematics, some biological controls, robotics and CAD/CAM.[8] Again, environmentalism can be seen as a matter of changing the value emphases of society; and different value priorities produce different technological choices.

In the past technology has been guided by the economic and political values of hierarchically structured societies. Technologies have largely been selected and developed in order to create profits for owners, power for political elites, or both.[9] Some environmentalists reject such values utterly. Others think that the present organization of wealth and power produces many benefits to society as a whole and need only be tempered further by another set of values: environmentalists' values. Most environmentalists fall between these two poles on the political spectrum, but they too share the same environmental values.

Thus most ways of looking at environmentalism lead to a concern with the value preferences of environmentalists. This is true regardless of the fact that environmentalism arises, in large measure, out of science. We are pushed towards an environmental perspective and position when we learn from science about the process of bioaccumulation of toxic substances in food chains, or about the impact on human health of such substances as PCBs or asbestos. Science also tries to define for us the physical limits of our renewable and non-renewable resources. Scientific understanding is absolutely essential to environmentalism. It is a necessary part, but only a part. In understanding environmentalism and in teaching about it we must deal with *both* scientific fact and environmentalist values.[10]

Values in the end must be taken as a matter of preference, of personal choice.[11] Nonetheless they can be articulated more, or less, clearly, and their implications for personal behaviour or public policy can be well, or little, understood. This paper seeks to clarify environmental values and some of their policy implications.

Environmental Values

Let me then offer here one possible list of the values of environmentalism:

1. An appreciation of all life forms and an understanding of the complexities of the ecological "web of life."
2. A need for evidence of the long-term sustainability of any human economic undertaking.
3. A revulsion with waste in the face of human need. In more extreme form an inclination to asceticism, and perhaps even to self-righteousness.
4. A love of simplicity.
5. An aesthetic sensitivity to season, setting, climate and inclination to natural materials.
6. An attraction to autonomy and self-management in human endeavours. Some appreciation of the appeal of political and/or demographic decentralization.
7. An extended time horizon.
8. A measurement of esteem, including self-esteem, in terms of non-material values such as skill, effort or integrity.

I believe we can go a very long way towards understanding what environmentalism is all about by seeing how important each of these values is within the literature of the movement.

The Ecologic Perspective

The first value links environmentalism to its historic antecedent: conservation. Beginning in the latter part of the nineteenth century, conservation was an influential intellectual and political movement deeply concerned with the threats to nature and especially threats to North America's forests. The ideas of such people as Thoreau and Audubon were widely felt and the political initiatives of John Muir, a preservationist, and Gifford Pinchot, a rational planner, were crucial. Conservation was primarily concerned with the careful, efficient use of natural, renewable resources. Radicals like Muir went further and we owe much of the beauty of North America's national parks to them. But on the whole, conservation reflected the "gospel of efficiency" so central to the thinking of the Progressive Era.[12]

Environmentalism has gone beyond conservation in several ways. As Brooks and McMullen put it in a recent article, conservation focused on the "... resources being used as raw materials for industry—in other words, on what was going into the production system..."[13] What these authors call the third environmental movement (the first two comprise what I call conservation here) shifted concern to the discharges of production systems rather than inputs. The new focus was on pollution. Pollution pressed the limits of the biosphere's ability to sustain life. Pollution is poisonous to humans, animals and plants—and pollution limits nature's ability to supply resources. Environmentalism thinks in ecological terms—a threat to any one species is a threat to the integrated whole. Species are inter-related in complex ways and the biosphere sustains all life. Many of humanity's intentional and unintentional interventions are not only immoral or wasteful, but suicidal. We live within a web of life and its continuity and diversity is an absolutely essential part of our being—morally, spiritually, intellectually and physically.

One consequence of this view is that in matters of human health and ecological well-being environmentalists require a shift in the burden of scientific proof. That is, suspected pollutants and toxic substances are presumed to be guilty, presumed to have health consequences, unless they are demonstrably safe. Reverence for life requires that we err on the side of safety, not on the side of risk. And further, ecological science teaches us that failure to rectify errors in such matters generally carries irreversible consequences.[14]

Another way of making our broader point here can be found in John Wadland's superb biography of Ernest Thompson Seton. Wadland writes:

> From the ecologist's perspective, there is no dichotomy between man and nature. In ecological terms, each organism constitutes part of the environment of all the other organisms. The complex, cyclical set of interdependencies thus established depends for its complete survival upon the continued existence of its own weakest link. There is, therefore, an immutable set of biological laws—ordered, organized and efficient—demanding the concurrence of all the species that live under them.[15]

Humanity is no longer seen as above nature—we are one part of the natural world. As a species we are vulnerable. We are also the only species whose activities put at risk virtually the whole of life as we know it. This power is new and has several dimensions: nuclear war, toxic wastes, and climatic alteration to name three. The simple weight of our numbers and needs for space and food now threaten the existence of thousands of our fellow species. Our new powers place on us responsibilities which are well beyond our present levels of moral consciousness. The development of an ecological consciousness, both globally and quickly, is perhaps environmentalism's leading value priority.

Long-term Sustainability

Second, environmentalism carries with it a special sensitivity to sustainability—the sustainability of human economic activities in terms of environment and resources. Forests must not be mined, they must be harvested at a sustainable rate. Metals must be recycled and all metals production must be kept in relation to supply both of the relevant ores and, crucially, of the energy needed to sustain extraction and processing. Metal production from recycled materials, of course, requires far less energy.[16] And in general, there is a preference for renewable over non-renewable resources, particularly in the most vital resource area, energy. The central thrust of Amory Lovins' work is to move us towards dependence on *renewable* energy sources. And here Lester Brown's *Building a Sustainable Society* subsumes almost all the concern of environmentalism in a thorough and upbeat volume.[17]

Achieving sustainability involves a long term transformation of most dimensions of our industrial economy. We would need to protect prime agricultural land and to learn to utilize biomass wastes as both sources of energy and enhancers of soil quality.[18] Processes such as pyrolysis would allow the production of both alcohol and fertilizer from sewage, manure or crop wastes. And, as Helliwell has demonstrated, much of Canada's massive forest industry could begin *now* to move economically towards being energy self-sustaining by using forest wastes.[19] What are now toxic wastes should come to be seen as chemical feedstocks.[20] Fossil fuel stocks can be stretched by radically enhanced building efficiencies and the widespread use of cogeneration and energy cascading.[21] And perhaps even more radically, communications systems can replace reliance on our far more energy intensive transportation systems.[22]

All in all, industrial society must transform the nature of its production process to new systems that are energy and materials efficient and, in a word, sustainable.

Concern for Wasteful Consumption

But while these changes are seen to be necessary, they are not seen to be sufficient, especially in the long run. Sustainability with minimal ecological disruption is indeed the goal and efficient use of resources the principal means. But environmentalism also embodies a strong inclination to restraint in goods consumption. Efficient production and careful use is seen as a second order question, foregone need is primary.[23] It is this view, I think, which most often separates environmentalism from the traditional political left in general and the contemporary trade union movement in particular.[24] It is also the view which Brooks and McMullen see as the distinguishing characteristic of the contemporary phase of environmentalism:

> What the previous three phases shared was their emphasis on industrial use of resources, in other words, on the supply side of the demand/supply equation. The fourth environmental movement made a significant break from the past when it put a 'why' to demand. For the first time in modern history, the goal of ever-increasing consumption was being challenged.[25]

Environmentalists find the waste present in contemporary North American society repugnant. Not only does it appear as gluttony in the face of global human want, but it is purchased at the price of damage to the global biosphere, potential exhaustion of our precious heritage of non-renewable resources, and with a clear cost in terms of human health.[26] What is crucial here is that environmentalists see limits to material and energy throughputs, if not to economic growth itself.[27]

Economics is increasingly taken to be a zero-sum game by environmentalists and non-environmentalists alike. What is used by one person, however unnecessarily, is thereby unavailable to another, however urgently it is needed. A family cruising North America in a Winnebago could well be assuring that someone else sometime soon will be unable to heat their home. In this light, shoddy products, planned obsolescence, excessive packaging, non-returnable containers, and frivolous appliances appear no longer as merely irritating or silly. They seem almost criminal.

That said, one rushes to add that on this point in particular self-righteous moral indignation flows quite easily into hypocrisy.[28] We still live in a very comfortable society and it is hard to know where one draws the line on con-sumption. One person's waste is another's profoundest pleasure, or even a basic need. Public transportation is more energy efficient but is also generally a hardship for the disabled. And the elderly are uncomfortable at household temperatures to which most of us can readily adapt.

In sum, people can have very different views of the desirability of nuclear power if one sees a nuclear station supplying the most necessary and another the most trivial 5% of electricity's applications. Environmentalists imagine nuclear plants servicing electric toothbrushes and hedge-trimmers.[29] Nuclear engineers see those same plants lighting dark staircases, baking cherry pies, and keeping the heat on in the children's room. The issue of what is wasteful and what is not is not as simple as it appears on its face. Nevertheless, having made this point, one is left with a sense that environmentalists are correct in saying that the North American sense of the quality of life is unduly materialist in conception and quantitative in measure.

Love of Simplicity

The fourth environmental value in our list can be seen as the positive side of the third: it is a love of and comfort with simplicity. Environmentalism implies that there is as much pleasure in a walk in the woods as in a snowmobile ride. And the walk does not disrupt the pleasure or peace of others, nor does it deny them non-renewable fuel.

A complete environmental ethic would carry a preference for painstaking production over hasty consumption. It would also stress the importance of the inter-relationship between production and consumption. Environmental values hold respect for craftsmanship and many environmentalists aspire to emulate its precepts in everyday living. Distinctiveness, functionality, design, and durability are highly regarded. Doing well for oneself what must be done in any case is seen as somehow a superior pleasure. Growing gardens, prepar-ing and preserving foods, and sharing leisurely meals are high-order pleasures. Not only can such activities substitute for those which might be environmen-tally problematic, such activities are taken to be superior in any case.

Environmentally Informed Aesthetics

The fifth value can be readily related to several we have looked at already; specifically it is an aesthetic which prefers the use of natural materials and fur-ther is highly sensitive to season, climate, and setting. An environmental aesthetic rejects quite out of hand most high-rise office towers and much of the contemporary "plastic" world. High-rise office towers are generally identical on all four sides—regardless of solar heat gain and heat loss and regardless of prevailing winds. Windows which cannot open prevail, thus necessitating air conditioning. Further, most modern office towers are virtually identical in design whether built for Nairobi or New York, Edmonton or Houston. Plastic *per se* is not always ugly, but it often is and the term "plastic" has come to refer to an artificial style of design of products of limited durability.

The "natural" materials question can, however, get complex. Plastic auto parts can reduce vehicle weight to such an extent that the oil feedstock used to produce the plastic is more than recovered in fuel. Further, plastic pipes do not readily corrode and in some cases take less oil feedstock than the energy necessary to produce and shape the metal in metal pipe.[30] Those concerned with an environmental aesthetic should look at questions like: what is it that makes plastic "unnatural"? What would be the total ecological effect of replacing synthetic fibres with wool and cotton?[31]

In the end one is left seeking an aesthetic informed by other environmental values: conservation of resources, avoidance of toxic byproducts and so forth. Nonetheless part of the basis of an aesthetic standard is irretrievably aesthetic. Wood products are beautiful, even if trees are in short supply. But fur coats made from the skins of rare and endangered animals are now ugly regardless of their appearance.

Decentralism

The sixth value on our list, decentralism, is the most explicitly political, perhaps excepting environmental consumption restraint (asceticism) taken as a rejection of economic growth. Environmentalism is often decentralist in character. For example, Energy Probe, an Ontario environmental organization, is seeking the breakup of the giant utility, Ontario Hydro. Further, many notable environmentalists are even self-proclaimed anarchists, of a gentle variety.[32] A soft energy path probably implies some decentralization of residential patterns, and organic agriculture implies a considerable rural repopulation if farm productivity levels are to be maintained. Such publications as *Harrowsmith*, *Rain*, and *Mother Earth News* have emphasized both environmental concerns and a preference for rural settings and rural virtues. The body of literature on building one's own solar home and/or returning to the land is awesome in volume and, I think, not without effect.[33] Demonstration projects such as the Ark in Prince Edward Island suggest that domestic settings can and should allow for a greater range of functions and even aspire to utter self-sufficiency in energy and food production. And Soleri's archologies envision the city rather than the family as the unit which might aspire to autonomy and a rural/agricultural setting.[34]

The values of self-management, self-reliance, autonomy and decentralization represent a profound challenge to contemporary industrial society. Yet it is my sense that these values are becoming manifest in many ways within the contemporary scene, and have been thus far inseparable from the other values of environmentalism. The appeal of an ability to autonomously supply the energy, shelter and food needs for one's family in these troubled times has obvious roots. To do so from renewable resources, including energy resources, allows one to imagine a secure future for one's descendants, perhaps these days the ultimate luxury.

There is, however, an important caveat with regard to the relationship between decentralization and environmentalism. However strongly environmentalists have sought a decentralized, self-managing future the *effect* of environmentalism as a whole, in the advanced industrial economies, has been to broaden and strengthen the powers of central governments. If one were to survey growth in the Canadian federal bureaucracy over the past twenty years one would see a disproportionate increase in "environmentally" relevant areas: energy, environment, and resource management. I for one do not take growing governmental power to be the least desirable political option. Autonomy and self-reliance as personal goals are not necessarily contradicted by a need for the political rival to centralized economic power.

Politically, environmentalists should not confuse their long-term decentralist dreams with the hard realities of the present situation. The existence of concentrated economic power assures a need for a strong political voice. Economic power is often, though by no means always, maintained at the expense of the environment. And in hard times the voice of environmentalists is one among many. Only with a strong political base for environmentalism and strong centralized political institutions for the nation as a whole can we hope to effectively impose the popular will on "our" institutions of private economic power.

Extended Time Horizon

The seventh value is less a value *per se* than a perspective—one with a differing sense of relevant time. Environmentalists, generally, are future-oriented and think in terms of long-term futures: their time horizon is extended. Others are content to bury toxic wastes in ways which render them likely harmless for a matter of decades. For most in industry, a century of safety is seen as an extravagance because it is tantamount to forever. Governments, alas, rarely see beyond the next election. Only environmentalists seem to ask the long-term questions: about hydrogeology, about bioaccumulation in food chains, and about potential long-term genetic effects. For an environmentalist there is really no such thing as "disposal" of toxic waste—there is re-use, there is containment, there is destruction and there is foregone need for manufacture. "Disposal" is an illusion, merely a deferral of problems into the future.

Many of the issues related to the extended time-frame perspective of environmentalism are discussed in Ernest Partridge's edited collection *Responsibilities to Future Generations*.[35] There the issue of nuclear power, particularly of the creation of nuclear wastes, is discussed extensively. A morally sensitive person must wonder if one generation has the right to put all future generations at risk in order to meet its own energy needs. But on reflection one must also realize that the depletion of fossil fuels also places future generations at risk, albeit a risk of a less dramatic sort. The point is that an environmental perspective disallows ignoring issues whose constituencies and victims (human as well as non-human) are as yet unborn. Civilization means nothing if we do not realize that the debt we owe our predecessors can only be paid to succeeding generations.

That paid, it does not automatically allow that environmentalists oppose particular forms of energy production out of hand. The issues are complex indeed and reach to the heart of the democratic system. Only living adults vote—yet many issues raised by environmentalists ask present governments to stop mortgaging the future—that is, to change present patterns in the interest of reducing future risks. There seems to be no other way; we can no longer plead ignorance on the whole range of toxic waste issues. Governments increasingly commit us for generations to come either by action, or by inaction.

One other matter should be mentioned here as well. Megaprojects impose ever-expanding time horizons on governments and citizens. Large-scale energy projects now require no less than a decade from planning to energy production. Money is committed and interest accrues for ten years before the first penny is earned. Obviously this is problematic for governments and for private investors. Soft-path energy production generally involves large numbers of small-scale projects and thereby avoids many of these time-frame and financing problems. However, one must also note that soft-path energy planners usually work on a 50-year time horizon.[36] That is, the production of most of all of Canada's energy from renewable resources involves such changes that it can only be imagined and planned on a time scale approaching a half-century. Thus, both in terms of sensitivity to problems and also in terms of proposed solutions, environmentalism requires a significant extension of the socio-political time frame. The environmentalist's time horizon is well beyond that of most individuals, corporate boards, and governments-of-the-day.

Interest in Non-material Values

The last value in our list largely follows from those which precede it. It is nonetheless worthy of separate identification and brief comment. A movement which questions the need for economic output at present levels, or at least in present mix is, of necessity, saying something about our society's basis for esteem. Broadly speaking, material measures of personal success, environmentalists would have it, are unduly emphasized within our culture. Success would be better determined in terms of less tangible attributes such as skill-level, achievement, taste or integrity. And material symbols of success, when employed, should emphasize qualitative and environmentally-guided standards, rather than quantitative measures.

Another way of characterizing this value is that environmentalists place greater emphasis on production values than on consumption values and within production values emphasize qualitative over quantitative production. For example, restoration of old and beautiful buildings is highly valued. So is writing a symphony or learning a language. Driving a big car or owning several homes is simply not important. Among the two economic implications of this perspective are these two: (1) quality (beauty, durability) is worth paying for, and (2) if advances in productivity can be continued, they should be translated at least as much into reduced work time as into increased production. "Work" here is used specifically in the sense of wage labour.

Conclusion

With this summary of what I take to be a list of environmentalist values, it is obvious that teaching science is not enough; we must also communicate values. I do not think it necessary to assert that the world will perish in fire, ice, poison and/or resource depletion if environmental values are not adopted wholesale and immediately. Environmentalist millenialism sometimes wears thin in the face of economic stringency.

The task left to environmental educators is an important one. Our society is unlikely to be able to achieve significant environmental improvement if we cannot reestablish the precedence of considered belief (values) over mere market preferences, the consumer whims of the moment.[37] In a democracy everyone's considered beliefs should count for something. And in an educational system which serves democracy, people must be given the opportunity to discuss value issues. Only when environmental values can be expressed and communicated will environmental improvement become possible.

Endnotes

1. This is the essence of many rebuttals to environmentalist claims. See, for example, John R. Maddox, *The Doomsday Syndrome*, (New York: McGraw: Hill, 1972).

2. The classic case here is Rachel Carson's *Silent Spring*, (Boston: Houghton Mifflin Company, 1962); its story is told in Frank Graham, Jr. *Since Silent Spring*, (Boston: Houghton Mifflin Company, 1970). Further, the notion that resource stocks were being depleted too rapidly and even frivolously was common in environmentalist publications well prior to the energy reckoning of 1973.

3. Paul R. Ehrlich, *The Population Bomb*, (New York: Ballantine Books, 1968), and Donella H. Meadows, *et al.*, *The Limits to Growth*, (New York: Universe Books, 1972). See also Robert Heilbroner, *An Inquiry into the Human Prospect*, (New York: W.W. Norton, 1975), and William Ophuls, *Ecology and the Politics of Scarcity*, (San Francisco: W.H. Freeman and Company, 1977).

4. David Brooks, and Alma *Norman*, "A Question of Choice," *Alternatives*, 3 Winter, 1974, 4-12.

5. Some response to this view is contained in a short paper which I prepared for the International Forum of this conference. The paper is entitled "Environmental Science and Environmentalism: Bridging the Two Cultures Gap" and is available on request.

6. See, for example, David Brooks' *Zero Energy Growth for Canada*, (Toronto: McClelland and Stewart, 1981), and David Brooks and Robert Paehlke, "Canada: A Soft Path in a Hard Country," in *Canadian Public Policy VI* (Summer, 1980), 444-453.

7. On the notion of a technological imperative see Jacques Ellul, *The Technological Society*, (New York, 1974).

8. I discuss the implications of some of these technologies for environmentalists in a paper presented in Washington, D.C., Summer, 1982. The paper is entitled "Telecommuting, Robotics and Hi Tech Environmentalism."

9. See David Dickson's *Alternative Technology and the Politics of Technical Change*, (Glasgow: Fontana/Collins, 1974).

10. *Supra*, endnote 5.

11. This issue is clarified in Arnold Brecht, *Political Theory*, (Princeton: Princeton University Press, 1959), in Chapter III, 117-135.

12. Samuel P. Hays, *Conservation and the Gospel of Efficiency: The Progressive Conservation Movement, 1890-1920*, (Cambridge, Mass.: Harvard University Press, 1959).

13. David Brooks and Doris McMullen, "The Trade-Off," *Nature Canada*, Spring, 1980, p.36.

14. See my article "Carcinogens: Guilty Until Proven Innocent," in *Nature Canada*, 9 (April/June, 1980), 18-23.

15. John Henry Wadland, *Ernest Thompson Seton: Man in Nature and the Progresssive Era 1880-1915*, (New York: Arno Press, 1978), p.10.

16. For some figures see Lester R. Brown and Pamela Shaw, "Putting Society on a New Path," *Environment*, 24 (September, 1982), p.32.

17. Lester R. Brown, *Building a Sustainable Society*, (New York: W.W. Norton & Company, 1981).

18. These issues are well discussed in *ibid.*, and loss of cropland in a Canadian context in Ralph R. Krueger and Bruce Mitchell, *Managing Canada's Renewable Resources*, (Toronto: Methuen, 1977).

19. John Helliwell and Alan Cox, "Wood Wastes as an Energy Source for the B.C. Pulp and Paper Industry: Economic Implications and Institutional Barriers," in Peter N. Nemetz, ed., *Energy Policy: The Global Challenge*, (Montreal: IRPP, 1979).

20. Monica E. Campbell and William M. Glenn, *Profit from Pollution Prevention*, (Scarborough: Firefly Books, 1982).

21. See Brooks, *Zero Energy Growth, op. cit.*

22. See *supra*, endnote 8.

23. William Leiss, *The Limits to Satisfaction*, (Toronto: University of Toronto Press), puts this assertion in perspective. See also Duane Elgin, *Voluntary Simplicity*, available through Gage Publishing, Toronto.

24. See my article "Environmentalisme et syndicalisme au Canada anglais et aux Etats-Unis," *Sociologie et Sociétés XIII (Avril, 1981), 161-179.*

25. Brooks and McMullen, *op. cit.* p.36.

26. Some of that cost is documented in Samuel Epstein, *The Politics of Cancer*, (San Francisco: Sierra Club Books, 1978).

27. The best collection on this issue is still Herman E. Daly, *Toward a Steady-State Economy*, (San Francisco: W.H. Freeman and Company, 1973).

28. For an example of heavy moral indignation regarding consumerism see Robert van den Bosch, *The Pesticide Conspiracy*, (New York: Doubleday & Company, Inc., 1978), p.17. This is not an uncommon perspective among environmentalists.

29. Paul McKay, "Survival or Suicide: The Choice is Ours to Make," in *Conserver Society Notes (Alternatives)*, 10 (Fall-Winter, 1982), Notes, p.9-13. Electric hedge-trimmers are mentioned on page 10.

30. Christopher Flavin, *The Future of Synthetic Materials: the Petroleum Connection*, (Washington: Worldwatch Institute, 1980).

31. This point was part of the notable Ehrlich/Commoner debate of the early 1970s.

32. Wadland, *op. cit.* makes this point and gives several references; see his pp.6-7, and 15-21.

33. See Robert G. Healy and James L. Short, "The Challenging Rural Landscape," in *Environment*, 23 (December, 1981), 6-11, 30-34.

34. For a discussion of Soleri's archology concept see Richard Faust Register, *Another Beginning*, (Berkeley: Treehouse Books, 1978).

35. Ernest Partridge, ed., *Responsibilities to Future Generations*, (Buffalo, N.Y.: Prometheus Books, 1981).

36. See Brooks and Paehlke, *op. cit.*, endnote 6.

37. These ideas are developed very effectively in Mark Sagoff, "Economic Theory and Environmental Law," *Michigan Law Review*, 79 (June, 1981), 1393-1417.

7

Is it Possible to Teach Environmental Ethics?

Peter Timmerman

Research Associate, Institute for Environmental Studies
University of Toronto, Toronto

Introduction

Information, exhortation, crisis reports—what can we use in the struggle to generate a sense of environmental concern?

For many people, this struggle to generate concern is best thought of as trying to instil in others a sense of "environmental ethics." It is, in the last analysis, a form of teaching; except that environmentalists are seeking to teach "environmental ethics" to citizens, industrialists, and people in positions of political power, not just to students. But is it possible to teach environmental ethics? And if it can be taught—in all senses of the word "teach"—how does one go about doing so?

Is it possible to teach environmental ethics at all? When I put this question—sometimes openly, sometimes surreptitiously—to most of the environmentalists of my acquaintance, I am struck by the consistency of their replies. By and large, environmentalists hold to what I would call the "pragmatic rapture" school of environmental education. It is somewhat analogous to the situation in Plato's famous dialogue, the *Meno*, where Socrates was able to show that an uneducated slave could learn geometry by being asked questions that brought out the slave's innate (and presumably prenatal) knowledge of the principles behind geometry.

In the same way, many environmentalists believe that putting people in touch with Nature will put them more in touch with themselves. By getting people to undergo wilderness experiences, by tapping their affection for familiar natural places, or by revealing to them scientifically the multitudinous connections and infinite complexity of ecosystems, there is a faith that the effort to understand, and the resultant feelings of awe, will somehow enable people to get back in touch with an innate love of Nature—a love that has been lost, stolen, or made to stray.

I am not saying this view is wrong. It is a curious amalgam of truths, truisms, Zen, existentialism, neo-Platonism, love of science, degraded pastoralism, and a bit of university academic thrown in for good measure. It could be right, since the truth is often a curious amalgam; however, it is difficult to use as a consistent basis for moral discussions, since it is ultimately grounded on either factual content or on the assertion of a personal existential experience.

A good example of this difficulty is provided by Livingston's book, *The*

Fallacy of Wildlife Conservation (1981), in which the author, having sliced away with glee all the tenuous threads of the second-rate utilitarianism, shadow cost-benefit analysis, and pure romanticism used by Lilliputian conservationists to restrain the technological Gulliver in our midst, is left only with the bald assertion that, having been a naturalist for over 40 years, his experience of life is richer than that of a non-naturalist. This being the case, it is Livingston's aim to convince others to undergo the same rich experience, so that they will then try to save wilderness areas in order that Livingston may continue to have his experience! Again, he may be right—he is certainly to be admired for not being mealy-mouthed—but it is not an argument. By what possible criterion could anyone prove that one person's experience of life, based on content alone, was richer than another's? I see no reason why William Blake spending his life cooped up in a Holiday Inn could not have as rich an experience of life as, say, James Watt in the High Sierras. Livingston's position is not susceptible of proof: it is the stance of a prophet.

Many of the moral arguments in the environmental literature are like this, though rarely are they so clearly and forthrightly stated. Many of the rest are held together simply by claims to sincerity and by improvisations around a few striking images. Lyrical statements about the beauty of an efficient ecosystem jostle against emotional responses to the distant eerie howl of a timber wolf; the doctrine of natural selection sits alongside the techniques of environmental management; and the mystical vision of the wilderness as sacred space somehow feeds into the necessary conversion of the swinish multitude.

Ethical arguments in environment contexts take this form in large part because environmentalism has up until recently been so loaded down with having to assimilate basic information about the environment into at least a preliminary synthesis, or with having to handle emergency cases of obvious value, that there has been little time to ask some basic ethical questions. Questions such as what it means to be ethical at all; what it means to have responsibility; what constitutes one's duties or obligations to others (including perhaps the physical world); and what it means to apply these issues to the environment. It was often just assumed that all that was required was an extension or some kind of "transformation" of existing ethical norms so as to include Nature.

One additional stumbling-block is the widely held belief that philosophy—and here I mean Anglo-American philosophy—which by rights should be providing the tools and framework for such a process of questioning of basic ethical positions, is largely irrelevant to all current issues, or at the very least occupied elsewhere.

If there was ever a kind of truth in this indictment, I think it is clear that its time is now past, and has been past for some time. At least since the 1960s—and in some quarters, well before that—moral philosophy has made the "metaphysical turn" back towards the discussion of pressing social, moral, and political issues. It is increasingly bringing its formidable critical and analytic abilities to bear on the analysis of issues ranging from bioethics to the distribution of food to Third World countries. While the most spectacular work has perhaps been carried out in political theory and law, there is a strong undercurrent or driving force being provided by new general theoretical arguments.

At the heart of these new arguments is the resurgence of a number of supposedly extinct traditional models of political theory that were driven underground by the liberal-utilitarian hegemony of the 19th and early 20th centuries: the social contract; the minimalist "watchman" state; moral sentiment; and natural law. The resurgence of these models has meant the recreation of a sense of importance for the role of moral philosophy in addressing social, moral and political issues.

This, I would like to argue, provides a new starting point for the consideration of a whole range of human and communal truths that seemed to have been expelled from the Garden of quantitative Eden. Moreover, as the philosophers I will now discuss show by their work, variations on these traditional views, as reformulated in the light of latter-day developments in moral philosophy, can be brought to bear on the environmental concerns of our time. For the teacher, there is the added bonus that it is also possible to discuss, act out, and perhaps even resolve moral issues in ways that the algebraic calculations of utilitarianism eliminated at the outset.

While, as I have indicated, this resurgence has been proceeding on a variety of fronts, it has been associated in moral philosophy mainly with the work of R.M. Hare, John Rawls, and their followers.

The Work of R.M. Hare and John Rawls

The main impetus behind Hare's moral philosophy was provided by the revolution in linguistic and metaphysical philosophy associated with the names of Russell, Moore, and Wittgenstein, a revolution which had as its basis a turning away from the notion that language was somehow transparent, or that the relationship between language and the world could be viewed without significant distortion as a simple one-to-one correspondence between a word and an object "out there". The clarifications of Russell and Moore set the stage for the revolutionary critique of language and logic put forward by Wittgenstein in his *Philosophical Investigations* (1953). The impact of this critique (too complex to be outlined here) was felt in a shifting emphasis towards determining to what extent our perceptions of what was "out there," and our actions in making the relevant correspondences, were being shaped by the structures, usages, and conventions of our ordinary languages.

Instead of focussing on some event or object that might be labelled "good" or "just," Hare and others began asking the question: "What in fact are people doing when they make moral judgements?" In other words, what is going on when people say: "This is good; you ought to do it."

Hare—who it might be noted had spent a lot of time in a Japanese prisoner-of-war camp in World War II, and thus had substantial experience in watching the construction of individual and communal moralities from scratch—was struck by the way that prescriptive language, language that tells us that we ought to do something, is primarily practical in intention. That is, somebody wants to get something done. At the same time, it is also evaluative. Somebody wants to get something done for a reason, the reason sometimes being a claim to the operation of a moral principle in that particular situation. Hare began by looking at prescriptive language or imperatives, breaking them down into ordinary imperatives like "Shut the door," and evaluative imperatives, such as "You should go and fight for your country." The basic difference between them is what is used to respond to the obvious question: "Why should I?" In the case of shutting the door, there will usually be a factual reason—"There is a draft"—or a power reason—"Because I tell you to." In the other case, there may also be factual or power reasons, but often one will come up against what Hare calls a universal, prescriptive, and overriding moral principle which is asserted: "In this situation, a citizen ought to fight for his or her country." It is universal, *"Anybody,* x, in this situation, should . . ."; and prescriptive, *"should"* or "ought to." Notice that Hare's position is formal; that is, it depends on the logical character which he says is part and parcel of using words like "ought" in a sentence. This means that if you say, "one ought to do x" and then, when you find yourself in the kind of situation where "one ought to do x" applies, you don't do x, and don't seem too bothered about not having done it, you obviously are not using the word "ought" properly. And one would be forced to conclude that you did not know the rules for application of the words used. For Hare, someone who knows what "ought" means logically, and uses it imperatively, must necessarily be committing himself or herself to the consequences.

Crucial to this logical meaning is the universality of the prescription. Anyone who says, "All blacks should be treated like second-class citizens" must be prepared to say that if he or she were black, he or she would be prepared to be treated as a second-class citizen. This involves a serious taking on of the viewpoint of the parties to be affected by the assertion of a moral principle.

Hare's position is thus a reformulation of Kant's famous ethical principle, "the categorical imperative," which states that "one should always act so that one's actions could be turned into a universal law"; as well as of Christ's ethical principle, "Do unto others as you would have them do unto you." What makes Hare's approach so appealing is that it provides a way of bringing both those principles together, by ensuring that moral principles are asserted on an individual basis, and from a universal point of view, a view that embraces universal sympathy. Moreover, it allows one to consider facts and evaluations at the same time, since issues are pared down to questions of fact, and questions of evaluation, without making the separation permanent. This is of special interest to environmentalists, who are usually involved in having to evaluate facts as facts before having to evaluate them as elements in a moral decision.

It might be said that Hare's universal prescription theory gives a reasonably useful set of guidelines for a personal morality; and, by its demand that the proposer of a moral principle be prepared to accept the consequences of its implementation, also gives a good negative test for the seriousness of someone's assertion of a moral principle. But there still remains the problem of somehow adjudicating the various individual assertions of principle. For example, how does one get from individual principles to the principles that should govern a society? Hare's position, if I understand it correctly, seems to be that the individual, by making a universally prescriptive statement, and thereby having to put herself/himself in the shoes of everyone who could possibly be affected by the statement, is in effect agreeing with an old utilitarian principle: "Everybody shall count for one, and nobody for more than one," in which case—as an ideal observer—the individual would make the right decision for everybody. The question then becomes: how do you set up a mechanism for putting everybody's shoes on the table, so to speak?

Before discussing a theoretical mechanism, it is worth noting that environmental educators already use a version of Hare's theory whenever they conduct a simulation game wherein certain people are required to play roles in handling an issue. This is not just a game: it is an exercise in testing both the interpretation and quality of arguments and facts; but it can also be seen as an external prototype for an internal moralizing process along Harean lines.

It has been noted by Hare and others, including Barry (1973), that Hare's theory bears a remarkable resemblance to that put forward by Rawls, a political philosopher, in his very influential book *A Theory of Justice* (1971). As I mentioned before, one fascinating aspect of current moral philosophizing is the extent to which previous imaginative reconstructions, such as the social contract and natural law, have been revived. Rawls' *Theory* is an attempt to put the theory of the social contract back on its feet, by emphasizing that what killed the old version of the social contract was that it was tied to an outmoded anthropology. The hypothesis that there was a time in history when people voluntarily gave up their aboriginal rights to club each other in exchange for mutual protection and advancement, came to seem less and less possible as more was learned about the sophistication of tribes under primitive conditions, and as the whole theory came to be seen as an inadequate justification for existing social conditions. Rawls suggests that the social contract should be interpreted instead as a theoretical exercise for determining the justice of present issues.

He does this by creating a story called "The Original Position." I suggest that it could be presented to students as such (see Appendix). The basic story is that a group of supposedly rational people are brainwashed—put behind a veil of ignorance, as Rawls states it—and asked to hammer out a set of principles for the society of which they are members. Having been brainwashed, they are unaware of their class, social position, their talents or abilities, their conception of the good, or what kind of social, economic, or political system they inhabit. Rawls devotes his long and immensely rich book to a defence of his view that in such a proposed imaginary contract situation, the group would naturally generate two principles:

1. Each person is to have an equal right to the most extensive total system of equal basic liberties compatible with a similar system of liberty for all;

and a principle which overrides the second basic principle:

2. Social and economic inequalities are to be arranged so that they are both (a) to the greatest benefit of the least advantaged . . . and (b) attached to offices and positions open to all under conditions of fair equality of opportunity.

There are a number of rules of ranking and priorities which have to be taken into account; but the general overall conception, as formulated by Rawls, is:

All social primary goods—liberty and opportunity, income and wealth, and the bases of self-respect—are to be distributed equally unless an unequal distribution of any or all of these goods is to the advantage of the least favoured.

I do not propose to evaluate in any detail the merit of Rawls' arguments supporting his position. What is most compelling about his theory, as even his sternest critics would admit, is the neatness of the story of the original position. It is so compelling that *A Theory of Justice* is probably the most cited book in current political philosophy, and there have been limited attempts to set up practical versions of the original position. One such attempt has been made in the environmental field by the U.S. E.P.A. in 1978, in social decision-making for high consequence/low probability accidents, specifically in the evaluation of suspending pesticide use.

I mentioned that there is a resemblance between Hare's universal prescriptive theory, and Rawls' rational social contract theory. Both philosophers deduce their moral principles from what have been called mechanisms of "constrained self-interest," which in their various ways ensure impartiality. Hare sums up the similarities in this way:

Impartiality is guaranteed by the fact that my prescription has to apply in all cases resembling this one (the asserted case) in their universal properties; since these will include cases (hypothetical or actual) in which I myself play the roles of each of the other parties affected. I am by this theory in exactly the same position as the rational contractors. (Hare, 1972.)

On the surface, then, we have what appears to be a compelling structure for rationally examining both individual moral principles, and the principles that a just society would adopt if it impartially tried to balance essential liberties with essential social aims.

Unfortunately, there are problems with both theories, many of which are revealed when one tries to apply them to environmental issues. The criticisms of these theories lead into the second and last part of my remarks, since they involve a completely different set of approaches to dealing with the ethics of the environment. But before doing that, I want to briefly return to Hare's approach, and make the assertion that his approach convinces me that it is possible to teach ethics, and to teach it in a way that brings out something of the essence of the operation of moral principles on issues of concern.

This was best brought out by Hare himself in his article, "Language and

Moral Education," in *The Domain of Moral Education* (Cochrane *et al.* 1979). In this article he describes, very sympathetically, the process by which children can learn about the formation and adoption of moral principles through the examples provided by their parents and teachers, and indeed, by anybody who attempts to live by moral rules. "Even if," Hare says, "the child later, in thinking morally himself, comes to reject the content of the parent's moral principles, she or he will still retain a knowledge of their form; she or he will still be thinking morally, which is the essential thing that moral education has to achieve." This, Hare points out, puts a special obligation on parents and teachers to articulate their moral rules if pressed, and to show at least some remorse if they don't find themselves always able to live up to them.

On Hare's terms then and probably on Rawls' too, although that might take longer to argue, it is possible to articulate the ethical process; and if that is so, then there seems no reason to doubt that it can also be taught, at least in the abstract.

What about *environmental* ethics? Is this kind of thinking amenable to thinking about the environment? On the most superficial level, I think it is reasonable to suggest that in both Hare's and Rawls' approach, a certain amount of "low-level" environmentally ethical attitudes to the environment could be generated based on ordinary self-interest constrained by consideration for the needs of others. Some people would say that if we could only get people to operate this way, all our problems would be solved without having to bring in any bigger guns. I doubt this, but I would like to talk about this doubt purely in the context of critiques of Hare's and Rawls' approaches.

Critiques of the Theories

There have been a number of critiques of their approaches. From the environmental standpoint, one relevant critique of Rawls' "original position" has been concerned with the conditions of the bargaining sessions. One aspect of this is the exclusively human-oriented nature of the bargains struck, since it is hard to imagine a tree as a reciprocating rational agent. This is another version of that long-standing issue—pardon the double pun—"Should trees have standing?" This is also true of Hare's universal prescription, where it seems to be impossible (except Buddhistically) to imagine oneself in the position of a tree for the purposes of determining whether or not one should be cut down for the benefit of humanity. I am not ruling the possibility out: many naturalists are prepared to speak up for the loon; it is the act of imagination that poses the problems when one gets down to rare orchids or endangered insect species.

A second critique—mainly aimed at Rawls' social contractarians—contends that the whole approach collapses when considerations of time are brought into play. Because of the nature of the veil of ignorance, and the fact that the principles set down by the contractors are to be followed throughout the future by the society, it appears to be inevitable that the rational agents will be most concerned about the redistribution of present patterns of income, rather than with organizing for the future. Rawls tries to get around this by having each of his rational agents represent himself or herself, *and* all future generations each might produce. Rawls also postulates that people will prefer to live in a continuously stable society; and he further postulates that the agents will have a consistent psychology. This is all to ensure that the contractors will stick to their principles once proclaimed.

All these necessary underpinnings slowly ruin the neatness of the original position, and bring into the open much of Rawls' American individualist middle-class liberal approach to the creation of a contract. Hare has himself criticized Rawls for this appeal to intuitively necessary postulates which turn out to be Rawls' intuitions in disguise.

But both Hare and Rawls have come under more serious attack in the recent work of Alaisdair MacIntyre, especially in *After Virtue* (1981). In this book and in his earlier book *A Short History of Ethics* (1966), MacIntyre focuses on Hare and Rawls as highly articulate examples of modern deracinated individualism. He suggests that what Hare and Rawls have done (along with others) is to take to its logical extreme the essentially arbitrary assertive nature of the schemes they put forward. They begin by assuming that everyone has become a moral Robinson Crusoe, dumped onto a desert island devoid of any rules, and forced to create individual and social order from scratch. MacIntyre would not be surprised that Hare learned lessons from the prisoner-of-war camp; nor, I suspect, would he find anything surprising in the modern world's fascination with the kind of reporting one finds in Bruno Bettleheim's psychological studies of life in concentration camps. One of the most resonant images of our times is the life pared down to the bone, in Auschwitz, the Gulag, or elsewhere. What MacIntyre is saying is that this sort of thing appeals to us in our search for moral principles because we want to discover what, deep down, (or "pared to the bone") our moral principles are when you get rid of everything else. But, he would argue, this is in itself highly artificial and is just the result of our indoctrination into modern individualistic rootlessness. The very act of seeing indescribably stressful, massively authoritarian, and "life-at-the-limits" situations as definitive of the human condition reflects the state into which we have got ourselves.

MacIntyre contrasts this individual assertion of principle with what one can call the "classical" approach, after its long history in classical and humanistic culture. MacIntyre centres his discussion around "virtue"—hence, the society we are living in is "after virtue." The classical tradition received its first great formulation in Aristotle's *Nicomachean Ethics*, and then and thereafter was the code by which everybody lived, as naturally as breathing, for well over a thousand years. In this great tradition there were many variations, but holding everything together was a unified belief in a set of moral criteria or standards that everybody should live by, even if they failed to do so. This meant that there was a pattern by which one could tell if people were living virtuously; more than that, there was a pattern by which one could teach virtue. It was the basis of scholastic and humanistic education. Because of this, everything in society made sense morally, because it was part of a meaningful story. The Greeks could say: "Count no man happy until after he is dead," for they had a sense that every man's life had a shape, and that it could be assessed after-wards, almost by checking off a list.

This tradition—MacIntyre argues—is all around us, and we often subscribe to it (especially when fragments of our lives seem to make coherent patterns); but its unifying power for moral analysis collapsed with the collapse of belief in a moral order in the universe sanctioned by some form of divinity. The result has been that moral discourse is both made up of bits of different systems which are appealed to for justification, and is also unable to decide rationally between emotional claims and counter-claims for one system or another. The need for the constructivism of Hare and Rawls is symptomatic of the underlying moral disorder of the modern world-order.

What I would like to emphasize here is that in the previous world-order designated as "virtue-oriented," facts were inescapably evaluative. Just as one could describe a good watch by appeal to facts, so one could describe a good man by appeal to social facts. In the classical tradition, it was theoretically possible that all facts could have a moral meaning. This was because there was a coherent story into which everything could fit; and everyone had a role in that story, since it was everyone's story. In general, then, in MacIntyre's words, "to adopt a stance on the virtues will be to adopt a stance on the narrative character of human life," since the part that virtues play in life is precisely that, the part they play in life. The reverse holds true as well: a commitment to a particular narrative of life entails a certain set of virtues. The two are interchangeable.

The Continuing Story of Life on Earth

Is there a point to all this, interesting as it may be? It seems to me that at the heart of any true environmental ethic, or what I called at the outset "a sense of environmental concern," is the creation of a sense of responsibility for the maintenance of the environment—if you like for the Earth and everything on it. To create that sense of responsibility one needs to have an interest in some-thing, and have an interest in its continued well-being.

The last philosopher I will mention, John Passmore, in his book *Man's Responsibility for Nature* (1974), uses the analogy of a teacher or a researcher who feels a sense of responsibility for the subject being taught or studied. One wants to contribute to it, to be part of its past and to take part in the creation of its future, either by transmitting one's interest in it to others, or by adding to the general stock of knowledge about the subject. But all this requires a com-munal story, a heritage, a narrative which is the subject: a continuing coherence of imaginatively related truths.

This dovetails very nicely with MacIntyre's argument, and has special relevance for environmental ethics. Commitment to environmentalism is the commitment to a sense of responsibility for the continuation of one particular narrative: life on Earth. This is the burden of Jonathan Schell's analysis of nuclear war in *The Fate of the Earth* (1982), which demands that we not only make a commitment to this narrative, but we also commit ourselves to the possibility of future narratives which we cannot even fathom from our limited present perspective.

Taking a stance on that commitment—which, I would argue, is exactly the same commitment that one makes in trying to save wilderness or endangered species, i.e., fighting the possibility that a narrative will be eliminated before it has even been read properly, let alone allowed to go on "telling itself"—creates or perhaps "shows forth" a set of virtues, a set of ethical principles. It is not that we want to determine if the creation of ethical concern in an individual could be extended to include trees: commitment to the environment *is* taking a stance on a set of virtues, by virtue of the story to which one is committed. This is exactly comparable, for example, to what happened in the development of Renaissance humanism. The famous poet, Petrarch, who was instrumental in the formulation of that particular set of virtues, kept near him a copy of Homer's *Iliad* in Greek, although he could not read it, and could not, in 14th century Italy, find anyone who could teach him Greek. He was, however, committed to the intrinsic worth of something he could not understand, because he was committed to the unfolding of the story when it became available. In the same way, preservation of species is a commitment to the virtue of a genetic story we are only now beginning to read, haltingly.

One consequence of this reorientation is quite common-sensical. The relationship (or story) to which we become committed is one which sees the creation of self not just in a social context, but in a biological context as well. To make the narrative "work," it is necessary to make the connections, to show how the story fits together. That is what environmentalists do when they try to make people more aware of how they and their environment are intertwined. The more the connections are made the more sense the story makes.

An analogy which seems to be fruitful is the concept of "orientation" now widely used in landscape and urban planning. In the work of Kevin Lynch, e.g., *The Image of the City* (1960), the endowing of a place with a sense of meaning depends upon landmarks that give one a proper sense of orientation. The ability to develop coherent images of a place, or a path through various places, depends upon well-orchestrated narratives of connection. Without these, people get disoriented, or lost. Is not reorientation central to environmentalism?

If the original analogy to responsibility for the furtherance of a discipline is at all compelling, and if one thinks of the concept of responsibility in other contexts (as in a parent's responsibility for the furtherance of its child's welfare) that do not necessarily entail any reciprocity, then something else starts to happen: the notion of "rights" begins to disappear. While those who impart their understanding, and information, and even lives to a particular discipline have a stake in that discipline, they have no "rights" in it. What they have is obligations, which may be obligations to the scientific method, or peer review, or other criteria for contributing. Maintenance and advancement of the discipline is a duty, and not a right.

This bears directly on our relationship to the continuing narrative of life on Earth. One of the most mixed of the mixed blessings of the last three hundred years has been the rise to power of the never-ending search for rights as a political panacea. I say this very carefully, keeping in mind the hard and perhaps necessary struggle for rights in the past, and the horrors that currently overshadow the struggle for rights all over the world. Nevertheless, it should be said: there are no natural, inalienable rights of man. They are a social fiction—perhaps a necessary social fiction— that did not exist until well into the modern world. It has been strongly argued, by C.B. MacPherson, among others, that the rise of "rights" is coeval with the rise of industrialism. One could argue that, just as we are moving into post-industrialism, we might well be moving into a post-rights world. As it stands now, however, any glance at a daily newspaper will tell you that the air is thick with the clamour for various rights. Since "rights" as an attention-getter has had great success in the past it is not surprising that claims to legitimate aspirations should be labelled as rights. But I think it is not unfair to suggest that things have come to a pretty absurd state when, as I have already mentioned, we are going to have to protect trees by giving them human rights equivalence. And we are in grave danger of having substantial gains in human freedom eroded if—as seems likely—we just become oversaturated with "rights" claims.

It is time we looked at turning the whole thing inside out, and focusing instead on our duties and responsibilities. Basic to this inversion is a recognition that it has to be complete, in order to keep the worthy advances that have been made. An inversion that emphasizes personal duties, but leaves the rights of the state intact is a recipe for totalitarianism. What we want, for example, is to be able to ask if society is fulfilling its duties to us. A right to free speech becomes a duty on the part of society to hear what its citizens have to say.

There are at least two advantages to this approach. First, the fulfilment or non-fulfilment of duties and obligations is easy to measure and identify, since they are positive in nature, and can even be delineated. My right to wreck my property is now only restricted by nuisance laws and externally imposed regulations and zonings: there is no positive requirement to fulfill one's duty or obligations to its well-being. Even to articulate it, under the present system, is to sound absurd: to intimate that someone might be fired as an inadequate "steward" is to court incarceration.

Second, a sense of duties and obligations might give us something positive to work in, a story if you like. At the heart of "rights" there is a kind of emptiness, because what one has done is to stake out a territory into which others— or the state—may not stray. But all there is, is a boundary: the boundary encloses nothing but empty moral space that can be filled by the person asserting the right to do whatever does not stray into somebody else's moral space. Life becomes a series of forays out from one's fortifications into a no-man's land increasingly filled with barbarians of no fixed moral address.

The "duties of man," as I say, would give us a story to live in, although the details of the story must be left to another time and place. It would replace the morality of the desert island with the morality of the family, the community, and all those fragments of the world we have lost. It would bring back into consideration our duty to past generations to see that their lives were not mere run-ups to extinction; and our obligation to future generations not to leave them the dregs, if anything, of our riot through the world's resources.

But above all, and here I return to the question of what sort of environmental ethics we should try to teach, what the philosophers I have been discussing have all been aiming for are methods by which one can move towards the solution of moral questions through creating extensions of individual imaginative sympathy. Imaginative sympathy has to be extended to others who might be affected by our moral decisions, and, indeed, extended to the visualization of the consequences of our actions for all sorts of "others" we might never have sympathized with before. For the environmentalist, who is concerned with extending imaginative sympathy to future generations, to the legacy of the past, and even to other species, a framework for moral decision making of the kind I have been describing should be of great interest. Duties and obligations spring out of the commitment to the maintaining and sustaining of a meaningful shape to the social and biological narrative of life on earth.

"History," as James Joyce the Irish writer, once said, "is a nightmare from which I am trying to awake" (1922); but, in fact, we need the opposite response: history is the dream into which we should be waking. As it is, we seem to wander around through the disconnected fragments of dull artifacts constructed with occasional bursts of sense by people and groups of people who were half-asleep when they thought them up. They are examples of what Northrop Frye somewhere calls, "failures of the imagination," and they litter the barren flatness of the moral sprawl in which we live.

The job of teaching environmental ethics, as I see it, is somehow to wake up the imagination to the work it needs to do. This requires that we tell it a story that has some point, that shows what role the imagination can play in the story, and that has a narrative and images rich enough, full enough, that with each telling the imagination gets more and more compelled into making the meaningful connections itself. And surely the story awaiting its tellers is one of the richest, fullest, and most compelling stories around. Especially since, in the last analysis, it will not be you that will be telling the story; it will be the story that will be telling you.

Appendix—"The Original Position"

Consider the following science-fiction story:

The society you are living in has to make a series of hard decisions about allocation of resources, animal rights, preservation of wilderness areas, and other issues that are a complex mixture of practical and ethical problems that demand a just solution. It is decided that some new mechanism for deciding on the justice of these issues must be created, since the old ones obviously don't work or are manifestly unjust.

You are sound asleep one night, and there is a knock on the door. You open the door, and five hooded people jump you. You are blindfolded and hurried away into the darkness. You have the sensation of movement, but you have no idea where you are going or why you have been kidnapped. Eventually, you are taken into a room, where you are drugged, and put to sleep. Just before you fall asleep, you hear what appears to be the sound of heavy machinery being rolled into place.

You suddenly wake up. You are no longer blindfolded, but you are in a strange cubicle, which is wired for sound. In some way, you realize that you are only one of a number of people (say 20) in cubicles in one large room. You have no idea what the other people in the room are like, nor who they might be—if they are rich, poor, ill, well, dying, male, female, black, white. It also suddenly occurs to you that you haven't the slightest idea what or who you are yourself. You have had all that part of you erased. All you know is that you have normal intelligence, and that you are a member of the society.

A voice comes over the universal intercom:

"Greetings. One of our eminent philosophers has convinced us that the only way our society can decide about questions of justice is by creating a panel of citizens like yourselves to formulate a set of basic moral rules. As you have no doubt learnt by now, you do not know where you are, what rank you now hold in society, what your advantages or disadvantages may be. Nor do you know about the qualities of the rest of the panel. All that you do know is that whatever you decide as a group will become the rule for everyone in the society, including yourself. Go to work."

References

Aristotle. *Nichomachean Ethics.* 1976. J.A.K. Thomson (trans.). Harmondsworth: Penguin Books.

Barry, Brian. 1973. *The Liberal Theory of Justice.* Oxford: Clarendon Press.

Cochrane, D.B., C.M. Hamm and A.C. Kazepides (eds.). 1979. *The Domain of Moral Education.* New York & Toronto: Paulist Press and Ontario Institute for Studies in Education.

Environmental Protection Agency. 1978. *Social Decision-Making for High Consequence, Low Probability Occurrences.* EPA-600/5-78-121, October.

Hare, R.M. 1952. *The Language of Morals.* Oxford: Clarendon Press.

Hare, R.M. 1963. *Freedom and Reason.* Oxford: Clarendon Press.

Hare, R.M. 1981. *Moral Thinking: Its Levels, Method and Point.* Oxford: Clarendon Press.

Joyce, James. 1922. *Ulysses.* Paris: Shakespeare & Co.

Livingston, John A. 1981. *The Fallacy of Wildlife Conservation.* Toronto: McClelland & Stewart.

Lynch, Kevin. 1960. *The Image of the City.* Boston: The MIT Press.

MacIntyre, Alaisdair. 1966. *A Short History of Ethics.* New York: Macmillan Publishing Co.

MacIntyre, Alaisdair. 1981. *After Virtue.* New York: Macmillan Publishing Co.

MacPherson, C.B. 1962. *The Political Theory of Possessive Individualism.* Oxford: Clarendon Press.

Passmore, John. 1974. *Man's Responsibility for Nature.* London: Gerald Duckworth & Co., Ltd.

Plato. *Meno.* (Various translations).
Rawls, John. 1971. *A Theory of Justice.* Oxford: University Press.
Schell, Jonathan. 1982. *The Fate of the Earth.* New York: Avon Books.

8
Coping with Science and Technology in the Eighties

David T. Suzuki

Professor, Department of Zoology
University of British Columbia, Vancouver

Introduction

We live in a time of crisis, a fact brought home to us every day by the media: war, urban crime, unemployment, inflation, high mortgage rates, energy shortages, and so on. There is, however, another crisis which is rarely recognized by the media—a science crisis. As used by the military, industry, and medicine, science affects our lives to a much greater extent than any of the other topics that either the media or the politicians feel are important.

This lack of attention is not a result of stupidity, but rather a lack of understanding. Media figures and politicians are as ignorant, prejudiced, and fearful of science as the average person in the street. Yet, they have to make important decisions about environmental issues in which science plays a major role. Such decisions include the following:

- What should be the future of the Candu nuclear reactor?
- Should we delay nuclear dependence and opt for conservation, while we search for alternate forms of energy as the fusion reactor or hydrogen energy?
- Should we allow drilling for oil in the Beaufort Sea, the building of the Mackenzie Valley pipeline, the building of liquid natural gas plants in New Brunswick, or the transport of oil in the High Arctic using atomic tankers?

These are all issues that cannot be decided without a solid understanding of science. Yet, the people we elect are not competent to make these decisions.

There are a number of other problems which influence the way that environmental issues are handled in Canada. One is the political system itself. Of necessity, the politicians are all short-sighted. Their vision is limited to the distance between elections; they simply cannot make commitments two or three elections away. The consequence of this limited time horizon can be illustrated by the case of high technology. Politicians are assigning massive amounts of money to private companies and universities in order to build a high-technology industry so that Canada can compete with other countries in such areas as computer technology and biotechnology. It is folly to believe that the government can simply give millions of dollars to a Canadian university and that in five years Canada will be a world-class biotechnology organization. It simply will not happen.

The reason that it will not happen is that we do not believe in ourselves; we do not believe that we can compete. As a small country, we have seen generations of our best people going to the United States or Europe to succeed at a world-class level. It has come to the point where the proof of Canadian quality is success somewhere else; if you are still in this country, it is believed that you cannot be any good. As long as we believe this about ourselves, there is no way that we can compete with Japan, Germany or the United States. This lack of self-confidence is a serious problem.

Another problem with environmental issues is that over 50% of the scientists around the world carry out their work for the military, with most of the rest working for private industry. So long as science and technology are being applied for destructive purposes and for private gain, such issues as the long-term consequences of new innovations for the environment and for the public at large will seldom become a priority.

For these reasons, environmental issues have either not been dealt with at all or have been dealt with in an *ad hoc* way. Yet, we have a society committed to progress where progress is defined as technological innovation and with an underlying faith that any detrimental consequences of that technology can be dealt with by further technological innovation. There is a fundamental flaw in this outlook: technology cannot always solve technological problems.

An Evolutionary Perspective

In order to understand how we developed this belief in technology, we have to go back in time and take an evolutionary perspective of the human brain. This is helpful in understanding why we are not completely rational entities.

Ancient creatures evolved with concentrations of nerve cells in ganglia. The part of the body that became known as the cephalic or brain area gradually increased in size until the cephalic complex controlled the automatic systems—breathing, heart rate, excretion, etc.—without the organism having to think about it. These control systems came to be located in the primitive brain stem at the top of the spinal cord. With the evolution of more complex behaviours, the primitive brain stem no longer sufficed. The result is what has been called the "R complex" or the reptilian complex, an enlargement of the cephalic region covering the primitive brain stem which is responsible for reptilian, aggressive, and territorial behaviour. When mammals evolved, they developed a mammalian aspect that overlays the R complex; it is responsible for such traits as loneliness, the need to play, group socializations, and parental caring. In fact, if specific parts of that mammalian portion of the brain are removed from a mammal—a monkey or a rat, for example—the animal will lose the corresponding mammalian properties; it will lose interest in playing, in parenting, etc.

When the earliest humans appeared, another thin layer or outer part of the brain—the neo-cortex—evolved. Those aspects of the human brain that are regarded as unique seem to reside in the neo-cortex: the ability to dream, to imagine, to think, to remember. I am making this point about the human brain because there seems to be a dominant idea or mythology that humans are rational creatures and that we must evaluate people on the basis of their rational activities. It is true that we do have the ability to think logically, but underlying the neo-cortex—supposedly the core of rationality—are ancestral structures. Emotions and instinctive behaviours and responses play a very strong role in the way we respond to stimuli as well.

The evolution of the neo-cortex gave rise to what seems to be a uniquely human characteristic: the need to create order out of chaos. To the emerging consciousness of our early ancestors, the world must have seemed a chaotic place, where nothing made sense, where things seemed to appear and disappear and happen for unknown—and perhaps unknowable—reasons. Chaos is terrifying, because it is unpredictable. But those early humans began to recognize order and regularity in the world around them: day and night, the seasons, tides, the lunar cycles, the movements of animals, the progression of plants during the seasons, and so on. By relying on these regularities, they could begin to create order around them; they could begin to predict; and they could begin to have some hope of controlling the world.

Control—that seems to be the operative word. By understanding the events occurring around them, they could control them in some way. Of course, there were still floods, storms, earthquakes, solar eclipses, and other things that did not make sense. In order to explain them, humans invented gods and goddesses: when these things happened, they could be blamed on the will or anger of the gods. There developed then what anthropologists call a "world view"—a cosmology in which everything is explained and linked together in a single explanation. Anthropologists argue that members of any other species faced with a stress situation or a given environmental input will invariably respond in the same way. They are programmed to respond in certain ways to various stimuli. In contrast, while the brains of an Australian aborigine, an African bushman or a North American are physically the same, each of these humans will react in totally different ways when faced with the same environmental signals. Unlike other animals, all humans share the same brain structure, but we each have the capacity to interpret and to fashion environmental stimuli in totally different ways. Thus, humans are characterized by an unbelievable amount of flexibility in the way that they look at the world.

The Judaeo-Christian World View

Human groups have held thousands of world views over time. Only a few of them survive today. About 3000 years ago, a world view emerged that has evolved into the most powerful one ever held: the Judaeo-Christian world view, as embodied in the Bible. We see embedded in *Genesis* an indication of the human position of this world view. Man is made in God's image and is enjoined to be fruitful, to multiply, and to go forth and fill the Earth and subdue it. Man is to have dominion over the fish of the sea, over the birds of the air, over every living thing that creeps upon the Earth. Therefore, the essence of this tradition is the injunction to dominate the world, to subdue it, to commit it to man's will. We have come to see progress in the Western World defined on the basis of the extent to which humans can realize that biblical injunction: if humans can dominate or subdue something in nature, they have progressed.

With the beginnings of the Scientific Revolution in the 16th and 17th centuries, scientists such as Kepler, Copernicus, Galileo, and Bacon began to recognize that within nature are certain regularities that could be recognized and understood; these came to be defined as laws or principles. Bacon said that knowledge is power; he recognized that, by looking at the world through this new methodology of science, humans could gain enormous power over nature and that that power would be a fulfillment of God's injunction to have dominion. These early scientists, however, were initially not so much interested in using the powers of science to control nature, but more in understanding how God works. Very quickly, however, they shifted to the notion that not only can humans understand how nature works, but they can also control it.

Descartes was able to show that there were underlying mathematical principles that could explain many natural phenomena. Mathematics, very early on, became an essential part of scientific analysis, as exemplified by Newton who, through the laws of gravity, laid the basis for understanding the complex motion of the planets and stars. To Newton, the universe seemed to behave as though it were a giant machine, with its components governed by simple laws. If the universe is a machine that could be understood through science, Newton wondered whether all aspects of the world could be understood in the same way. If the elements of nature could be reduced to their most elementary parts, could we then not reconstruct the entire universe and not only understand it, but predict it and know it all? Science then could become a powerful way of knowing not only about the cosmological motions of the universe, but also about the activities of human beings and all other creatures on the planet.

The church, which had earlier held such power over the people, recognized that science represented a great threat to its authority and chose to fight. It chose to fight, however, in the one area in which science was bound to be a winner: the realm of scientific information. It fought Galileo and won—for a while. It was a hollow victory because in the end, by clinging to the doctrine that the Earth was the centre of the universe, it created a very complicated universe. It is possible to derive the mathematics placing the Earth in the centre of the universe, but it is very complicated; it is much simpler to have the Sun at the centre. So, the church won the battle over Galileo, but in the end it lost the war.

In the 19th century, as biologists began to say that the Earth was probably hundreds of millions, if not billions, of years old, the church chose to fight them. For example, Bishop Usher claimed that the Earth was created in the year 4004 BC on a particular weekday afternoon, based on his interpretation of biblical history. The church held that humans were special creatures placed on Earth by God in God's image, and battled the Darwinian notion that humans had evolved like all other living forms on this planet. While there are still today some believers in creationism, such battles have generally been lost. In each case, the church chose to fight in the realm of science and, as it lost each battle, seemed to lose more of its moral authority. That, I believe, is the great tragedy of these battles. If God were indeed the ultimate mystery—beyond the ability of human beings to comprehend—then science kept pushing God further and further away from the image of the old man in the long beard sitting on a cloud looking after each one of us on Earth. Science kept extending its power and view further and further out to the range of the Universe and into the smallest levels of organized matter. I believe that God was killed by the very forces originally set in motion by devout people who saw science as a way to realize God's injunctions.

Thus, I believe that in the 20th century—with the death of a personal God, with the apparent loss of the church's capability and moral authority, and with the apparent victory of science—we are left with the sense that all we have is our lives: we are born, we live, and we die. There is nothing else. What science has done is to cut us adrift from any kind of sense of continuity as a part of the stream of life. We are now individuals who just happen, who live out a life, who die, and who disappear. We have been cut loose from any cosmological significance: we are on one of many planets circling billions of stars and billions of galaxies. We seem to have evolved as a product of chance with no purpose—one tiny flash in the eternal Universe.

Science and Technology

Today, science and technology have become an indispensable arm of national economies and policies. There is no doubt that science and technology in this century have been enormously successful in improving the quality of our lives. Machines have taken over dangerous or difficult tasks. Many health problems have been conquered by improved sanitation, antibiotics, and better nutrition. We are very different from our ancestors of only a few hundred years ago: we are technological beings and, as such, we are different from other organisms. Our dependence on science and technology has made us incapable of carrying out the most elementary acts of survival. We have created an entirely new class of people that never existed before in the history of human beings: the elderly. In 1900, the average life expectancy of North Americans was 47 years; today it is 74 years; by the end of this century, it will reach its theoretical maximum of 85 years. Today, 16% of the population is over the age of 60; this will increase to 20% by the end of the century. At the same time that science and technology have created this new group, they have also accelerated the speed with which our society is evolving so that these older people have become more obsolete and less relevant at a more rapid rate than ever before. It is most striking to see people at 60 or 70 in Africa who are still in the Stone Age, but who are living in the same house as children who are watching television; technology has created a leap of thousands of years.

We have become technological creations. Science has become a means for dominating nature, both environmental and human. I believe, therefore, that this scientific domination has resulted in a need to control the natural environment for human reasons. For example, we regard forest and animal populations as resources to be exploited. We regard people of the Third World as a resource to be exploited or as a potential market for our goods. Canadian history is rooted in the exploitation of a seemingly endless supply of resources, but if one examines that history it becomes obvious that we have not harvested these resources: we have mined and plundered them. We regard soil, water, and air as limitless in this country and then spew our wastes over the land. Take, for example, the problem of air pollution in Sudbury from nickel smelting: the "solution" was not to clean up the plant, but to build a higher stack in order to dilute the pollution and spread it over a wider area. I have never understood how that can be considered to be a solution to an environmental problem.

Science: The Ultimate Truth

Now that religion has diminished in its relevance to our lives, we look more and more to scientists for our ultimate truths. Indeed, science has itself become a world view, a means for understanding the entire world. But there is a flaw in such a view: we expect science to provide all answers and solve all problems. For example, we are afraid to die, so we call aging a disease and look to science for its cure. Science, however, is not and was never meant to be a world view. Science can supply a methodology, a way of probing nature. A world view must, by definition, explain everything and must be completely self-contained—a cosmology.

Science does exactly the opposite. It begins with the proposition that one cannot explain everything; the world is too complicated. All you can do with science is to focus on one tiny aspect of nature and try to understand it. When you understand it, you gain power and influence over it. But you cannot understand in any way how that little aspect of nature fits into the bigger picture. We know, for example, that even if we understand the elementary particles that make up matter and the behaviour of electrons and protons in atoms, we cannot anticipate what will happen when two atoms of hydrogen join with one atom of oxygen, for we cannot predict higher levels of complexity by the simple particles that make them up.

Moreover, in the reductionist approach to science, there is no equation or formula to take account of such things as emotions, values, ethics, morality, beauty, or love—the questions that we as people feel are important. Let us take the cases of whooping cranes or the great whales that are on the verge of extinction. From a scientific standpoint, it is impossible, I believe, to argue that these species should take the enormous amount of effort that is going into preserving a handful of them on the basis of some possible ecological collapse. I do not believe that the loss of one hundred whooping cranes now will have any significant effect on the environment. The loss of a few hundred whales of a particular species will not significantly affect the ecology of the oceans. I do not believe that we can justify or rationalize the attempt to save these organisms on any scientific basis. What I do believe is that these are issues of values. I started with the proposition that humans are very different and special, because we are able to look at whales and whooping cranes and to appreciate their beauty and, in so doing, create something that did not exist before: human appreciation. Whooping cranes, I believe, do not have this ability of appreciation; they merely act out what their DNA tells their RNA to tell their proteins to do. It is the human ability to appreciate and value that makes us different from other animals. When we destroy other species, we show such self-contempt for ourselves that it seems to reduce some of that dignity and specialness about humans. Therefore, I can justify putting an enormous amount of effort into protecting endangered species, not on any scientific basis, but because it diminishes me to see that humans would do such a thing—that is not in the scientific tradition.

We cannot deal with the issues of science, society, and the environment until we realize what the limits of science are; however, we cannot recognize those limits as long as we see science as providing a world view. The very methodology of science is based on a reductionist approach which does not allow such a comprehensive picture. Science's problem is its very success: we have come to expect far too much from it. In the process, we have become its victims. Scientists must take some of the responsibility for that, for they promulgate the notion that many of society's ills can be solved if we simply pump more money into science. They fail to see that the solutions to these problems are far more complex than that.

The Victims

Let me use nuclear weapons as an example of the fact that we have become victims of science and technology. Such weapons represent the greatest threat that we face today as a species and as a civilization. Weapons are, of course, designed to maximize our survival. Even the simplest early weapons—sticks or stones—were valuable for protection, gaining territory, and killing food. They were part of a survival strategy that came out of the human brain. By the 20th century, however, weapons have become totally counter-productive. They threaten human survival, for proliferation of atomic devices is literally out of control.

There are many people who argue that to talk about an arms freeze or an arms reduction is totally ridiculous. They argue that we must continue to support the United States so that it does not lag behind the Soviet Union. I would like to submit, however, that at the present time nuclear technology is out of control. I say this, not because of the degree of access to nuclear weapons, although this is a serious problem. In the United States, for example, over 100 000 people every year have direct access to a nuclear weapon. These people are heavily screened from a security point of view: psychological stability, capacity for social interaction, ability to obey orders, absence of drug problems, etc. Yet every year between four and five thousand of these 100 000 people are fired from their jobs because they have refused to take orders, because they have been found taking drugs or alcohol on the job, because they have had nervous breakdowns, and so on. Four to five thousand unstable people with direct access to nuclear weapons—that seems to me to pose a terrifying hazard.

There is, however, an even more profound issue than that. These weapons have the potential to hit their targets within a very short time—30 minutes if fired from a land base and 15 minutes if fired from a submarine. The United States Pentagon claims that, through the use of satellites, they can detect a missile within seconds after it leaves the ground or water and that they can identify within minutes the type of missile, its nuclear pay-load, its trajectory, its landing site, and the time when it will hit. They also claim that, within that 15-30 minute time frame, they will be able to evolve a strategy to respond. Further, they claim within minutes after the missile is detected, the President will have been transported to a lead-lined Boeing 747 and will be in the air, circling, presumably, above the danger of the fall-out or explosion zone or on his way to a giant fort in Colorado under a mountain where he will direct the response and win the nuclear war.

Such a strategy sounds great and might indeed work if the alarm sounds on a Tuesday morning at 11:00 a.m. when everyone is feeling well and is ready to respond quickly. I submit, however, that, if I was on the other side and I was going to fire a missile, I would probably wait until there was a big party in the White House on a Saturday night. After everyone went to bed at 2:00 a.m., I would wait until everyone was asleep and then fire the missile at 4:00 a.m. Imagine the poor guy sitting at the computer screen when he sees the information that a missile has been fired. The first thing that he will do is to kick the machine to make sure that it is working! Remember that in the past 15 years there have been over 100 mistakes detected, where computers have misdiagnosed flocks of geese or friendly airplanes as Russian missile attacks. In one case, a technician loaded the wrong computer tape and for several minutes the entire American military went on a "red alert" because they assumed the Russians were attacking.

Let us assume, however, that this will not happen. A few of the 15-30 minutes available have been lost ensuring that there has not been a computer mistake. Then someone has to get up the nerve to wake up the President and explain the situation. While the President is getting his pants on, he will have to decide whether to call the Russians to find out if it is a mistake or to order counter-measures to shoot down the missiles. What happens if not all the missiles are shot down? What about civilization? What about his own family? I do not believe that any human being is capable of functioning under these conditions.

The Pentagon argues that, if they are granted enough money, they will develop even better super-computers that will monitor the situation in that 15-30 minute window and will decide what the options are. The problem is that with every passing minute, the number of options decreases. It comes to a point when you absolutely have to respond or it will be too late. At that point, you will have to trust the machine because no human being is able to respond. For that reason, I think that we have turned ourselves into a technological people, not only the products of technology, but also totally dependent on that technology to the point that it is out of our control.

The Role of Education

How do I bring this discussion back to me and you? When I began working in the public media some 20 years ago, it was my belief that what was needed was a public that understood and had access to scientific information, that was scientifically literate, and that was therefore capable of handling the great forces affecting their lives. I thought that through the media, such as television, we might be able to raise the consciousness of people to a point where they could demand more of their politicians and be more critical about issues that affect them. In the past few years, I have had to ask myself whether this is a tenable position. I am afraid that I have come to the conclusion that it is not.

The reason for this conclusion is that we have access to more information at a popular level than ever before in human history: magazines, television, newspapers, books, radio, etc. All of these things suggest that people are more informed today than ever before. The problem is not getting more information to people; the problem is information overload. There is a wealth of information, but people have not learned to evaluate it. Alvin Toffler says that the amount of information available doubles every seven or eight years. Yet five or 10 years from now, we will know that 95% of all that information is wrong or irrelevant. The major problem, it seems to me, is how to evaluate the information and draw out the 5% that might be useful. People consume information at an outstanding rate, but simply cannot distinguish that which should be taken seriously and that which can be forgotten. Too much quasi-scientific information is presented in the popular media for entertainment purposes; the problem is that people accept it as fact.

The challenge then, I believe, to those of us who are interested in environmental issues and who are educators is that we must provide people not just with a sense that science is important and that science is limited, but that science is a way of looking at information. The essence of science is to be sceptical: not to take someone's word for something, but to ask for evidence and to evaluate that evidence using as many techniques as we have available to us.

I believe that the challenge for educators is to convey the importance of being able to look at knowledge, assess it, and then use it to influence our lives in a more profound way. That is the challenge for all of us.

Part 3:

Energy and the Conserver Society

This Part focuses on energy as a primary environmental issue and illustrates the complexity of environmental problems which involve ecological, social, economic, technological, and educational aspects. Berger focuses on the environmental and social impacts of frontier energy exploration in Canada. Arguing that the exploitation of such energy resources is ultimately futile because they are non-renewable resources which eventually must run out, Commoner lays the basis for a transition to a new type of society based on renewable energy resources. The paper by Brooks and Robinson shows how this could be accomplished in terms of one of the world's most serious environmental problems, the challenge of energy conservation.

9
Conflicting Views of the "Frontier"

Hon. Thomas R. Berger

The Clash Between the Dominant Society and Native Peoples

We in the Western nations tend to think of the history of the last 400 years as the history of the triumph throughout the world of Western ideals in science, industry, and technology. There is much truth in such a perspective; indeed, it is a perspective which many of the countries of the Third World have adopted. Western ascendancy in science and technology has made us think that there is nothing that the nations once colonized by Europe can teach us, for we regard the world we live in as a world conceived by science and built by technology. Indeed, we used to think that the changes wrought by science and technology would be altogether benign. In recent years, however, another view has begun to take hold: the advance of science and technology—especially large-scale technology—may entail social, economic, and environmental costs which must be reckoned with. The pace of change—and the cost that it entails—is only now beginning to be understood in the industrial world. In North America, the metropolis' requirements for energy and resources—energy and resources now being sought at the frontier—are bringing industrial activity to communities which may not be prepared to cope with the impact.

Many of us are aware of the impact of industrial advance on Third World countries, but we in Canada have our own domestic Third World: it is the world of the native or indigenous peoples—the Indians, the Inuit, and the Metis, who number altogether more than a million. The recent clashes of culture and of values that have occurred in Canada between the dominant society and the native peoples have forced a reconsideration by Canadians of the assumptions by which we live and of the means by which we hope to prosper in the future.

Perhaps the best-known recent encounter between the dominant society in Canada and the native peoples was that which occurred when the oil and gas industry proposed to build a gas pipeline from the Arctic to the mid-continent. The pipeline was to run along a route from Alaska through Canada along the Mackenzie Valley and down to the Lower 48 states, across environmentally sensitive lands claimed by the native peoples of the North. The Government of Canada appointed a Commission of Inquiry to examine the social, economic and environmental impact of the proposed pipeline. The Mackenzie Valley Pipeline Inquiry[1] provided a focus for consideration of the consequences of the advance of the industrial system to Canada's last frontier and beyond the necessity for the preservation of the Northern environment and, above all, the rights of the native peoples living on the frontier. The Inquiry had to weigh the value of establishing large-scale extractive industry in the midst of native communities trying to preserve traditional values and to reestablish local self-sufficiency.

Two ways of looking at the world were in conflict. Throughout the New World, since the time of Cortez and Pizarro, men have sought wealth at the frontier—wealth to enrich the metropolis. Ever since the days of New Spain, men have wished for another Montezuma's treasure, another Atahualpa to be ransomed. The drive to extract the wealth of the New World continues today. John Armstrong, Chairman of Imperial Oil, in a speech given in August, 1980, said: "The Canadian oil industry should be moving into our most promising Atlantic and Arctic properties like an army of occupation."[2] The language he chose epitomizes a value judgment about the future and the predominant place of large-scale, capital-intensive technology in that future. His preferences are, indeed, widely shared. Our notions of progress have, in fact, acquired a technological and industrial definition.

There has always been another strain running through our attitude toward the land and its resources. It is exemplified by the members of the first European settlement in North America, north of Florida, the Frenchmen who established Port Royal on the Bay of Fundy in 1605. One of them, Marc Lescarbot, a lawyer from Paris, wrote in his diary:

> . . . *farming must be our goal. That is the first mine for which we must search. And it is better worth than the treasures of Atahualpa for whoso has corn, wine, cattle, linen, cloth, leather, iron and lastly, codfish, need have naught to do with treasure.*

It is not surprising that these settlers, who came to be known as the Acadians, had the most harmonious relations of any European group with the native peoples. The view of man's occupation of the land that they exemplified is one which has an increasing number of adherents today in Canada.

The Growth of Ecological Awareness

The debate still goes on. It was the underlying theme of the Mackenzie Valley Pipeline Inquiry. The Arctic Gas Pipeline was to be the greatest project, in terms of capital expenditure, ever undertaken by private enterprise anywhere. It was to be a major construction project across our Northern territories, across a land that is cold and dark in winter, a land largely inaccessible by rail or road, where it would be necessary to construct wharves, warehouses, storage sites, airstrips—a huge infrastructure—just to build a 1.2-metre diameter pipeline. There would be 130 gravel-mining operations. There would be 600 river and stream crossings. There would be a network of hundreds of kilometres of roads built over the snow and ice. There would be pipe, trucks, heavy equipment, tractors, and aircraft. The capacity of the fleet of tugs and barges on the Mackenzie River would have to be doubled. There would be thousands of construction workers required to build the pipeline and to build plants and gathering systems. There would be thousands of in-migrants seeking jobs and opportunities. If a gas pipeline were built, it would result in enhanced oil and gas exploration activity all along the route of the pipeline throughout the Mackenzie Valley and the Western Arctic, and an oil pipeline would follow. So, the Inquiry had to examine the social, economic and environmental impact on the North of an energy corridor from the Arctic to the mid-continent.

In recent years, we have seen the growth of ecological awareness and a growing concern for wilderness, wildlife resources and environmental legislation that parallels—although it does not match—the increasing power of our technology, the consumption of natural resources, and the impact of rapid change.

Let me be clear about the importance that I accord to environmental values. I do not urge that we seek to turn back the clock, to return in some way to nature, or even to deplore, in a high-minded and sentimental manner, the real achievements of the industrial system. Rather, I suggest that environmental values constitute an invaluable aspect of modern-day life: the preservation of the environment is a contribution to, not a repudiation of, the civilization upon which we depend. It may be said that this is all very well in the case of urban amenities, recreation areas, campgrounds, and national parks. But of what use is a far-off landscape or seascape which urban dwellers may never see? Why should it matter to the urbanite whether the caribou still make their annual journey to the Arctic coast, whether the white whales of the Beaufort Sea still find a haven in the Mackenzie Delta in summer, whether the snow geese still feed on the islands of the Arctic archipelago? I think it matters because wilderness and wildlife are essential to mankind's sense of order in the universe. They affirm a deeply felt need to comprehend the wholeness of life. They offer serenity and peace of mind.

If a pipeline were to be built from Alaska along the Arctic coast of the Yukon, it would open up the calving grounds of the Porcupine caribou herd. This is one of the last great herds of caribou (110 000 animals) in North America. Every spring, the caribou journey from the mountains in the interior of the Yukon to the calving grounds on the Arctic coast. There they are able to leave the wolves behind; they can forage on cotton grass and bear their young before the onset of summer mosquitoes and bot flies.

In late August as many as 500 000 snow geese gather on the Arctic Coastal Plain to feed on the tundra grasses, sedges, and berries, before embarking on the flight to their wintering grounds. They must build up an energy surplus to sustain them; indeed, so must all other Arctic waterfowl and shore birds, for their long southward migration to California, the Gulf Coast, or Central and South America.

The peregrine falcon, golden eagle, and other birds of prey nest in the Northern Yukon. These species are dwindling in numbers because of the loss of their former ranges on the North American continent and because of toxic materials in their feed. Here in these remote mountains they still nest and rear their young, undisturbed by man.

Thus, the proposal by Arctic Gas to build a pipeline across the Northern Yukon confronted us with a fundamental choice. It was a choice that depended not simply upon the impact of a pipeline across the Northern Yukon, but upon the impact of the establishment of an energy corridor across it, for if a gas pipeline were to be built, an oil pipeline would logically follow along the same route.

This ecosystem, with its magnificent wilderness and scenic beauty, has always been protected by its inaccessibility. With pipeline construction, the development of supply and service roads, the intensification of the search for oil and gas, the establishment of an energy corridor, and the increasing occupation of the region, it would no longer be inaccessible to man and his machines.

Another international resource is the white whales of the Beaufort Sea. I recommended that a whale sanctuary be established in Mackenzie Bay. In summer, the white whales of the Beaufort Sea converge on the Mackenzie Delta to calve, because the Mackenzie River, rising in Alberta and British Columbia, carries warm water to the Arctic. So the whales (some 5000 animals) remain in the vicinity of the Delta throughout the summer, then leave for the open sea. For these animals, the warm waters around the Mackenzie Delta, especially Mackenzie Bay, are critical habitat, for here they have their young. In these warm waters, the whales stay until the calves acquire enough blubber to survive in the cold oceanic water. Nowhere else, so far as we know, can they go for this essential part of their life cycle. The evidence—and it was not contested— was that oil and gas exploration and production activity could so disturb the whale herd that they would be unable to reproduce successfully. In time, the herd would die out. I concluded that we must preserve these waters from any disturbance that would drive the whales from them.

Economic Development in the North

The Mackenzie Valley and the Western Arctic constitute a region as large as Western Europe. Though it is sparsely settled (only 30 000 people live in the region: 15 000 white, 15 000 native), it is inhabited by four races of people (White, Indian, Inuit, and Metis) speaking six languages (English, Slavey, Loucheux, Dogrib, Chipewyan, and Inuktitut). The region has a mixed economy. The people living in the Mackenzie Valley and the Western Arctic had a long-established renewable resource sector, based on hunting, trapping and fishing, and some limited logging and sawmilling along the upper reaches of the Mackenzie. Native people have traditionally found employment in this sector. There was, as well, a non-renewable resource sector, based on mining and, in recent years, oil and gas exploration. The mining industry largely employed white people. The oil and gas industry has sought to employ native people, although the largest number of employees in the industry are white. By the 1960s and 1970s, the Federal and the Territorial Governments had become the principal employers of both the white and the native population.

We had been committed to the view that the economic future of the North lay in large-scale industrial development. An atmosphere of expectancy about industrial development had been generated, especially among Northern business. There had always been a traditional renewable resource sector in the

North, but instead of trying to strengthen it, we had for a decade or more followed policies by which it could only be weakened or even destroyed. We believed in large-scale industrial development and depreciated the existing economic base. Indeed, people who tried to earn a living by hunting, trapping, and fishing had often been regarded as unemployed.

I found that the development of the non-renewable resources of a region can bring serious pressures to bear on its population: people who try to continue to live on the renewable resources may experience relative poverty and may be faced with the loss of a productive way of life. Gradually more and more people may give up one kind of work and therefore relinquish the way of life associated with it, in favour of another kind of work and life. Where this has happened, they often feel they had very little choice in the matter. If the neglected sector of the economy represents a preferred or culturally-important way of life, if it is a means of self-identification and a source of self-respect, then the devaluation of that way of life can have widespread and dismaying consequences. These consequences are exacerbated if the industrialized economy offers rewards that are only short-term.

This implied a new set of priorities for northern development: the strengthening of the traditional hunting and trapping economy; the development of local logging and sawmilling operations where there are merchantable stands of timber on the Mackenzie; the development of the fishing industry; the development of recreation and conservation; an orderly program of petroleum exploration in the Mackenzie Delta and the Western Arctic; and in due course a pipeline along the Mackenzie Valley. Native people—given this set of priorities—could participate in all of these economic activities. The advance of the industrial system could be orderly and beneficial to all.

If there is one overarching lesson to be learned from the work of the Inquiry, it is this: it is imperative to build on existing social and economic strengths. None of the provinces in Canada which is enjoying the benefits of oil and gas and mineral wealth regards it as the permanent mainstay of its economy. Alberta knows that its agricultural sector was there to provide the underpinning of the province's economy before oil and gas were found and will still be there when the oil and gas are gone. Saskatchewan's mineral wealth has arisen on an agricultural base. Those provinces are thriving today because of diversification. That is what I urged for the North. Newfoundland, which expects to gain considerable benefit from the oil that has been discovered offshore, wishes to regulate the pace at which the development of these oil discoveries takes place, in order to protect the fishing and lumbering industries on which its economy has been based for centuries.

The pace of industrial development is the key. I concluded that, in the Mackenzie Valley and the Western Arctic, industrial advance on a massive scale would gravely weaken the renewable resource sector and that its social impact would be disastrous. I urged that the rate of advance should be calculated so as not to overwhelm the existing base.

We think of the city, of the metropolis, as the mirror of progress. So hunting, fishing, and trapping in the far North are not thought of as a way of getting a living that any people who believe in development would want to pursue. In the same way, we in the industrialized nations often think that the model of economic development that our own experience represents is the only one to which Third World countries ought to aspire. Such a model, however, invariably requires an emphasis on large-scale centralized technology at the expense of traditional values and local self-sufficiency.

If the sole emphasis of government policy is on the development of non-renewable resources, the social impact of such activity will be magnified throughout the entire region. People will be drawn into it for want of any alternative and the social impacts will proliferate in places far from the project itself. There will be a massive shift in employment, disruption of family and community life, and a plethora of problems in urban centres. Only balanced development can ameliorate or avoid such effects.

We have seen in many countries that where there has been undue policy emphasis on the non-renewable resource sector, undue dependence on that sector results, with corresponding losses in the renewable resource sector. Iran under the Shah and Nigeria today are examples of regimes where the concentration of development in oil and gas led to a loss of self-sufficiency in agriculture. The same results can, of course, occur when agricultural development is seen as essentially a means of obtaining cash crops, and the need to feed a nation's people is neglected. A great number of Third World countries have followed this path and now find themselves utterly dependent on the fluctuations of world commodity markets, while at the same time they are unable to supply their own basic nutritional requirements. This kind of monolithic economic mode is not what people want.

Our inclination in Canada has been to think in terms of expanding our industrial machine to the limit of our country's frontiers. It is natural for us to think of developing the frontier, of subduing the land, populating it with people from the metropolitan centres, and extracting its resources to fuel our industry and heat our homes. We have seldom had to consider the uses of restraint.

The question that we and many other countries face is: are we serious people, willing and able to make up our own minds, or are we simply driven, by technology and egregious patterns of consumption, to deplete our resources wherever and whenever we find them?

I do not want to be misunderstood about this. I did not propose that we shut up the North, as a kind of living folk museum and zoological gardens. I recommended that no pipeline should be built and no energy corridor established across the Northern Yukon because of the likelihood of substantial and irreparable losses to wilderness, caribou, and migratory birds—losses which would indeed extend into northeastern Alaska. I also recommended that no pipeline should be built and no energy corridor established across the Mackenzie Delta because the occupation of the calving grounds of the white whales of the Beaufort Sea would mean the eventual loss of 5000 whales. I did, however, advise the Government of Canada that a pipeline corridor is feasible, from an environmental point of view, to transport gas and oil from the Mackenzie Delta along the Mackenzie Valley to the Alberta border. At the same time, however, I recommended that we should postpone the construction of such a pipeline for 10 years, in order to strengthen native society and the native economy—indeed, the whole renewable resource sector—and to enable native claims to be settled.

This recommendation was based on the evidence of the native people. Virtually all of the native people who spoke to the Inquiry said that their claims had to be settled before any pipeline could be built. It should not be thought that the native people had an irrational fear of pipelines. They realized that construction of the pipeline and establishment of the energy corridor would mean an influx of tens of thousands of white people from all over Canada seeking jobs and opportunities. They believed that they would be overwhelmed, that their native villages would become white towns, and that they would be relegated to the fringes of Northern life. They believed that the building of the pipeline would bring with it complete dependence on the industrial system and that it would entail a future which would have no place for the values they cherish. The native people insisted that their culture is still a vital force in their lives.

The culture of native people amounts to more than crafts and carvings. Their tradition of decision-making by consensus, their respect for the wisdom of their elders, their concept of the extended family, their belief in a special relationship with the land, their regard for the environment, their willingness to share—all of these values persist in one form or another within their own culture, even though they have been under unremitting pressure to abandon them. Their claims are the means by which they seek to preserve their culture, their values, and their identity.

I think a fuller understanding of the Northern environment emerged during the course of the Inquiry. The proposals made for the creation of an international wilderness area in Alaska and the Yukon, a whale sanctuary in Mackenzie Bay, and bird sanctuaries in the Mackenzie Delta and the Mackenzie Valley, attracted widespread support in Canada and the United States. There is a felt need and a perceived responsibility to preserve critical habitat for caribou, whales, and other wildlife and for wilderness, and there is an understanding of special vulnerability of migratory species in the North to industrial advance. The foundations have been laid for the development of a firm policy designed to protect the Northern environment. In fact, the goal lies within our reach.

The Government of Canada rejected the Arctic Gas Pipeline proposal and decided that, if a pipeline were to be built, it should be along the Alaska Highway route, that is, along the alternate route that I urged be considered. Now the Government of Canada and the Government of the United States have agreed on the construction of a gas pipeline along the Alaska Highway route.

Mr. Hugh Faulkner, then Canada's Minister of Indian Affairs and Northern Development, announced in July, 1978, that he was withdrawing the Northern Yukon north of the Porcupine River—an area of 3.9 million hectares—from future industrial development, with a view to setting aside the area as Canada's first wilderness park, subject to traditional native hunting, trapping and fishing rights in that area. In 1984 the federal government established a national park covering much of the area, and in 1985 reached an agreement with the native people regarding a management regime.

The Carter administration proposed, in the Alaska National Interest Lands Conservation Act, that 17 million hectares in Alaska be set aside as wilderness, including the lands comprising the Arctic National Wildlife Range in Northeastern Alaska. The House of Representatives approved the legislation in April, 1980. The Senate approved an amended bill in December, 1980, and this amended bill was signed by President Carter that same month.

As to native claims, the decision not to build the Arctic Gas Pipeline gives us, and the native people, the time to achieve a fair settlement of native claims in the Mackenzie Valley and the Western Arctic—an opportunity to meet what I believe is Canada's greatest challenge in the North. An agreement was reached in 1985 between the Committee for Original People's Entitlement (COPE), representing the Inuit of the Western Arctic, and the Government of Canada; negotiations are now under way between the Indians and the Metis of the Northwest Territories and the Government of Canada. For the native people, their claims are the means to the preservation of their culture, their languages, their economic mode—the means by which they can continue to assert their distinct identity in our midst and still have access to the social, economic, and political institutions of the dominant society. This is an unusual, perhaps unprecedented outcome: a recognition that industrial goals do not at all times and in all places take precedence over environmental values and native rights.

As a result of the decision to postpone the construction of the pipeline for 10 years, a number of developments have taken place in the Northwest Territories. There has been a renewed emphasis on the possibilities of the development of non-renewable resources. The report, "Fish, Fur and Game in the Northwest Territories," issued in September, 1980 by The Science Advisory Board of the Northwest Territories discussed the importance of wildlife as a source of income and food. The report says that "intensive management can increase substantially the fish and wildlife that can be harvested," and that "the economic importance of fish, game and furs can be greatly expanded." It concluded that the fish and mammal resources of the Northwest Territories could provide sufficient protein for a human population in the Northwest Territories two to four times as large as the present one. There must, of course, be a greatly expanded program of wildlife management and a carefully regulated harvest, and native people in the North must become actively involved in resource management. The native people of the Northwest Territories have elected a native majority to the Legislative Council of the Northwest Territories, a majority reflecting native interests. The Council now works closely with the native organizations in the Northwest Territories. The Canadian Radio and Television Commission, in July, 1981, handed down a decision providing for access to satellite transmission for native radio and television programming in the Northwest Territories and the Yukon. The Dene, the Inuit, and the Metis are advancing proposals for two new provinces in the Northwest Territories. Their proposals are far-reaching. Whatever their outcome, they are evidence of a renewed determination—and a new capacity—on the part of native peoples in the North to establish a distinct and contemporary place for themselves in Canadian life. The native people are now a political force to be reckoned with in the the North and in the country.

This has become apparent most recently in connection with the proposal by Imperial Oil to construct a 30.5 cm pipeline from Norman Wells south to Alberta. The project was approved by the National Energy Board. The Federal Cabinet decided that the pipeline should go ahead, but that there should be a two-year moratorium on construction, that is, oilfield expansion would not begin until the summer of 1983 and pipelaying in the Northwest Territories would not start until November, 1983. The pipeline has now been completed. Who can doubt that this postponement is a manifestation of the increasing political strength of native people in the Northwest Territories?

The judgments that we had to make about these questions were not merely scientific and technical. They were value judgements. It is impossible—indeed it is undesirable—to try to lift scientific and technological decisions out of their social and environmental context, to disentangle them from the web of moral and ethical considerations which provide the means of truly understanding the impact they will have.

Growth as a Questionable Goal

The pipeline debate is over. But it has precipitated another debate, a debate about some fundamental issues which were highlighted by the proceedings at the Inquiry. Since the Industrial Revolution, we have thought of industrialization as the means to prosperity and well-being. And so it has been, to many people and to many parts of the world, but the rise of the industrial system has been accompanied by a belief in an ever-expanding cycle of growth and consumption. We should now be asking whether it is a goal that will suffice. Ought we and our children to continue to aspire to the idea of unlimited growth? And, equally important, ought the Third World to aspire to this goal?

Our belief in an ever-expanding cycle of growth and consumption conditions our capacity and our willingness to reconsider or even to contemplate, the true goals of the industrial system. There is a feeling that we cannot pause to consider where we are headed, for fear of what we shall find out about ourselves.

Certainly if anything is plain, it must be that we in North America shall have to get along with a smaller proportion of the world's energy and resources. This entails a reconsideration of conventional wisdom, for, to a large extent, we have conditioned ourselves to believe that the onward march of industry and technology cannot and must not be impeded or diverted. I am not urging that we dismantle the industrial system. It has been the means to the material well-being of millions and an engine of prosperity for many countries.

I do say, however, that we must pause and consider to what extent our national objectives are determined by the need for the care and feeding of the industrial machine.

The issues are in fact profound ones, going beyond the ideological conflicts that have occupied the world for so long—conflicts over who was going to run the industrial machine, and who was going to get the benefits. Now we are being asked, how much energy does it take to run the industrial machine, where does the energy come from, where is the machine going, and what happens to the people who live in the path of the machine?

Even our terminology has become eccentric. Those who seek to conserve the environment and traditional values are often regarded as radicals and those who are undertaking radical interventions in the natural world that threaten the future of existing communities think of themselves as conservatives. Thus, the debate about the future often tends to become a barren exchange of epithets. But we do not face a choice between unrestrained growth and consumption on the one hand and stagnation on the other hand. To reject the philosophy of endless and unlimited growth does not mean that we must choose scarcity and reject abundance.

I urge that we adopt a policy of rational and orderly development. The implications of unrestrained growth and expansion are becoming apparent all over the world. Examples of the pervasiveness of large-scale technology and marketing out of control can be seen everywhere: tankers cracking up on the beaches; infant formula being peddled indiscriminately in the Third World; the continuing destruction of the rain forest of the Amazon; the mining of soils in many countries. The oil blowout at Ixtoc 1 in the Gulf of Mexico, which ran uncontrolled from June, 1979 until February, 1980, should have been a useful reminder of the tendency for enthusiasm for untried technology to outrun present scientific and engineering knowledge.

The great agency of change throughout the world is industrial man. He and his technology, armed with immense political and administrative power and prepared to transform the social and natural landscape in the interest of a particular kind of society and economy, have ways of soon becoming pervasive. Industrial man is equally the creature of East and West. And of the Third World too: many of the governments of the Third World share our commitment to endless growth, even though they may have no real prospect of achieving it. This is so whether they purport to share the ideology of the West or call themselves Marxist.

Our ideas are still the ideas of the mid-19th century: the era of the triumph of liberal capitalism and the challenge of Marxism, the era of Adam Smith and the Communist Manifesto. Both of these creeds are the offspring of the Industrial Revolution. Capitalism (and I include under this heading all the regimes of the industrialized democracies, as variants on the capitalist economic model) and communism constitute two forms of materialism competing for the allegiance of men in the world today. Neither has yet come to grips with the necessity for rethinking the goals of the industrial system.

Can the nations of the Third World achieve the levels of growth and consumption that have been achieved by the industrialized countries? If they cannot—if the consumption of natural resources at a rate necessary to enable them to do so (not to mention the concomitant increase in pollution) is not possible in a practical sense—then what? We have been unwilling to face up to the moral and ethical questions that this would raise for all of us.

Dr. Ian McTaggart-Cowan, one of Canada's most eminent biologists, has said:

> Is the only way to improve the lot of a country's citizens the way of industrialization, whether it be the western way or the forced march of the U.S.S.R.?. . . Almost inevitably, diversity is sacrificed to a spurious efficiency.
>
> The loss of diversity is not merely a matter for sentimental regret. It is a direct reduction in the number of opportunities open to future generations.
>
> As we look toward the end of the twentieth century . . . we see . . . this diversity threatened by dominant societies pursuing goals that, though they have produced a rich material culture, are already eroding the sources of their original stimulus.[3]

We need a philosophy to sustain us in the post-industrial era, an era for which we have no name, since we cannot yet discern its lineaments. We shall have to consider the question that Adam Smith, the prophet of capitalism, asked:

> For to what purpose is all the toil and bustle of this world? What is the end of avarice and ambition, of the pursuit of wealth, of power, and preeminence?[4]

This is a question that not only individuals must address, but nations also. In seeking an answer, we in the Western nations may discover that the experience of other countries and other cultures can offer insights not only to the countries where they have arisen, but also to the industrialized nations only now coming to grips with the problems of scarcity of resources, environmental crises, and massive unemployment and underemployment which have been the lot of the Third World for so long.

I think we can venture some thoughts about the post-industrial era. There is no reason to suppose that it will necessarily mean a return to scarcity, a foregoing of abundance. Nor does it mean that the Third World must be relegated to a condition of permanent poverty. It would be a mistake to believe that the choice that we face is growth or no growth. A mindless debate along such lines will not get us anywhere.

It is rather the rational application of industry and technology that we must pursue; however, we cannot expect that within a week, or a month, or a year, a new philosophy can be worked out in all its details. We must realize that if we are to postulate, let alone erect, an alternative to a system established 400 years ago, and which has ramified throughout the world, we must be prepared to begin on a small scale. Small can be beautiful, and that applied to theorizing as much as to anything else.

The intellectual challenge of comprehending the shape of the post-industrial era, of comprehending the lineaments of the moral, social and economic goals that will inform that era, will soon be facing us all.

So we stand on the leading edge of history, driven by forces that require greater and greater use of energy, and greater and greater consumption of dwindling resources. Can we change direction? Upon the answer to that question depends the future of each nation, of our environment, and of humankind itself.

Endnotes

1. The Inquiry was established on March 21, 1974. Hearings began on March 3, 1975 and were completed on November 19, 1976. The report of the Inquiry was handed in to the Government of Canada on May 9, 1977.
2. The Toronto *Globe and Mail*, August 30, 1980.
3. From an address to the Pacific Sciences Congress, Vancouver, April 26, 1975.
4. *The Theory of Moral Sentiments*, 1775.

10
The Solar Energy Transition

Barry Commoner

Professor and Director, Center for the Biology of Natural Systems
Queens College (CUNY), Flushing, New York

The Relationship Between Energy and the Economy

This paper deals with what we need to do to solve the energy crisis. That may appear to be a foolish thing to write about since the cover of a recent edition of *Atlantic Monthly* declared that there was no energy crisis, that there was an oil glut, and that the price of oil was falling. On the other hand, we know that the world is in a serious depression, that unemployment in North America and Western Europe is over 7%, and there is a serious decline in the world's economy. I suggest that the current economic depression is to a very significant degree the expression of two factors: the energy crisis and the arms race. In this paper, however, I will deal only with the former.

Because I am proposing that the physical relations in the energy system are responsible for a serious decline in the economy, it is necessary to explore the relationship between energy and the economy. Physics textbooks provide no information on the economy, nor do they say what energy really is. They do say what energy does—work—and that work is a force exerted through a distance. Obviously, that tells us nothing about the economy. Therefore, I must lay out the science of energy in a way that is both physically accurate and obviously related to the economy. Accordingly, I will define work as what you have to do if you want something to happen that does not happen by itself. There is only one way to accomplish work: you must have an energy source arranged in such a way that the energy flows from that source to some destination, so that, as the energy flows, you can arrange to have it do work. For example, the gasoline in a car ends up by heating the inside of the cylinder; that, in turn, causes energy to flow from the inside of the cylinder through the engine, through the radiator, out into the air, and, in doing so, moves the piston which drives the wheels and moves the car. The energy represented by the heat of the exploding gasoline does the work of moving the car. Another point is that whenever work is extracted from energy, that source of energy loses some of its ability to do work; therefore, a constant source of energy is needed to do work. In an economic system, work is essential to produce all the goods and services yielded by the production system, the source of all the economic output of the economy. Without a constant input of energy, therefore, the economy would grind to a halt.

It is also obvious that work has to be done by diverting some of the output of the economy back into the production of energy: oil well drilling equipment, pumps, pipelines, etc. The proper relationship between energy and the economy, therefore, is a feedback cycle: energy drives the economic system and the economic system, in turn, provides the necessary financial support to produce the energy that drives the economic system.

We are in economic trouble, therefore, because we use a system of energy production which supports the economy and destroys it at the same time. Each year a larger proportion of the output of the economic system has to be diverted into the production of the energy needed to run the system. That is, the fraction of the economic output that is needed simply to get a unit of energy is escalating. The economic consequences are extremely serious. In order for the economy to continue to provide goods and services for us to use, it requires capital to renew and rebuild the factories, produce the energy, build the homes, etc.

What, then, is the impact of the energy system on the capital available for sustaining the economy? In the United States, for example, in 1966, 15% of the capital available for business investment had to be used to produce energy. In 1970, that figure was 18%; in 1975, 25%; and in 1981, 31%. This means that, regardless of how the economy is operating, a larger and larger portion of it is being required to produce the energy that makes the economy run. This, in turn, simply depletes the capital available for rebuilding the economy that is so obviously needed in these days of serious economic difficulties. We must ask why we have an energy system which is literally cannibalizing the economy as it continues to operate. The answer in the United States is that 95% of the energy used is non-renewable: oil, coal, natural gas, and uranium. (The figure is somewhat less for Canada because of the higher proportion of hydro-electricity.) Non-renewable sources of energy inevitably become progressively more costly to produce as they are depleted. In fact, even when inflation is taken into account, there is an exponential increase in the real cost per unit of energy as more energy is produced; that is perhaps the most important fact about energy and its relation to the economy. Take, for example, oil. Oil is distributed in various types of deposits: shallow, deep, large, small, under-water, etc. Obviously, the ease with which oil can be removed differs according to the nature of the deposit. It is a rule in the exploitation of any natural resource that the easiest, most accessible source is used first. In other words, the cheapest oil is produced first. That means that every time a barrel of oil is taken out of the ground, it is automatically necessary to go deeper or to a more difficult source to get the next barrel. In mathematical terms, that is an exponential relationship.

This exponential relationship is the basic rule of non-renewability. The major issue of non-renewability is not that the source of energy is going to run out—for all non-renewable resources must run out eventually—but that their use automatically means a progressive increase in the cost of production. For example, if the cost per unit of energy of producing natural gas in the United States in 1966 was 100, it was 180 in 1970, 400 in 1975, and 800 in 1981—an eight-fold increase in 15 years! The reason is very simple: it became necessary to go deeper and deeper (up to 10 000 metres deep in the Southwest United

States) because the more superficial areas had been exhausted. Therefore, the problem that we face with the present energy situation, which is largely based on non-renewable forms of energy, is that it necessarily becomes progressively more expensive and, therefore, erodes the economic system that it is supposed to support. Not only does this deprive the economy of necessary capital, but it also lowers the standard of living for individuals. For example, in the United States in 1978, the poorest fifth of American families spent over 25% of the family budget to buy energy; the richest fifth about 5%. Families that are poor or on fixed incomes will, of necessity, have to divert a larger and larger percentage of their family budget into buying the energy that is necessary to stay warm, to cook, and to get to and from work and school. As the cost of energy rises, there will be less money left for such a family to spend on other things. I guarantee you that this winter there will be families in the United States and Canada who, after paying their energy bills, will not have enough to eat. One result will be vast sums of government aid spent to sustain a minimal standard of living for people whose energy costs become very great in the winter. In fact, the energy cost index—which reflects the amount of money (discounting inflation) spent on energy per capita—has gone up seven-fold in the United States since 1966. It is eroding the standard of living, particularly for poor people, and diminishing the ability of the economy to accumulate capital for its rebuilding. That is why the energy crisis persists.

The Transition to Solar Energy

How can this problem be solved? One step would be to conserve energy, through such measures as improved home insulation. Valuable as that is, however, energy conservation will not stop the escalating exponential process of the rising cost of energy. The only way to stop it is to find sources of energy which do not become less accessible as they are used. There is, of course, such a source of energy: the sun. The sun constantly pours an enormous amount of energy down on the earth; no matter how little or how much of that energy is used, the emission of solar energy will remain unaffected. As a result, the cost of solar energy, no matter how high it is, will be constant. We must begin to think immediately and act immediately to move from our present cannibalistic energy system to a system of solar energy. I would like to discuss how that transition can be carried out.

What is solar energy? Solar energy is derived directly or indirectly from the sun. It takes various forms: direct solar heating from sunshine; ethyl alcohol from corn; wood; hydro-electric power; and wind. All of these depend on energy provided by the sun. The ethyl alcohol from corn or the heat produced by the combustion of wood depend on photosynthesis which is fueled by the sun, as is the water cycle which is necessary for the continuous flow of water required for hydro-electric power. Wind is caused by the sun heating air, which then rises, allowing cold air to rush in underneath. All of these are forms of solar energy. There are also high-technology ways of utilizing solar energy, as in the electricity produced by a photovoltaic cell.

Humans have been using solar energy for a long time; for example, agriculture relies on solar energy, as does a sailing ship. The question that faces us now is how to accommodate a transition so that the sun becomes the source of all the energy we use. It is often argued that solar energy is impractical because it is so diffuse. This attitude highlights our dependence on centralized, concentrated production of energy (for example, from a coal-burning or nuclear power plant) which then has to be distributed over vast areas in order to be used. The situation with solar energy is quite the reverse: the energy itself is distributed widely, so that it must be used where it is needed, rather than transmitted long distances. Also it does not make sense to transmit energy unnecessarily because a substantial proportion of energy may be lost in transmission. On average, 30% of electric power is lost in the transmission system in the form of heat as it runs through the wires. Therefore, a solar system is inherently a decentralized system which ideally depends on the local forms of solar energy best delivered to each particular area. (For example, the largest source of solar energy available in the state of Minnesota is that of marsh cat-tails). After the best possible source of solar energy in a particular area has been identified, it is necessary to match it to energy needs.

Compared with conventional forms of energy, solar energy requires a large initial expenditure. The fuel costs nothing, but the solar collectors (e.g., photovoltaic cells, solar stills) can be very expensive; that is what economists call a large front-end cost. Therefore, any transition from the present system to a solar system will require a very large capital investment. However, one of the features of the corrosive effect of the present energy system on the economy is the diminishing accessibility of capital. What then would be the source of this large amount of capital when there is little capital available? The answer is that a process of transition is required. It is necessary to determine which of the present fossil fuels—coal, natural gas, oil, uranium—and its ancillary systems is most compatible with a solar future. Not all of the present fuels can readily facilitate conversion to a solar system. If a future solar system is decentralized, that means that electricity will be produced where it is needed and that there will be no wires running across the countryside conducting electricity, which, is, of course, wasteful and ugly. It would not be wise, therefore, to invest huge amounts of capital in central power systems and extensive transmission lines if eventually these will not be needed. Rather, it would make more sense to invest in ways of producing and using electricity locally in order to promote decentralized power systems that will match the solar future.

Natural Gas Co-generation

There is a way of producing electricity locally which is far more efficient thermodynamically than a central power station. It is a fundamental law of thermodynamics that, when a fuel is converted into work, two-thirds of the energy in the fuel is converted to heat and only one-third into electricity. Thus, in an ordinary power plant, regardless of whether it is coal, oil or nuclear powered, two-thirds of the energy is expelled into the environment in the form of heat, through air-cooling towers or warm water. It would be useful to recapture that lost heat through the process of co-generation. A co-generator is a power plant that produces both electricity and heat in a form which can be used. The co-generator must be located near the end-uses of the heat as it is inefficient to transmit heat over long distances; thus a system of scattered, decentralized co-generators is required. Examples of such systems exist today: Starrett City, a large housing development of approximately 5000 units in Brooklyn, New York, uses large diesel engines (run on natural gas) located in the basements of the buildings, to provide electricity and space heating (through a hot-water system). Such systems are approximately 90% efficient, resulting in an energy bill that is about a third less than normal. Natural gas is an obvious fuel for such systems, because it avoids the pollution problems of other fuels such as coal.

If all the residential buildings in New York City were to switch to co-generation, the city's energy bill would be cut in half. Most of the energy used in New York is for residential buildings; at the present time, these buildings use 220 trillion BTU's of heat each year, for a peak electricity demand of approximately 5000 megawatts and an annual cost of $6 billion. If all of these buildings had gas-driven co-generators, the heat created would be 315 trillion BTU's, 50% larger than the present demand for heat, and the electricity capacity would be 5200 megawatts, resulting in excess electricity which could yield an annual income of $800 million. This income plus the efficient use of fuel would yield a saving of more than $3 billion per year—half the city's energy bill. (These figures include amortization of the initial capital cost of the co-generators.)

Starrett City has further advantages which make it a good example of the energy transition. It is across the street from a large sewage treatment plant. Sewage is, in effect, organic matter because it is a result of consumption of food by humans, that food being dependant on solar energy; the most convenient way to liberate the solar energy is to allow the sewage to decompose anaerobically (i.e., in the absence of air), converting the organic matter to methane which is the fuel in natural gas. There is now a project underway at Starrett City to pipe methane from the sewage plant into the co-generators: Starrett City will then be operating on solar energy, a completely renewable resource. Incidentally, the excess heat from Starrett City will be piped back across the street to the sewage plant because the methane generators operate best when they are kept warm.

This symbiotic relationship between Starrett City and the sewage treatment plant demonstrates that a natural gas co-generator can be converted into a solar energy system simply by putting methane into the system from a solar source, such as sewage. This is done with no extra equipment; also, a mix of commercial natural gas and solar methane could be used if necessary. Natural gas, therefore, is the most suitable fossil fuel for the transition to solar energy because it can eventually be replaced by methane from a variety of sources: sewage, garbage, manure, algae, etc. There are two additional advantages: the distribution network of gas pipelines is already in place; and the process is equally suitable for both residential and industrial purposes. Thus, a process of using natural gas co-generators would save an enormous amount of energy, reduce the cost of energy to the consumer, and lay the basis for switching to solar energy with no additional expenditure. This is the kind of thinking that is necessary for the solar transition.

The Transportation Sector

Opportunities also exist to begin to recapture the transportation sector which was lost to non-renewable energy with the invention of the automobile. "Recapture" is the proper word because for a few years after the first gasoline-driven car was produced, ethyl alcohol was widely used in France for fuel; over the years, the oil industry took over. Indeed, solar cars exist today: Brazil has a large ethyl alcohol production system based on sugar cane. President Reagan recently signed a bill to foster the production of ethyl alcohol in the Midwestern United States, despite the fact that the Department of Energy has cut the support for solar energy by 90%. Critics of ethyl alcohol production argue that it can take more energy to produce alcohol than can be obtained from it; this can happen, but only if the production process is badly designed. This highlights my view that it is possible to be in favour of solar energy and to be stupid at the same time; there are smart and stupid ways of producing and using solar heat.

How can ethyl alcohol be produced from the solar energy that falls on Midwestern agricultural fields? First, it is important to realize that food is now being produced for certain specific purposes; for example, 90% of the food grown in the United States is used to raise animals. The function of food in raising animals is two-fold: protein to allow the animal to grow and develop; and carbohydrate to provide the energy that drives the biological machinery. Agriculture in the Midwest is designed to produce a net assemblage of crops that have a ratio of protein and carbohydrate suitable for raising animals. In order to produce fuel for automobiles, corn is fermented to produce carbon dioxide and alcohol; about 40% of the food value of the original corn is left over to be fed to animals. Since about 60% of the nutritional food value is lost if alcohol is produced from corn, there would be a decrease in the amount of food available if alcohol production were to be undertaken on a large scale, thus raising the price of food; however, this would happen only if the present system of agriculture were to continue. Remember that engines do not require the protein part of the corn, only the carbohydrate. Therefore, instead of growing crops that have exactly the right ratio of protein and carbohydrate to raise animals, crops could be raised that have an excess amount of carbohydrate which could then be drawn off and converted to alcohol, leaving behind the protein and carbohydrate to raise animals. For example, a new crop system can be designed for a typical Illinois farm which substitutes sugar beets for soybeans, resulting in the same amount of protein and twice the amount of carbohydrate per acre; the excess carbohydrate can be converted into alcohol, with no net loss in the availability of food. With such a system, Midwest farms could produce enough alcohol to replace over 20% of the present demand for gasoline, with no diminution of food production. (Incidentally, soil erosion would be reduced as sugar beets are less damaging to the soil than soybeans.)

One problem with such a transition is that alcohol can be mixed with gasoline in present engines in any ratio up to 20%; for technical reasons, beyond that it will be necessary to introduce newly-designed engines that run on 100% alcohol. This has already been done in Brazil, which now produces approximately 30% alcohol relative to the demand for gasoline. Several years ago, the Brazilian government and the automobile industry made a pact in which industry agreed to produce cars using pure alcohol, while the government would produce the requisite distilleries. Unfortunately, there was a strike which reduced the production of cars; then there was a depression; then there was an oil glut and the price of oil did not go up; then they had more alcohol than they needed. As a result, they had to export alcohol to the United States, much of which ended up as gasohol in American gas stations. It is clear, therefore, that in order to carry out the transition, co-ordinated and integrated planning is required among farmers, government, and industry—a planned set of decisions regarding how to invest in producing energy. Similarly, in a solar transition, it would be necessary to cut back on central power stations and the use of all fossil fuels except natural gas, and gradually introduce solar energy in various forms. Also, it is important to realize that cities like New York will never be self-sufficient in energy; they will have to import energy, but the only sensible way is via methane pipelines.

Conclusion

The need for such co-ordinated decisions, however, presents serious economic and political problems. In the United States, particularly under President Reagan, all investment decisions are governed by the free market: whatever a corporation decides is most profitable is assumed to be good for the country. Obviously, that is not true: the market has created gas-guzzling automobiles, destroyed the railroads, and damaged such industries as steel.

Contrary to present practice, therefore, the transition to solar energy will require that production decisions cannot be based on profit maximization for the corporation, but on what is good for the people of the country. That is a very radical idea; I can say it because I am a radical person. The question arises as to whether the rest of the people can face this problem. It was recently addressed by Pope John Paul II in an encyclical on human labour, in which he stated that capital is created by the labour of workers; therefore, the workers have the moral right to determine how that capital ought to be invested. Translated into action, this would mean that, when the United States government helped support the Chrysler Corporation several years ago, the American people had the right to tell Chrysler to build distilleries and alcohol-driven cars; instead, Chrysler is making money by going back to gas guzzlers.

I am convinced, therefore, that in order to carry out the solar transition, which—along with cutting the military budget—is the only way to restore any vitality to our economy, we will have to extend democracy into the marketplace.

11
2025: Soft Energy Futures For Canada

David B. Brooks
Principal, Marbek Resource Consultants, Ltd.
John B. Robinson
Assistant Professor, Department of Man-Environment Studies
University of Waterloo, Waterloo

Introduction

The purpose of this study was to investigate the potential, in Canada and in each of the provinces and territories, for energy policies that are based on the principles of "soft energy paths"—that is, energy policies that are based primarily upon the development of energy conservation and renewable energy sources. The study was intended to assess the technical and economic potential for such soft energy technologies over the period from 1978 to 2025. Some attempt was also made to examine potential social and environmental impacts of the soft energy scenarios developed in the study and to derive policy implications of, and possible implementation measures for, those scenarios.

The results of this study can be summarized most briefly as follows: under the economic and demographic conditions projected in the scenarios, it would be technically feasible and cost-effective to operate the Canadian economy in 2025 with 12% less energy than it requires today, and, over the same 48 year period, to shift from 16% reliance on renewable sources to 77%, even though gross domestic product grows by 275% and population by over 50%. In addition, should the economy grow by only 130% to 2025 (with the same population growth), and should the real cost of soft technologies drop slightly, it would be feasible and efficient to use 34% less energy in 2025 than in 1978, with 82% of that energy provided by renewable sources. (Technical feasibility is defined in terms of the availability today of either off-the-shelf or prototype technology. Cost-effectiveness is defined in terms of the long-run marginal costs of alternative ways of supplying energy in Canada.)

It is important to recognize that these results are not intended to be forecasts of future energy supply and demand in Canada. That is, the scenarios are not predictions, nor do they imply anything about the likelihood of the energy futures that they describe. Rather, the study tested the technical and economic feasibility of soft energy path options. Given the assumptions underlying the analysis, the results illustrate efficient energy futures, but whether these futures will in fact occur is a political and not an analytical question.

Because this study focuses on soft energy systems, certain possible future energy options were excluded from consideration. Options were sought that were not just more efficient, but also more decentralized, smaller in scale and environmentally less damaging than those typical of today. In particular Arctic oil and new nuclear power plants were excluded, and coal and big hydro were de-emphasized, in the supply analysis. However, some large-scale non-renewable energy developments were included, notably oil from Hibernia, Sable Island natural gas, one additional tar sands or heavy oil plant, and those nuclear plants already under construction in 1978—the base year of our study.

Soft energy studies have been undertaken for most industrialized countries of the world, including Canada, and even for some Third World countries. For the most part, the results of studies in other industrialized countries are similar to those described above for Canada, though, of course, they vary enormously in detail. This study represents the third phase of soft path analysis within Canada. The first phase included a number of broadly focused national studies. In the second, provincial analyses were undertaken using a similar broad approach. In this study, the provincial base for analysis has been retained, but the analyses have been done in a much more controlled and detailed fashion.

Method of Analysis

All soft path studies follow a common sequence of analysis. They focus, first, on the services provided by energy; second, on the techniques for and cost of providing those services with less energy than in the past; third, on the techniques for and costs of using renewable sources to supply whatever energy is demanded; fourth, on supplying the remaining energy needs, if any, with non-renewable energy; and, fifth, on the implications and impacts of following the demand—supply route identified. With the exception of the last step, this is almost exactly the reverse of the sequence of analysis in a conventional energy study. In further contrast to many such studies, both supply and demand options in soft path studies are compared at long-run marginal costs rather than at Canadian prices. For example, the cost-effective level of investment in energy-efficient construction is determined not by comparison with today's price of oil or of natural gas but with existing (and projected) levels for real (inflation-free) replacement costs, which in the case of oil and gas are roughly equivalent to world market prices.

As in most energy studies, the steps of a soft path analysis are applied in the context of economic and demographic scenarios which are developed in order to test the potential over time of the energy systems being studied. That is, as described below, certain economic and demographic projections were used to construct two scenarios within which soft energy technologies were analyzed. Hence, it is not the future economy itself that was analyzed, but only the energy aspects of that economy together with their economic, social and environmental implications. Figure 1 is a flow chart that illustrates the principal stages and sequence of analysis in this study.

Two methodological advances have been made in this study over earlier soft path studies in Canada and, to our knowledge, other countries in the world.

Figure 1
Flow Chart of Method: Soft Energy Path Study

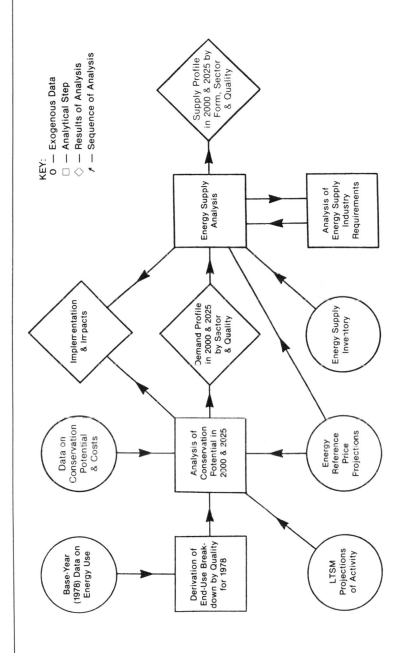

KEY:
O — Exogenous Data
□ — Analytical Step
◇ — Results of Analysis
↗ — Sequence of Analysis

Supply Profile in 2000 & 2025 by Form, Sector & Quality

Energy Supply Analysis

Analysis of Energy Supply Industry Requirements

Implementation & Impacts

Demand Profile in 2000 & 2025 by Sector & Quality

Energy Supply Inventory

Data on Conservation Potential & Costs

Analysis of Conservation Potential in 2000 & 2025

Energy Reference Price Projections

Base-Year (1978) Data on Energy Use

Derivation of End-Use Breakdown by Quality for 1978

LTSM Projections of Activity

First, soft path studies have tended to adopt rather simplistic projections for the economy under study, projections that expand all parts of the economy at some proportionate rate. Instead, this study has adopted as its base an integrated input-output simulation of the Canadian economy (the Long Term Simulation Model (LTSM) developed at Statistics Canada) that can be moved forward in time in such a way as to ensure that supply and demand match perfectly in a physical sense for every commodity and every industry. It assures, for example, that there is enough iron ore mined and steel manufactured to produce the trucks required for the growing transportation sector, and also that the highways system expands to accommodate the growing volume of truck traffic. While use of the simulation model involved limitations on the flexibility of analysis (for example, because different transportation modes were explicit components of the input-output base, it was not possible to consider the energy effects of, say, shifting some truck traffic to rail), and requires that the analysis be tied to fixed technological coefficients, it does ensure that the economy being projected is truly operable. Moreover, it avoids the problem, inherent in price-based econometric projections, of basing the economic projection on precisely those variables (price elasticities) that one wishes to analyze.

Second, few soft path studies have been regionally disaggregated, and those that were have generally been analyzed from the top down. This study was instead built up from 12 separate (10 provincial and two territorial) energy analyses developed within national control totals. This unique blend of national controls and provincial/territorial analysis allowed the study to reflect regional variations in supply and demand patterns and at the same time permitted each provincial analysis to be consistent—in energy, economic and demographic terms—with the others, which in turn allowed them all to be added together to produce consistent Canadian totals.

The national economic projections of the LTSM for the period 1978 to 2025 were first allocated among the provinces and territories, allowing for a continuing westward shift of employment and industry. Where appropriate, as with automobile design and construction techniques, national "standards" were adopted for future years to represent the cost-effective targets for energy efficiency, but within each province or territory it was possible to vary the rate of implementation of such standards to allow for local conditions.

A common base for energy costs from both conventional and nonconventional energy sources was then developed for use in the study. Long-run real costs for oil, natural gas and electricity were adapted from information provided by the Federal Department of Energy, Mines and Resources. In brief, oil and gas prices were assumed to rise at real rates of 3% to 2000 and 2% thereafter; electricity prices at 2% and 1%. Long-run real costs for conservation and renewable energy options were developed from both operating experience and literature reviews for each specific technique adopted for use in this study. Where relevant, resource limitations were incorporated into the analysis. (Such limitations are of concern for renewable as well as nonrenewable resources; notably, the supply of biomass resources is highly limited by the quantity and quality of land available and by management practices.) And appropriate quantities of energy were allocated for the operation of the energy production and distribution system itself.

Finally, throughout the study, certain decisions were made at the national level where this was necessary to ensure coordination. Such decisions included the choice of methanol as the renewable-based fuel for inter-urban vehicles, as well as the allocation of inter-provincial flows of energy and of national exports and imports.

The future energy economy of Canada was studied under two scenarios, one termed "Business as Usual" and the other "Consumer Saturation." The two scenarios were originally developed by Statistics Canada for the Privy Council and reflect alternative courses of development for the Canadian economy over the next 50 years. Both incorporate the same population growth and demographic characteristics, both assume that full employment is maintained, and both allow for labour productivity to grow at about 1% per year. The main difference is that under Business as Usual conditions, Canadians opt to work the same number of hours per year as at present, whereas under Consumer Saturation they opt to work about 30% less per year. Hence, while the economy, and per capita income, grow in both scenarios, they grow substantially more in the Business as Usual scenario because of the choice for income over leisure (Table 1). To this economic difference between the scenarios, were added two generic differences so far as energy options were concerned. First, whereas soft energy options were selected for the Business as Usual scenario according to strict cost-effectiveness criteria (at present or projected marginal costs), the economic criteria for the selection of both conservation and renewable energy options for the Consumer Saturation scenario were relaxed somewhat. Second, in the Consumer Saturation but not the Business as Usual scenario, modest changes in lifestyles to cut energy demand (e.g. reduced per capita usage of hot water, as by laundering in warm or cold water) were permitted. Thus, results from the two scenarios reflect differences in both

Table 1
Economics Growth Rates for Canada
(LTSM Scenarios, 1978 — 2025)

| | | | | GDP | Labour |
Scenario	Population	Output	GDP	/capita	Productivity
Business as Usual	1.0	2.2	2.8	1.3	1.1
Consumer Saturation	1.0	1.5	1.7	0.8	1.2

(%/a)

GDP: gross domestic product

economic growth and in energy choices, but neither scenario represents an extreme case. The Business as Usual scenario uses less energy than would an all-out growth scenario, and the Consumer Saturation scenario uses more energy than would a conserver society. A Canadian of today viewing either of our two projected societies in 2000 or 2025 would find them entirely recognizable.

Results

The results of this study can be conveniently grouped into four sections: energy uses, energy sources, supply/demand balances and the provincial distribution of energy. They will be discussed sequentially.

Table 2
Total Energy Use in Canada By Sector and Scenario

	BUSINESS AS USUAL SCENARIO		CONSUMER SATURATION SCENARIO	
	(PJ)	*(%)*	*(PJ)*	*(%)*
1978				
Residential	1271	21	1271	21
Commercial	808	14	808	14
Industrial	2242	37	2242	37
Transportation	1687	28	1687	28
TOTAL	6008	100	6008	100
2000				
Residential	839	13	833	18
Commercial	689	11	525	11
Industrial	3160	51	2239	47
Transportation	1574	25	1117	24
TOTAL	6262	100	4714	100
2025				
Residential	673	12	675	17
Commercial	576	11	423	11
Industrial	2585	49	1852	47
Transportation	1476	28	996	25
TOTAL	5310	100	3946	100

Average Annual Growth Rates

1978-2000: 0.2%	1978-2000: −1.1%
2000-2025: −0.7%	2000-2025: −0.7%
1978-2025: −0.3%	1978-2025: −0.9%

Uses of Energy

Table 2 shows the changes over time, in each of the two scenarios, in energy use in Canada, broken down into the four energy-using sectors: Residential, Commercial, Industrial and Transportation. Also shown are the overall average annual growth rates for energy use from 1978 to 2000, 2000 to 2025 and over the whole study period from 1978 to 2025. It can be seen that energy demand grows slightly to the year 2000 in the Business as Usual scenario then falls so that by the year 2025 it is only 88% of the 1978 level. In the Consumer Saturation scenario, energy use falls throughout the 1978 to 2025 period, reaching a level of 66% of the 1978 level in 2025.

With regard to sectoral energy use, the table shows that in both scenarios the major changes in sectoral shares of energy use occur between 1978 and 2000; changes thereafter are relatively minor. The largest changes are the fall in the share of energy used by the residential sector, a result of the vastly improved levels of thermal integrity that are cost-effective, and the growth in the share used by the industrial sector. Energy use in the commercial sector declines more slowly as rapid economic growth in this sector in part offsets improved construction practices. The share of energy used in the transportation sector falls at first and then recovers, which reflects the growing role for commercial transportation and the relatively smaller efficiency gains expected for commercial vehicles than for automobiles.

For the most part, the share changes exhibited by the two scenarios are very similar. Residential use retains a larger share under Consumer Saturation because new construction is lower. Similarly, the share of industrial use grows less because economic growth is lower. Also, the initial fall in the share for transportation is greater, and the subsequent rebound less, under Consumer Saturation because of reduced usage of automobiles and higher load factor in commercial transportation.

Sources of Energy

Table 3 shows the changes in the forms of energy used to provide for secondary energy requirements in the two scenarios.

As shown, the use of coal and peat grows modestly in both scenarios. This growth occurs because, in addition to being used as a source of electricity, coal is used as a source of steam to propel ocean-going ships, and because peat is used as a source of heat and of fluid fuels for transportation. Even in 2025, however, coal and peat provide no more than 8% of annual secondary energy demand compared with 3% in 1978. Refined petroleum products (RPP's) exhibit a steady decline, despite expected new production from Hibernia and from an additional tar sands plant, from around half the supply in 1978 to less than one-quarter in 2000 and just a few percent (mainly for non-energy products) in 2025. The pattern for natural gas is different yet, partly because of a stronger resource base, including development of Sable Island fields in the East. For the first half of the projection period, its share of the supply mix is constant, which means effectively no change in the level of production under

Table 3
Total Energy Use in Canada By Form and Scenario

	BUSINESS AS USUAL SCENARIO		CONSUMER SATURATION SCENARIO	
	(PJ)	*(%)*	*(PJ)*	*(%)*
1978				
Coal and Peat	177	3	177	3
Natural Gas	1366	23	1366	23
RPP's	3245	54	3245	54
Electricity	1009	17	1009	17
Biomass Solids	211	4	211	4
Biomass Fluids	0	0	0	0
Active Solar	0	0	0	0
TOTAL	6008	100	6008	100
2000				
Coal and Peat	367	6	248	5
Natural Gas	1390	22	1074	23
RPP's	1412	23	971	21
Electricity	1352	22	1065	22
Biomass Solids	838	13	707	15
Biomass Fluids	776	12	526	11
Active Solar	127	2	123	3
TOTAL	6262	100	4714	100
2025				
Coal and Peat	423	8	310	8
Natural Gas	517	10	243	6
RPP's	172	3	82	2
Electricity	1229	23	961	24
Biomass Solids	927	17	771	20
Biomass Fluids	1735	33	1299	33
Active Solar	307	6	280	7
TOTAL	5310	100	3946	100

Average Annual Growth Rates

1978-2000: 0.2%	1978-2000: −1.1%
2000-2025: −0.7%	2000-2025: −0.7%
1978-2025: −0.3%	1978-2025: −0.9%

Business as Usual conditions and a 20% decline under Consumer Saturation. However, between 2000 and 2025, usage falls off substantially so that it provides only 10% of supply in the Business as Usual scenario and 6% in the Consumer Saturation. The supply of electricity exhibits still a fourth pattern. From about 17% of the supply mix in 1978, it grows to provide around 23% in both scenarios and both projection years. In absolute terms this means electrical production peaks about the year 2000 and then declines slowly thereafter as total energy use falls—a pattern that suggests that only a little additional electrical generation capacity will be needed in Canada. In the Consumer Saturation scenario, moreover, the year 2000 peak is very little higher, and the year 2025 level much lower, than the 1978 level.

The share of energy supplied by renewable forms of energy of course increases over the study period. Ignoring hydro-electricity and other renewable sources of electricity, the share starts at 4% supplied by biomass solids, mainly wood wastes used as fuel in the forest industries. The share grows over the study period to 56% in the Business as Usual scenario and to 60% in the Consumer Saturation scenario. Within that growth, the three categories fare quite differently. Use of biomass solids increases between three and four times up to 2000, but increases little either absolutely or relatively thereafter. Active solar grows steadily but modestly as a fuel for water heating and low-temperature process heat, and even in 2025 is only providing 6 or 7% of secondary use. The real change occurs with biomass fluids (mainly methanol but including some biogas), which start at nil, climb to provide more than a tenth of secondary supply in 2000 and a third (both scenarios) in 2025. In absolute terms, of course, the growth is not so strong because total energy production and use are declining. Nevertheless, as shown by the way the increase in the use of biomass fluids mirrors the decrease in the use of refined petroleum products in the table, one of the principal results of the projections, so far as energy supply is concerned, is the gradual substitution of renewable biomass for non-renewable crude oil.

If the share of electricity supplied by renewable energy sources is included, the shift to renewables described above is even more marked. In 1978 about 68% of all electricity was produced from renewable hydraulic sources. In both scenarios, the renewable share of electricity climbs: slightly to around 72% in 2000 and rapidly thereafter to over 90% in 2025. During the first period the increase is largely due to the construction of new hydro capacity; after 2000 other renewable-based electricity (wind, solar and wood) begins to contribute significantly.

When the shares of renewable-based electricity are added to those of other renewables, the total share of energy supplied by renewable sources in Canada grows from 16% in 1978 to 33% in 2000 and 77% in 2025 in the Business as Usual scenario and, in the Consumer Saturation scenario, to 45% in 2000 and 82% in 2025.

In summary, the patterns of supply developed here would move Canada toward the objectives of a soft path. Not only is the share of renewables increased relative to non-renewables, which means greater sustainability, but the supply mix has also become more diverse which means greater resiliency. Moreover, as will be indicated in the next section, energy production is no longer so heavily concentrated geographically, but is shared by all provinces. Note finally that the transition envisaged here is a gradual one. Even in 2000 renewable sources provide less than half of the total supply. However, their production base is growing, and the year 2000 represents a transition toward an energy system dominated by renewable sources in 2025 and beyond.

Table 4
Total Energy Use in Canada By Quality and Scenario

	BUSINESS AS USUAL SCENARIO		CONSUMER SATURATION SCENARIO	
	(PJ)	*(%)*	*(PJ)*	*(%)*
1978				
Heating & Cooling	1801	30	1801	30
Process Heat- Intermediate	812	13	812	13
Process Heat-High	639	11	639	11
Electricity Specific	756	13	756	13
Liquid Fuel	2000	33	2000	33
TOTAL	6008	100	6008	100
2000				
Heating & Cooling	1195	19	1075	23
Process Heat- Intermediate	1084	17	746	16
Process Heat-High	1055	17	732	15
Electricity Specific	1028	17	795	17
Liquid Fuel	1900	30	1365	29
TOTAL	6262	100	4714	100
2025				
Heating & Cooling	885	16	792	20
Process Heat- Intermediate	743	14	540	14
Process Heat-High	986	19	683	17
Electricity Specific	991	19	747	19
Liquid Fuel	1705	32	1184	30
TOTAL	5310	100	3946	100

Average Annual Growth Rates

1978-2000:	0.2%	1978-2000: −1.1%
2000-2025:	−0.7%	2000-2025: −0.7%
1978-2025:	−0.3%	1978-2025: −0.9%

Energy Balances

Table 4 shows the supply-demand balance for energy in terms of the services that energy supplies, that is in terms of the type or quality of energy needed to meet the end-use demands resulting from the scenarios.

The two biggest changes in the quality categories are the reduction in the shares of energy used for heating and cooling (including low-temperature industrial process heat) and the increase in the share used for high-temperature process heat. The need for energy for heating and cooling declines steadily over the projection period with the gradual introduction of construction techniques that practically eliminate the need for space heating in the residential and commercial sectors. The need for high-temperature energy sources increases partly because of the growing share of total energy used by the industrial sector and partly because relatively smaller energy savings are available for subsectors that need high-temperature heat. This is a notable result of the study, for it is not immediately obvious how soft sources could be economically developed to provide for high-temperature process heat in the years beyond the end of the study period.

A few other changes in the shares for energy quality categories are worth noting. The share of energy used as mid-temperature process heat grows at first but declines during the second half of the projection period as a result of growing investment in energy cascading techniques. The share of energy used for electricity-specific purposes grows slowly but steadily over the whole study period (though the absolute level declines after 2000), which reflects the use of motors and equipment as well as some use of electricity as back-up for heating and as motive power for transportation. Finally, the liquid fuel share declines at first and then partially recovers, which not surprisingly parallels the pattern of change for the transportation sector.

A more detailed look at energy balances is provided in Figures 2 to 6, each of which provides a snapshot of the energy situation in Canada, in 1978 and in 2000 and 2025 for each scenario. Reflecting the end-use approach of this study, each of these figures expands outward from the services provided by energy (shown in the inner circle), to the sectors in which each of these services is used (in the outer circle), and finally to the fuel mix used for each of these sectoral services (in the bars around the margin). By indicating the interrelationship among energy services, sectoral use and the forms of energy supply for each of the years analyzed in each scenario, these charts collectively illustrate the general results of this study.

Provincial Use and Production

One of the general objectives of a soft energy path is to develop decentralized sources of energy appropriate to regional and local conditions. This thrust is given added weight by the low energy density of most renewable energy sources, such as solar heat, which means that they cannot economically be transported very far, if at all. Thus, soft paths tend toward national, regional and even local self-reliance.

This effect is illustrated in the results of this study which, with very few exceptions, show a decreasing movement of energy across provincial or national borders. (Results for the two scenarios are quite similar, with smaller flows occurring in the Consumer Saturation than in the Business as Usual scenario.) In the case of crude oil, this is simply a result of declining resource availability, but in most cases it is a result of the gradually diminishing need in each province for energy resources from other provinces. Of the two exceptions (coal and biomass fluids) only one involves energy per se (the increased trade in coal is primarily for coke used as a non-energy product). By the year 2000 biomass fluids have become an energy form important enough to move from provinces

Figure 2
Energy End-Uses and Forms in Canada in 1978

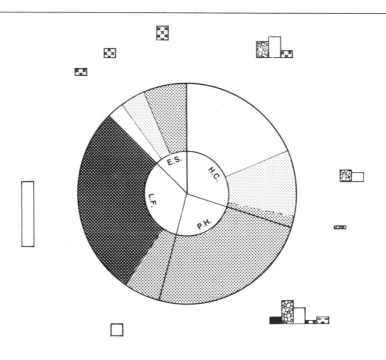

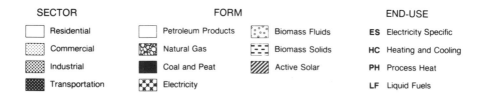

SECTOR	FORM		END-USE	
Residential	Petroleum Products	Biomass Fluids	ES	Electricity Specific
Commercial	Natural Gas	Biomass Solids	HC	Heating and Cooling
Industrial	Coal and Peat	Active Solar	PH	Process Heat
Transportation	Electricity		LF	Liquid Fuels

with a biomass surplus to those with a deficit. However, total trade never comes close to rivalling the scale of today's shipments of natural gas or crude oil.

In some cases interprovincial flows of energy stemmed from social or environmental choices pursuant to soft path objectives. For example, Ontario has a number of options for hydro-electric developments on north-flowing rivers, but they were deemed to involve serious conflicts with environmental preservation and with native land claims. Instead, the choice was made to import surplus hydropower from Quebec (which, as indicated in the provincial report, will have excess electrical capacity throughout the study period even if no new construction is undertaken).

Figure 3
Energy End-Uses and Forms in Canada in 2000—BU Scenario

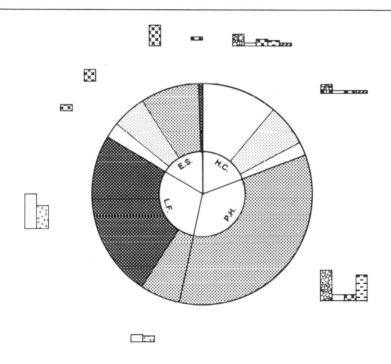

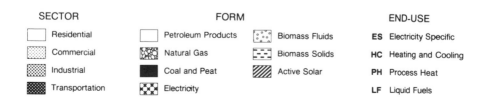

SECTOR	FORM		END-USE
Residential	Petroleum Products	Biomass Fluids	**ES** Electricity Specific
Commercial	Natural Gas	Biomass Solids	**HC** Heating and Cooling
Industrial	Coal and Peat	Active Solar	**PH** Process Heat
Transportation	Electricity		**LF** Liquid Fuels

Imports of energy into Canada would be greatly reduced from present levels under either Business as Usual or Consumer Saturation conditions. On the other hand, energy exports could be larger. Soft paths do not aim for self-sufficiency as an objective but only use it as a working hypothesis. There is no inherent objection to energy trade when the production, processing and transportation are economically efficient and do not violate environmental and other objectives. Thus, natural gas exports from Alberta are left open as there do not appear to be environmental problems or resource limitations over the time frame of this study. The figures even suggest the possibility of renewed exports of high-cost oil in the second half of the study period and even earlier under Consumer Saturation. On the other hand, there would be great hesitation about expanding the hydro-electric system or growing biomass for export.

Figure 4
Energy End-Uses and Forms in Canada in 2025—BU Scenario

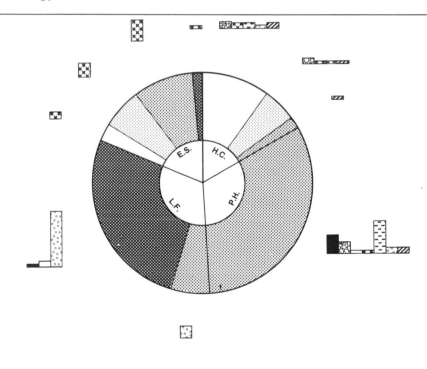

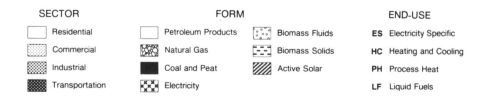

SECTOR	FORM		END-USE	
☐ Residential	☐ Petroleum Products	⊡ Biomass Fluids	ES	Electricity Specific
Commercial	Natural Gas	Biomass Solids	HC	Heating and Cooling
Industrial	Coal and Peat	Active Solar	PH	Process Heat
Transportation	Electricity		LF	Liquid Fuels

In summary, Canada's international balance of trade would improve under either the Business as Usual or the Consumer Saturation scenario. Within Canada each province would become substantially more self-reliant. There would still be plenty of movement of energy, mainly from biomass sources, but relatively little of it would cross a border. However, the growth of shipments of biomass fluids does indicate, once again, that the development of an alternative transportation fuel is the most difficult problem within the soft path framework.

Conclusions and Implications

The main conclusion of this study is that, under the relatively buoyant economic and demographic conditions projected in the scenarios, a soft energy

Figure 5
Energy End-Uses and Forms in Canada in 2000—CS Scenario

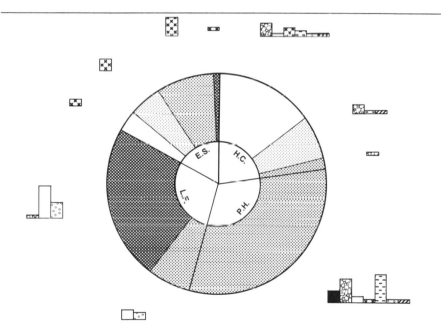

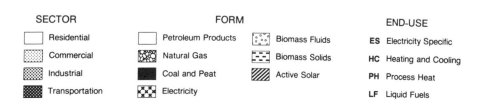

SECTOR	FORM		END-USE
Residential	Petroleum Products	Biomass Fluids	**ES** Electricity Specific
Commercial	Natural Gas	Biomass Solids	**HC** Heating and Cooling
Industrial	Coal and Peat	Active Solar	**PH** Process Heat
Transportation	Electricity		**LF** Liquid Fuels

future for Canada is both technically feasible and economically efficient. That is, Canada can make a cost-effective transition to primary reliance upon ecologically sustainable and geographically distributed renewable energy sources without any reductions in material standards of living or significant lifestyle change. Indeed, because for methodological reasons this study excluded certain soft technologies and actions that could be expected to have significant results (e.g. transportation modal shifts, greater product durability, district heating, changes to more efficient urban form), it almost certainly does not indicate the full potential for soft energy paths. Instead, it presents two more or less moderate and manageable scenarios for a transition to such energy futures.

Figure 6
Energy End-Uses and Forms in Canada in 2025—CS Scenario

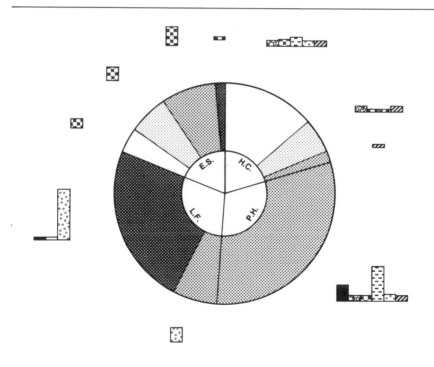

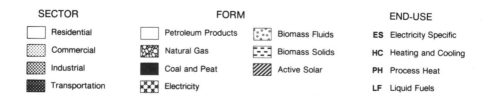

SECTOR		FORM			END-USE	
☐	Residential	☐	Petroleum Products	Biomass Fluids	**ES**	Electricity Specific
	Commercial		Natural Gas	Biomass Solids	**HC**	Heating and Cooling
	Industrial	■	Coal and Peat	Active Solar	**PH**	Process Heat
■	Transportation		Electricity		**LF**	Liquid Fuels

There are, however, some more disquieting results of the study. Most important are those related to the use of methanol from biomass. While adequate quantities of non-agricultural land appear to be available to support the amount of biomass harvesting implied in the scenarios, the scale of harvesting required to meet liquid fuel needs raises some serious concerns about forest management and environmental impacts. Also, the strong cost-effectiveness of using biomass as a heating fuel (probably as wood chips or pellets) in this study implies much more organization of production and marketing than is typical of the industry at present. Clearly, these are areas that require additional study.

The relatively large demands for high-temperature process heat, especially in Ontario, are also of concern since these requirements are hard to meet with soft energy sources. Further work is also required in this area.

On the other hand, the relative abundance of electricity in most provinces in both scenarios is a more positive result. In particular, the ability of existing capacity to meet most electricity needs to 2025 in the scenarios has important implications for electricity system expansion plans. Avoiding such capital intensive expansion may be one of the major economic benefits of a soft energy path future; at the same time this suggests that the role of electric utilities in such futures needs to be carefully examined.

One important conclusion implicit in the results of this study has to do with the role of energy prices. Since the study was primarily based upon an economic test for assessing the feasibility of energy technologies, the price assumptions were clearly critical in influencing the results. Moreover, the use of long-run marginal costs points up the present difference between economically efficient energy prices and those prevailing today in Canada. Since energy prices in Canada, as elsewhere, are the result of pricing policy decisions, this means that future Canadian energy pricing policies will be a critical factor in influencing the development of soft (as well as hard) energy systems in Canada. Exactly the same is true for the wide variety of institutional barriers and financial incentives that determine, perhaps more than prices themselves, inputs and investments in the energy system. This study has abstracted from the specifics of barriers and incentives, but it is clear that at present they strongly favour hard, at the expense of soft, energy systems.

These points can be generalized to perhaps the most important conclusion of this study. The overall potential for soft energy path futures for Canada turns out in almost every case not to be limited by technological, nor even economic, factors. Instead, the extent of that potential is policy-determined, in the sense that the potential will essentially be determined by policy decisions, made primarily by the federal and provincial governments. Put another way, the results of this study indicate that a soft energy path is feasible and attractive for Canada, but whether such a path will be chosen is primarily a political question.

List of Analysts and Authors of Provincial Reports

Newfoundland - Geoff Stiles and Jeff Harrison,
Island Energy Associates, St. John's.

P.E.I. - Kirk Brown,
Institute for Man and Resources, Charlottetown.

Nova Scotia - Susan Holtz,
Ecology Action Centre, Halifax.

New Brunswick - Bonny Pond and Auguste Gallant,
Senopi Consultants, Petit Rocher.

Québec - Hélène Lajambe et Richard Lalonde.[*]
Montréal.

Ontario - Ralph Torrie,
Torrie, Smith and Associates, Kitchener.

Manitoba - Yvonne Penning,
Ottawa.

Saskatchewan - Herman Boerma,
Saskatchewan Environmental Society, Saskatoon.

Alberta - Bill Ross,
Faculty of Environmental Design, University of Calgary,
Calgary.

B.C. - Jay Lewis,
Society Promoting Environmental Conservation.
Vancouver.

Territories - Tony Hodge and Lynda Ehrlich,
Yukon Conservation Society, Whitehorse.

[*]Prior to July 1982

Part 4:

Economics, Development, and the Environment

This Part provides a number of examples of the environmental impacts of development. Hall presents a view of the costs and problems of the use of pesticides versus the use of biological control. Loucks explores the impacts of pollution from industrialization and urbanization on agriculture and forestry, while Troughton analyzes the impacts of industrialized agriculture on the environment. Two very different environmental problems are discussed in the next two papers. Gibbs describes the Love Canal disaster as an example of long-buried and -forgotten pollutants coming back to haunt later generations, while Tuntawiroon shows that many environmental problems are "exported" when industrialized nations undertake development in other countries because they do not want them "in their own backyard."

12
Pesticides: As Much a Political Problem as a Technical Problem

Ross Hume Hall

Professor, Department of Biochemistry
Health Sciences Centre, McMaster University, Hamilton

Introduction

The Cinnabar moth is a spectacular black and crimson insect. Its larvae, no less spectacularly coloured, voraciously chew up entire plants in their growth to adult moths. Is it a foe—a pest? In this case, the host plant, a tenacious weed that spreads relentlessly throughout open pasture land on Canada's east and west coasts, is the foe. This weed, the Tansy ragwort, once caused severe losses to farmers whose animals graze on the land. The Cinnabar moth was established through the work of Dr. Peter Harris and associates of Agriculture's Canada Weed Research Station at Regina, Saskatchewan. The Tansy ragwort, especially on the east coast, is one of some two dozen pests successfully controlled in Canada by introduction of a specific predator.

The alternative to the use of the Cinnabar moth is to spray large areas of pasture land with herbicides. In spite of the success of biological control of pests such as the Tansy ragwort, most weeds and insects designated as pests in Canada are controlled by chemical pesticides. These chemicals by their very nature are poisonous not only to their targets, but to a variety of natural organisms, including humans. Although Agriculture Canada, the responsible federal agency, requires extensive testing of chemical pesticides before they are licensed for use, it cannot guarantee that these chemicals will not injure non-targets. The difficulty lies in the current approach to toxicological testing. Although pesticides that pass government-prescribed tests will not likely poison immediately (as long as label directions are followed), the same testing system offers no protection from cancer, birth defects, and a legacy of harmful mutations in future generations.

Chemical pesticides remain active long after they assault their targets. They and/or their breakdown products percolate through the soil and contaminate ground water. They become residues in animal and human food and in drinking water, exposing the entire Canadian population. The more we learn about continued exposure to such residues, the more we must ponder the price that has to be paid in order to grow food and fibre. Yet, the use of chemical pesticides in Canada continues to project ever upward.

Just as Scrooge once asked the Ghost of Christmas Future if the Ghost's projection was the way the future had to be or whether there was an alternative, we should be asking whether there is an alternative to almost total reliance on chemical pesticides. The answer implies greater use of biological controls, but these controls require highly sophisticated research and field application and, above all, public policies that encourage their development and implementation. Government policy, whether intentional or not, favours a chemical approach to pest control and actively discourages the introduction of biological alternatives. This article looks at some of the obstacles to biological alternatives and suggests ways of overcoming them.

Natural Predators or Sterile Males Can Control Pests

Biological control refers to a deliberate manipulation of natural control agents to increase their attack on the designated pest species. It takes many forms. Here are two more examples.

The cereal leaf beetle attacks the leaves of young grain plants, weakening the plant and reducing yield. It began to move into Ontario in the early 1970s from the American Midwest where it caused significant economic loss in oat crops. Agriculture Canada officials became concerned that the pest would spread into other grain-growing areas of Canada.

Some years previously, in efforts to cope with the pest, American scientists had imported several natural enemies of the leaf beetle from Europe. One of them, a parasitoid (*Tetrastichus julis*) became established. When the beetle migrated into Ontario, the parasitoid migrated with it and fortunately established itself. The parasitoid keeps the beetle population below an economic threshold, i.e., the damage caused is acceptable with respect to the profit on the crop.

It is interesting that, although the leaf beetle is now satisfactorily controlled in Canada, it continues to inflict significant damage in the United States. One possible explanation is that the parasitoid finds Canadian climate and agricultural practices more similar to the conditions of its European origins.

Once a predator such as the Cinnabar moth or the cereal leaf beetle parasitoid becomes established, no further intervention is required. The control becomes a "free-good." The lady bug, introduced 100 years ago to control the cottony-cushion scale (a devastating pest of citrus trees), still controls this pest at no cost to the growers. Other forms of biological control, however, require sophisticated yearly management, as illustrated by the successful biological control of the codling moth in the Okanagan Valley. This moth lays one or two eggs in an apple bud just after the blossom drops. The egg hatches into a larvae which burrows inside and eventually becomes a worm resident in the ripe fruit. A program worked out at the Agriculture Canada Research Station at Summerland, British Columbia in the 1950s exploits sterile male moths. Male codling moths raised in captivity are subjected to a dose of gamma-rays sufficient to sterilize but not kill them. The males are released in the spring by the tens of millions; they retain their sexual vigor and dilute the population of the natural (fertile) males.

In the mid-1970s, a three-year large-scale trial was run in the Similkameen Valley. This area, comprising 4200 hectares of apple and pear orchards, was relatively isolated, an important feature in preventing reinfestation. All of the growers agreed to forego their normal chemical spray program. Sterile codling moth males were released over the three seasons and the program reduced fruit damage to an acceptable minimum. The program was originally subsidized by Agriculture Canada, in the hope that growers would eventually assume the costs, but the growers looked strictly at the economics. Sterile moth control costs about $250 a hectare and chemical sprays $100. The growers opted for the chemicals, considering that they were spraying for other pests and hence had all the expensive equipment on hand. A full economic analysis that included all environmental effects might have been instructive, but no such analysis was done.

Modern Agricultural Practice Makes Biological Control Difficult

The codling moth episode shows how biological control can fail, but because of failure of government policy to follow through. No accounting was made of the costs of not using the sterile-male technique, costs which were registered in human and environmental injury by the chemicals. This example highlights the dichotomy in agricultural research and policy. Excellent scientific groups in government and university laboratories across Canada research biological controls. Much of this research does not reach the field due to government policy. It is not a simple matter of reversing that policy by saying "let's have more biological control," because the problem goes deeply into the way farmers practice agriculture. The difficulty can be illustrated by attempts to control the onion root maggot.

This maggot, if left alone, can ruin an onion crop. Control now consists of 30-40 chemical sprayings a season. Scientists of Agriculture Canada for years have tried to establish biological control of this pest. Predatory wasps were tried, but they failed to survive. Currently, a sterile-male technique similar to that used against the codling moth is being tried. So far, it has achieved only limited success and the sprayings continue. A very simple solution to control of this pest, however, waits in the wings: stop growing onions for two or three seasons and grow something else. Dismissal of this simple solution points up the single-minded orientation of agricultural research and production in Canada. Research activity tends to be segregated in tight compartments, each devoted to a single crop. In other words, the objective is to grow and market onions year after year regardless of the price paid in loss of soil quality and environmental contamination, to say nothing of the problem of chemical residues reaching the eaters of the onions. When the same crop is grown in the same field year after year, insect populations literally explode as they quickly adapt to unchanging favourable conditions. Similarly, weeds which have to compete only with a single crop, readily penetrate that pattern.

Supporters of chemical pesticides are fond of saying that "if chemical pesticides were withdrawn from the market, reduction in crop yield and loss of quality would devastate Canadian agriculture." They are probably right. The varieties of plants that form the backbone of Canadian agriculture are a highly inbred lot, ill-equipped to withstand the rigours of nature. Although we have entered the space age, the basic biology of plants has not changed since the time of the Egyptian Pharaohs. A plant captures a fixed amount of energy from the sun. That energy is divided between formation of the fruit (or edible parts) and growth of the leaves, roots and plant reserves. Though the yield of traditional varieties of plants may be lower, their superior plant structure can withstand drought, competition from weeds and attack by insects and disease.

The modern cultivar with the same total energy available has been selected to put most of that energy into its fruit at the expense of its root, stem, and leaf structure. The biology of such cultivars functions well only when supported by ample water, heavy application of fertilizer, and the protection of chemical pesticides. To suddenly withdraw pesticide protection from these plants is like kicking a crutch out from under a crippled person. It is no wonder that farmers, agricultural scientists, and market managers—all specialists in one-crop agriculture—react so negatively to suggestions that use of chemical pesticides be restricted.

To be effective, in most instances, biological control must go beyond a one-on-one predator/pest relationship. It must include crop rotation; economic incentives to encourage farmers to adopt less damaging forms of pest control; marketing programs flexible enough to handle these changes. Fragmentation of research, farm economics, and marketing all too often block implementation of biological controls. When new techniques do reach the field and fail, as in the case of the onion root maggot, agricultural policy makers too often fault the techniques themselves rather than their unfavourable policies.

Pesticide Technology Has Peaked

The almost blind faith in chemical pesticides is rather puzzling, especially since the basic technology has peaked and the effectiveness of the pesticides is declining. To understand why, we must look at how chemical pesticides are invented and then registered for use by Agriculture Canada, a process which is itself very much part of the selection of a chemical as a pesticide.

The essence of a good pesticide is a chemical that kills or damages the indicated pest, but does not harm non-target species with which it comes in contact. It is this selectivity that must be established and around which the registration procedure revolves.

Search for a marketable pesticide occurs in two stages. The first stage is to find chemicals that kill. Candidate chemicals are tested to find out if they kill insects, weeds or other pests. The initial screening turns up numerous killers which are further tested in refinements of the primary screen in order to learn their range of targets. The initial search is relatively easy. Having been selected, candidate chemicals pass into a time-consuming second stage which is expensive and generally indecisive. The second stage asks the following questions: is this chemical safe to non-target organisms and what are its long-term effects?

Limits to toxicological testing have long been recognized and research on new and more sophisticated testing procedures proceeds briskly. Although the methodology has a long way to go, especially with respect to the effects of trace amounts of chemicals, it is much improved over the procedures of even 10 years ago.

It is customary to subject the candidate pesticide to several tests in a number of organisms. The objective of each test is to prove the chemical unsafe; that is, does it exhibit harmful effects in the test system? The fact that any one procedure shows no evidence of harm does not prove safety; other tests may indicate harmful effects. It should take only one test showing harmful effects to fail a candidate. Thus, the more testing protocols applied to a candidate pesticide and the more sophisticated they become, the less likely the candidate pesticide will pass. This situation has an important implication for registration of new pesticides and review of old ones.

The determinant of a good pesticide is the ratio of its ability to kill its target versus minimal effects on other organisms. Since the advent of the new pesticides 40 years ago, the first part of the ratio—the ability to kill the target organism—has not changed much. DDT, which ushered in the modern era of chemical pest control, has not been surpassed in kill ability and in range of targets in spite of several million chemicals being screened. All chemicals have undesirable side-effects. Therefore, as the stringency of safety testing tightens, the second part of the ratio—the effect of the pesticide on organisms other than the target—inexorably moves toward the first part. The so-called selectivity of the pesticide diminishes and consequently its utility diminishes. The selectivity in absolute terms actually does not change; what changes is how much we know about the pesticide.

Pesticide technology could be said to have reached its limit. It is unrealistic to expect that some new miracle chemical pesticide will be discovered that will control pests and not harm non-target organisms in any way. This limitation poses a dilemma. Should registration criteria be maintained at the relatively relaxed level that now prevails or should Canadians insist on more stringent criteria? The presently administered criteria probably represent the upper limit to what can be applied to candidate pesticides in order to allow a few to be registered.

Canadian agriculture faces yet another dilemma in the development and manufacture of chemical pesticides. A chemical company may spend $20-50 million developing a single pesticide. Few chemical companies have the resources to invest that much money, and no such companies have their head-quarters in Canada. Moreover, in order to recoup their investment, the companies design their products for use on major world crops, such as cotton, corn, wheat, and soybeans. In effect, Canadian agriculture must adapt to its own uses pesticides which were designed for quite different conditions.

Canadian agriculture has become dependent on a pest-control technology over which it lacks influence. It cannot generate new pesticides itself. It lacks the clout to compel foreign chemical companies to develop pesticides designed for Canadian crops and Canadian conditions because on a world-scale Canadian agriculture is a minor actor. Although the multinational companies are glad to exploit the Canadian market, they can choose to pull out if Canadian authorities become too restrictive.

We can only conclude that the selectivity of chemical pesticides is not going to improve. As long as Canadian agriculture maintains its dependence on these chemicals, 25 million Canadians will continue to be exposed to the hazards of genetic and other long-term damage.

A New Approach to Pest Control

How can Canadian agriculture be weaned from its dependence on chemical pesticides? First of all, changes in attitude need to take place. Pest control has been viewed mainly as a technical problem. In order to implement biological alternatives, the science and application of pest control must take into account farm economics, product marketing, and traditional agricultural practices; above all, this requires a desire to invest in an ecologically-sustainable system of food and fibre production. It is difficult to see how all this is going to come about within a government framework that designates chemical pesticides as the principal means of controlling pests.

As one means of facilitating a comprehensive approach to pest control, the Canadian Environmental Advisory Council, a body that advises the Federal Minister of the Environment, recommended strongly that the Federal Government create a Pest Control Commission, independent of Agriculture Canada and other operating departments (Hall, 1981). This commission, with its own statutory authority, would address pest problems by focusing on comprehensive strategies for their successful resolution. It would review all aspects of the problem, integrate economic policies, and promote ecologically-sound technical approaches. Its deliberations and the reasons for its decisions would be open to the public. A strong economic case can be made for greater use of biological controls. Not only are they cost-effective, but, because they also have to be designed and developed in Canada for Canadian conditions, they create numerous new job and economic opportunities.

As more and more biological controls were implemented over a period of years, the use of chemical pesticides would be minimized. The private sector would continue to play a major service role in agriculture; the difference would be that their role would shift from selling chemical pesticides to providing control services. It would be naïve to suggest that biological controls in themselves are totally benign. They do present risks that must be assessed and they can never be final. In the words of Dr. Peter Harris, "once you have one weed species under control, another pops up." Nevertheless, eliminating risks to human health, lessening the environmental burden and improving the sustainability of agriculture are worthy objectives.

Reference

Hall, Ross H. 1981. *A New Approach to Pest Control in Canada.* Canadian Environmental Advisory Council, Report No. 10, July. (A free copy of this report may be obtained from the Canadian Environmental Advisory Council, Environment Canada, Ottawa, Ontario, K1A 0H3.)

13
Impacts on Agriculture and Forestry from Fossil Fuel Combustion Residuals

Orie L. Loucks

Research Scientist, Holcomb Research Institute
Butler University, Indianapolis

Introduction

Beginning late in the 1970s, many studies have reported that the farmlands and forests of both the Eastern and Western United States, Eastern Canada, Europe, and parts of Asia are being exposed to significant concentrations of gaseous air pollutants, suspended particulates, and acidic deposition (Loucks, 1980; Wolff and Lioy, 1980; NRC, 1981). Given what is known about the functioning of soil, water, and biological components in ecosystems, all of these alterations in atmospheric chemistry suggest a likelihood of deleterious direct or indirect effects. Since annual effects are small, but, on forests, are cumulative, the productivity of natural resources could be impaired over a period of a few decades.

The objective of this paper is to evaluate the evidence and geographic scope of pollutant-induced stresses on crops and forests, most specifically those from fossil fuels. The potential for alteration of ecosystem processes and of resource productivity represents an aggregate response to subtle pollutant effects, some of which derive from combined action of pollutants at levels not otherwise significant for plants or animals. Long-term effects are those in which the species composition and age-class distribution of forests are changed over large regions. Thus, the material presented here provides a foundation for an analysis of effects, extrapolating where possible from experimentally derived dose/response relationships to the responses of entire ecosystems and regions.

Pollutant Sources and Air Quality in Eastern North America

The problems of pollutant sources and ambient concentrations can be considered from several perspectives. The principal sources of sulfur dioxide (SO_2) for the Eastern United States and Canada are located in the urban centers and industrial sites, many of which are distributed along the Ohio River Valley, while the nitrogen oxide (NO_x) sources correspond to the major urban centers. Ambient concentrations associated with the release and transport of these pollutants have been summarized in various ways. For example, in 1978, 79% of the 67 counties in Region V (Minnesota, Wisconsin, Illinois, Michigan, Indiana and Ohio) with ozone (O_3) monitors were in violation of the National Ambient Air Quality Standards for O_3 (0.12 ppm); 14% of the 160 counties monitored for SO_2 were in violation of the SO_2 primary standard (0.14 ppm averaged over 24 hours); and 27% of the 122 counties monitored for total suspended particulates (TSP) were in violation of the primary standard (260 $\mu g/m^3$ averaged over 24 hours). These data originate in counties which are predominately urban or suburban in character, but they are adjacent to the central agricultural breadbasket in the United States Midwest.

Effects of Primary Emissions

The significance of pollutant concentrations for natural resources probably is best known for SO_2 (Dochinger *et al.*, 1970; Loucks, 1980). Effects on crops and some forest species have been studied extensively and yield reductions can occur at the concentrations cited above for counties in and around urbanized areas. Exposures at 0.05 to 0.1 ppm for a few hours have been shown to cause leaf injury and reduced needle length in a sensitive species such as eastern white pine, particularly when in conjunction with moderate regional O_3 concentrations. Although the studies of NO_x effects on plants have been less thorough, they indicate considerably less toxicity than for SO_2. Current concerns for improving NO_x control relate primarily to the role of NO_x in producing secondary pollutants such as acid rain and ozone. However, synergistic interactions between NO_x and SO_2 of significance to crops and forest have been demonstrated experimentally and may occur near major pollutant source areas. Bormann (1985) has provided a comprehensive summary of how multiple pollutants at relatively low doses produce a long-term stress on forests as a system.

Long-Range Transport and Chemical Transformation of Pollutants

The fate of primary emissions released into the atmosphere depends on several factors, some meteorological and others a property of the pollutants themselves. Long reaction times and long-range transport are facilitated by tall stacks, a stable lower atmosphere (i.e., where the temperature does not increase rapidly with altitude), and the absence of precipitation events. The meteorological factors which influence long-distance transport are primarily those associated with clockwise circulation of air around high-pressure systems and the counter-clockwise flow of low-pressure centers. These tend to facilitate transport from south to north and vice versa, while the prevailing air mass circulation moves from west to east. Hence primary emissions from the industrialized Midwest are the precursors for the elevated pollutant concentrations and deposition elsewhere in the Midwest as well as in Eastern Canada and the United States. Occasionally, in advance of frontal systems, major incursions of polluted air move into northern Minnesota, Wisconsin and Michigan, and have been linked to air masses originating southeastward in the Ohio River Valley (Bowen, 1978; Wolff *et al.*, 1980; NRC, 1983). Thus, for example, 45-74% of the total deposited sulfur in Ontario is estimated to come from outside the province. This pattern is complicated by seasonal trends which show a stronger southerly component in the summer and a more northerly component in winter.

In the course of the long-distance transport the concentrations of primary emissions can be decreased, but the concentrations of secondary pollutants can increase (especially SO_4 aerosol particulates, O_3 and acids in precipitation). Important threats to resource values of the Eastern United States and Canada are associated with the constituents in visibility reduction (from particulates, primarily SO_4), effects of O_3 on terrestrial vegetation, and the reactions following acidic deposition on soils in poorly buffered watersheds. Each of these will be discussed in turn.

Photochemical Oxidants

Photochemical oxidants, principally O_3, have been thought of until recently as pollutants of urban areas. However, rural and forested areas some hundreds of miles downwind of urban areas are seriously influenced by persistent regional episodes of O_3. Effects on vegetation and crops are being confirmed now over the entire Eastern United States and adjacent Canada (OTA, 1984).

Visibility Reduction

Numerous studies have demonstrated that atmospheric reactions involving SO_2, NO_x, O_3, and ammonium compounds contribute strongly to the formation of large amounts of aerosol-sized particulate matter, primarily ammonium sulfate and nitrate particles. During periods of slow-moving anticyclonic activity, these reactions, combined with uptake of water by the particles from humid air masses, lead to increased haze and visibility reduction over most of the Eastern United States (U.S. EPA, 1979). In much of the Eastern United States and Southern Canada, visibility is now frequently less than a few miles during air stagnation episodes, seriously reducing the scenic value of residential properties, lake recreational sites, and state, provincial or national parks.

Acidic Precipitation

The chemistry of precipitation throughout Eastern North America appears to have been changed significantly over the past half century in association with increases in the use of high-sulfur coal. Elevated concentrations of sulfuric and nitric acids in the lower atmosphere are the most widely recognized change (Likens, 1976; Galloway and Cowling, 1978; Glass and Loucks, 1980). Currently, acidity in precipitation in Eastern North America continues to be high, a condition that has raised concern about effects on the long-term productivity of both aquatic and terrestrial resources (Loucks, 1983).

Effects of Pollutants

SO_2/NO_x

Several extensive reviews of SO_2 effects (e.g., Braunstein *et al.*, 1977) show that a wide variety of organisms are sensitive to slightly elevated SO_2 concentrations (EPRI, 1976). Many species exhibit synergistic reactions to combinations of SO_2 with other pollutants such as O_3, or NO_x under field and laboratory conditions (Dochinger *et al.*, 1970; Kress and Skelly, 1977; Houston, 1974; EPA, 1984). Along with the effects of photochemical smog and acidic precipitation, these reactions pose one of the greatest threats to resources (NRC, 1981; OTA, 1984).

SO_2 and Trace Element Effects on Plant/Insect Interactions

The complex effects of environmental contaminants on insect-plant interfaces may be reciprocal, acting on the insect through the plant and on the plant through the insect (Glass and Loucks, 1980; Smith, 1981). Air pollutants reported to have significant effects on insect behaviour and population dynamics include sulfur and nitrogen oxides, ozone, hydrocarbons, fluorocarbons, smog, dusts, acid mists, major and trace elements, and radionuclides. Known effects of air pollutants on insects include death of sensitive species, proliferation of pest insects in forests and croplands, loss of parasitic and predacious insects, loss of saprophagous insects, loss of pollinators, temporary or permanent changes in behaviour, reduced hatchability and fecundity, and genetic alterations, such as chromosome disjunction. Although responses by insects to threshold exposures of pollutants have not been well established, a number of insect groups with strong sensory systems, particularly saprophagous and predacious beetles, social bees (pollinators), and parasitic wasps have been shown to be reduced in abundance at relatively low concentrations of air pollutants. The response, apparently, results from pollutant avoidance or disorientation, or both. Several plant-feeding insect groups increase rapidly when the activity of parasite or predator-control insects is reduced, or the vigor of host-plant species is reduced, both of which have been shown to occur from gaseous air pollutants. The available literature suggests that disturbances in the population dynamics of these insect species can occur at pollutant levels below those manifesting visible injury to the host forest species.

The Effects of O_3 on Agricultural Productivity

Photochemical oxidants are recognized as the air pollutant causing the most significant economic losses in the United States (OTA, 1982). For example, experimental yield-loss data indicate that for the cumulative O_3 exposures observed in the Ohio River Basin in the late 1970s, the loss would be 5-26.% for soybeans; 4-15% for corn, depending on exposure and variety; and 3-10% for wheat. These results should be applied to the less humid plains states, but, during humid years, may apply as far west and north as Minnesota (Loucks, 1980). For soybeans, the SO_2 loss coefficients range from a lower bound of 1% to an upper bound of 9%. The limited, short-term studies suggest that while chronic SO_2 effects on corn are small, they should not be discounted (Loucks and Armetano, 1982). Pollutant-induced crop losses, however, must be viewed as potential crop production gains from investments in cleaner air.

Potential crop production gains from O_3 abatement in the five Ohio Valley states are estimated in 1976 to have been: 18-144 million bushels of soybeans; 85-318 million bushels of corn; and 5-18 million bushels of wheat (Loucks, 1980).

Recently, the Office of Technology Assessment (OTA, 1984) of the United States Congress, utilized data developed by the National Crop Loss Assessment Network (Heck *et al.*, 1982), in combination with recent field O_3 exposure data, to determine the national impacts of pollutants on the productivity of corn, wheat, soybeans, and peanuts. The assessment estimates that approximately three billion dollars of agricultural productivity could be gained if current maximum O_3 levels were reduced below 25 ppb. Dollar values are based on 1978 crop prices, without accounting for price effects, to provide an overall estimate of the impact. Of the dollar impact, soybeans represent 64%, corn 17%, wheat 12%, and peanuts 7%. The corn-belt states of Illinois, Iowa, and Indiana would sustain the greatest potential gain from pollutant abatement. The OTA report notes that certain assumptions and caveats must be considered when interpreting the uncertainty associated with these or other similar assessments. However, they note that several important conclusions can be drawn from the assessment. First, it is readily apparent that a significant portion of the agricultural land area of the United States is experiencing levels of oxidants during the growing season capable of reducing crop yields. Second, the impact estimates further support earlier, independent estimates by Heagle and Heck (1980) which suggested annual losses of approximately two billion dollars.

Losses of Horticultural Plantings

To estimate the private residential losses of sensitive horticultural materials in the urban areas of the Ohio Valley, observations were made of annual mortality in the Indianapolis area during 1978-1980 (Loucks, 1980). Dieback and mortality were noted for major plantings (including mature conifers, shrubs, and garden plants) on which air pollution injury symptoms were observable each year. The mortality is not all directly attributable to air pollution injury, but all of this vegetation has been weakened by the air pollutants. Although every property owner is not affected every year, nearly every residence appears to lose important plantings on an average of once per decade. Although the final cause of mortality is often insect outbreak or disease, the weakening of urban horticultural and landscape plantings by air pollutants appears to be a crucial factor in the etiology of plant loss. To estimate precisely the horticultural loss, a total urban population study would be required. Rural areas and small towns are not considered in the following estimate.

In a recent insurance settlement in Indianapolis, one large specimen tree had an assessed value of $6000. Other data suggest that mature trees on residential properties have an average value of $4000. We have estimated the loss of such trees due directly and indirectly to air pollution as one tree per 200 properties each year. Fully established small trees and large shrubs were valued at $1000 each, with an estimated one property in 50 losing a plant of this type each year. Garden plants and flowering herb losses are estimated at $20 per year per property. Thus, total horticultural losses for an estimated 700 000 urban properties in the Ohio Valley having horticultural materials will be approximately $42 million per year. Total losses were assumed to remain unchanged in future years, since pollution-sensitive varieties may be replaced by more resistant ones over the next several decades.

Estimating Forest Growth Losses from Gaseous Pollutants

Questions regarding the effects of utility plant emissions on forests and other non-agricultural species require an approach much different from that applied to crops. The Eastern United States has in the order of 50 native forest tree species (with many more introduced as horticultural plantings). These species are exposed year after year to atmospheric pollutants, and for the conifers, which usually maintain several years' foliage, effects are expressed cumulatively over years rather than in a single growing season. In addition, the "product" value is the accumulating woody growth or the plant survival (as in the case of horticultural material), rather than an annual harvest that is removed from exposure each year.

Because of differences in duration of exposure, number of species, and limited experimental data base, it is difficult to differentiate effects on forests from primary gaseous emissions as opposed to those of secondary pollutants, such as oxidants and acid rain. The differences can be distinguished where one or another pollutant dominates, but over a large area responses tend to become integrated. Also difficult to assess are the effects on trees from elevated insect populations which take advantage of weakened host plants over a period of years. Air pollutants also have effects on natural insect control organisms, such as birds and hymenopteran parasites, which need to be considered.

Several studies have provided quantitative estimates of the impacts of air pollutants on forests. Some examples of these studies are: 37% reduction in radial growth and 83% loss of merchantable volume growth for trees under 30 years of age, and an annual mortality rate of 3% in ponderosa and Jeffrey pine in the San Bernardino Mountains of southern California (US EPA, 1977); 11% annual mortality rate on eastern white pine in the Appalachian Mountains (Skelly et al., 1979); and growth fluctuations caused by direct gaseous pollution effects from urban areas and factories (Karnowsky, 1980; Usher and Williams, 1982; Phillips et al., 1977a) and by increased wartime munitions manufacturing (Phillips et al., 1977; Stone and Skelly, 1974).

The results from the Indiana white pine foliage survey (Usher and Williams, 1982) provide detailed background on the intensity of air pollution effects in the Ohio River Valley area. As a comparison white pines were monitored in 1980 for symptoms of air pollution disease at four relatively "clean" sites near the Columbia Generating Station at Portage, Wisconsin. These stands had significantly less disease than those at the Indiana sites. The differences in disease at the various locations correspond to observable canopy changes; when trees lose foliage prematurely, canopy density deteriorates, and the trees experience a decline in stem vigor.

In 1980, a preliminary assessment was completed of prospective pollutant impact from expanded power generating capacity in the Ohio River Basin (Loucks, 1980). The normal forest growth rate for the region (37.3 million acres of forest), has been calculated (USDA Forest Service, 1978) to be about 40 ft³/acre/year for all species.

Softwood species (including air pollution-sensitive white, Virginia and shortleaf pines) comprise 4.2% of the forests, with hardwoods making up the remainder. The sensitive softwood species are assumed to experience a reduction in annual volume increment of 2.6 to 11.7% of the potential annual growth or 2.76 to 7.33 million ft³/year. This range encompasses Linzon's (1971) estimate of 5.6% per year and is near Skelly's (1980) estimate of 2% per year for sensitive eastern white pines and softwoods of equal sensitivity. However, it does not consider the effects of mortality in softwoods that may be induced, at least in part, by the long-term reduction in growth.

Based on work by West *et al.* (1980), it was estimated that the annual losses from the three sensitive hardwood species (black walnut, black cherry, and black locust) were similar to those of softwoods, i.e., 2.6 to 11.7% per year or 3.36 to 17.9 million ft³/year. The 10 species of intermediate sensitivity suffered losses of 1.1 to 5.9% per year or 4.85 to 25.7 million ft³/year. The resistant hardwoods suffered no losses. The total estimated reduction was between 10.97 and 50.93 ft³/year. The total annual wood production in the Ohio River Basin forests has been estimated by the USDA Forest Service (1974) at 1.49 x 10⁹ ft³ of wood (40 ft³/acre/year x 37.3 million acres). The 1976 loss from air pollution stress on all species, therefore, would be estimated to have been from 0.7 to 3.4%, attributable to a combination of O_3 and SO_2 effects. Again, however, this estimate does not include growth losses due to the mortality of hardwoods induced, in part, by the pollutant exposures.

Large-Scale Impacts on Forest Productivity

More significant than simply the mechanisms by which pollutant effects are expressed locally is the potential for subtle or chronic effects to be cumulative in long-lived species and to produce severe damage after two decades or more. The most recent reports from West Germany and other countries in central Europe (Ulrich and Pankrath 1983; AFZ 1984) document a severe dieback of both coniferous and broadleaf forests. This damage is strongly linked to foliage symptoms and is associated with pollutant concentrations (including acidity in rainfall) that lead scientists to conclude these large-scale effects are attributable to the pollutant inputs.

Regional Forest Losses from Pollutant Deposition

Given the widespread evidence of the sensitivity of tree species to air pollutants, numerous researchers have sought to document the potential for a similar response in forest growth to the annual deposition of acidic substances in rainfall. The results up to 1980, however, were inconclusive (Smith, 1981). These findings may have been due to imprecision in the methodologies being used to document height or diameter growth changes, at that time. However, studies of the effects of acidic deposition on forest growth have been underway for some years in Europe (Abrahamsen, 1980). Early work in Sweden used tree-ring analysis methods, and the finding of possible effects was couched in considerable uncertainty. A later study was not able to support the original findings of effects from acidic deposition, but more recent research in Sweden has found negative effects on tree growth under sensitive soil conditions (F. Anderson, personal communication).

A variety of experimental approaches for detecting effects of acidic deposition on tree growth have been undertaken in Norway (Abrahamsen, 1980). These have led to the conclusion that over the period of a few years, the initial beneficial effects (on some soils) from the nitrogen and sulfur content in acidic deposition can be reversed, and the negative influence apparently due to the loss of soil cations (and possibly the toxicity of moderately elevated aluminum concentrations) combine to reduce the growth of trees.

Studies in Germany (Ulrich and Pankrath, 1983) have led to the conclusion that mobilization of aluminum (under situations of unusually high H^+ concentration) has produced loss of growth and extensive mortality on Norway spruce. Similar effects on diameter growth in association with fluctuations in rainfall pH and a downtrend in stream pH have been reported by Johnson *et al.* (1981) for pitch pine in New Jersey. Other studies show greatly altered growth rates and considerable mortality for red spruce in Vermont. No definitive linkage has been found to acidic deposition as yet, but toxicity from free ionic aluminum (Al^{3+}) mobilized by acid deposition, particularly during flushing episodes, along with oxidant damage, appears to be the most plausible explanation.

Diminished Global Carbon Uptake as an Effect of Air Pollutants

An important new term emerging in studies of the global carbon balance and atmospheric CO_2 increases, is "diminished sequestering capacity." This term describes an increase in CO_2 accumulation in the atmosphere due to the reduction in photosynthesis caused by air pollutant exposures (Loucks, 1981). It is best explained in relation to the implications for carbon exchange of recent increases in O_3 concentrations in the lower atmosphere. For example, by 1978-1979, the recurring "episode peak" value in the Ohio Valley was 0.15 ppm, an increase in O_3 of 0.02 ppm per decade over the 50-year period since the 1920s (Loucks, 1980).

As part of the Ohio Valley study (Loucks, 1980), we examined the potential for further increases in O_3 by the year 2000 and its significance for vegetation and CO_2 uptake and release. Projections of increased O_3 concentrations for 1985 and 2000 indicate potential crop losses of 28% and 34%, respectively. Such responses are already the case for California, where they have been met by the development of somewhat resistant strains of the main crop varieties. In addition, the historic rise in O_3 is a very probable explanation for the leveling off of an historic upward trend in agricultural yields—low and relatively unchanged until the 1930s when a sharp increase began and continued until 1968. At that time a "plateau effect" seems to have occurred (Wittwer, 1979), in which yields no longer increase as much in relation to the continuing technological input and improvement in agricultural practice.

To determine the long-term implications of oxidants for CO_2 exchanges, we need to evaluate the large-scale effect of these O_3 concentrations on major carbon pools, such as forests. Evidence of O_3-induced foliage pathologies, reduced growth, and mortality of selected forest species has been noted already, not only for much of the Eastern United States, but also for areas such as California's San Bernardino National Forest, where the original standing crop already has been greatly depleted. The forest decline in California represents a major step toward emissions-induced species conversion—in this case, toward chapparal species of lower productivity—a widely anticipated response.

If the loss of annual forest growth through mortality (not previously estimated) is about equal to the reduced growth in the annual ring increment already discussed, forest production in Eastern North America under the increased pollutant load projected for the Ohio Valley by 1990 would be on the order of 5 to 15% below present levels. Acid rain effects also may interact with the air pollutants released from increased use of fossil fuels to increase the degree of damage (Loucks, 1980; Johnson *et al.*, 1981). Assuming these forest losses are applicable in 1990 over the Eastern United States and limited areas of Europe (e.g., see Ulrich *et al.*, 1980), the "diminished sequestering capacity" in the temperate-zone forests will be on the order of 0.5 to 1.0 x 10^9 Gt (Gigatons)/yr. Little effect is expected in the tropics from toxic pollutants at that time, although reduced sequestering capacity may occur from deterioration of soils and the invasion of low nutrient-demanding but slower-growing species. Thus, the reduction in the normal rate of biospheric storage of carbon could range from 10 to 20% of the total CO_2 release from all current fossil fuel combustion on earth. This new "source" of CO_2 constitutes a significant potential increase in the rate at which CO_2 accumulates in the atmosphere.

Conclusions

Although the data presented here are largely North American, the studies here and in Europe document the recent emergence of biologically-significant pollutant loads over large areas of these continents. Because most of the research during the 1970s concentrated on experimental plots and controlled environment studies, few people recognized the magnitude of the effects on crops and forests from present pollutant exposures. Of special importance, however, is the apparent lag time in the expression of pollutant effects on long-lived and deep-rooted species of forest ecosystems. The evidence of extensive mortality for sensitive species in North America and Europe suggests serious consequences for natural resource productivity. In the long term, air pollutant effects on plants have the potential to contribute still other alterations in the chemistry of the lower atmosphere and to affect global climate.

References

Abrahamsen, G. 1980. Acid Precipitation, Plant Nutrients and Forest Growth. pp. 58-63. In: D. Drabls and A. Tollan (eds.) *Ecological Impact of Acid Precipitation. Proceedings of an International Conference.* SNSF Project, Oslo, Norway. 383 pp.

Allgemeine Forstzeitschrift, 1984. Zur Diagnose und Klassifizierung der neuartigen Waldschäden. AFZ Nr. 14/15 Stuttgart.

Bormann, F.H. 1985. Air Pollution and Forests: An Ecosystem Perspective. *BioScience*, Vol. 35: 434-441.

Bowen, B.B. 1978. "A Study of the Large Scale Transport of Low Level Ozone Across the Central and Eastern United States." M.S. Thesis. University of Wisconsin-Madison.

Braunstein, H.M., E.D. Copenhaver, and H.A. Pfuderer. 1977. *Environmental, Health and Control Aspects of Coal Conversion: An Information Overview.* Vol. 2, Oak Ridge National Laboratory, ORNL/EIS-95.

Dochinger, L.S., F.W. Bender, F.L. Fox, and W.W. Heck. 1970. "Chlorotic Dwarf of Eastern White Pine Caused by an Ozone and Sulfur Dioxide Interaction," *Nature*, 225:476.

Electric Power Research Institute. 1976. *Sulfur Oxides: Current Status of Knowledge.* EPRI EA-316, Project 681-1, Final Report, December.

Galloway, J.N. and E.G. Cowling. 1978. "The Effects of Precipitation on Aquatic and Terrestrial Ecosystems: A Proposed Precipitation Chemistry Network," *APCA Journal*, 28(3):299-235.

Glass, G.E. and O.L. Loucks (eds.). 1980. *Impacts of Airborne Pollutants on Wilderness Areas Along the Minnesota-Ontario Border.* EPA-600/3-80-044.

Heagle, A.S. and W.W. Heck. 1980. "Field Methods to Assess Crop Losses Due to Oxidant Air Pollutants," pp. 296-305. In: P.S. Teng and S.V. Krupa (eds.), *Assessment of Losses Which Constrain Production and Crop Improvement in Agriculture and Forests, Proceedings, E.C. Stkaman Commemorative Symposium.* Misc. Publ. No. 7, Agricultural Experiment Station, University of Minnesota.

Heck, W.W., O.C. Taylor, R. Adams, G. Bingham, J. Miller, E. Preston and L. Weinstein. 1982. "Assessment of Crop Loss from Ozone," *Journal of Air Pollution Control Association*, 32:353-361.

Houston, D.B. 1974. "Responses of Selected *Pinus Strubus.* L. Clones to Fumigations with Sulfur Dioxide and Ozone," *Canadian Journal of Forest Research*, 4:65-68.

Johnson, A.H., T.G. Siccama, D. Wang, R.S. Turner and T.H. Barringer. 1981. "Recent Changes in Patterns of Tree Growth Rate in the New Jersey Pinelands: A Possible Effect of Acid Rain," *Journal of Environmental Quality*, 10(4):427-430.

Johnson, A.H., R.S. Turner and D.G. Lord. 1983. "Assessing the Possibility of a Link Between Acid Precipitation and Decreased Growth Rates of Pitch Pine (*Pinus Reqida*), Short-leaf Pine (*Pine Echinata*), and Red Spruce (*Picea Rubens*)." In: *Direct and Indirect Effects of Acid Deposition on Vegetation.*

Presented at American Chemical Society Symposium on Acid Precipitation. Las Vegas, Nevada, March.

Kress, L.W. and J.M. Skelly. 1977. "The Interaction of O_3, SO_2, and NO_2 and its Effect on the Growth of Two Forest Tree Species." In: *Cottrell Centennial Symposium on Air Pollution and its Impact on Agriculture.*

Likens, G.E. 1976. "Acid Precipitation," *Chemical and Engineering News,* 54:29-44.

Linzon, S.N. 1971. "Economic Effects of Sulfur Dioxide on Forest Growth," *Journal of the Air Pollution Control Association,* 21(2):81-86.

Loucks, O.L. (ed.) 1980. *Crop and Forest Losses due to Current and Projected Emissions from Coal-fired Power Plants in the Ohio River Basin.* Report to the Ohio River Basin Energy Study. The Institute of Ecology, Indianapolis.

Loucks, O.L. 1981. "Recent Results from Studies of Carbon Cycling in the Biosphere," pp. 3-42. In: *Carbon Dioxide Effects Research and Assessment Program.* Proceedings of the Carbon Dioxide and Climate Research Program Conference. US Department of Energy, CONF-8004110. Washington, DC.

Loucks, O.L. 1982. "The Concern for Acidic Deposition in the Great Lakes Region," pp. 21-41. In: F.M. D'Itri (ed.) *The Effects of Acid Precipitation on Ecological Systems in the Great Lakes Region.* Proceedings of a Conference, East Lansing, Michigan, April 1-3, 1981. Ann Arbor Science Publishers, Ann Arbor, Michigan.

Loucks, O.L. 1983. "Use of Forest Site Index for Evaluating Terrestrial Resources at Risk from Acidic Deposition." In: *Direct and Indirect Effects of Acid Deposition on Vegetation.* Proceedings of a 1982 American Chemical Society Symposium. R.A. Linthurst (ed.), Ann Arbor Science.

Loucks, O.L. and T.V. Armentano. 1982. "Estimating Crop Yield Effects from Ambient Air Pollutants in the Ohio River Valley," *Journal of the Air Pollution Control Association,* pp. 146-150.

National Research Council, Committee on the Atmosphere and the Biosphere. 1981. *Atmosphere-biosphere Interactions: Toward a Better Understanding of the Ecological Consequences of Fossil Fuel Combustion.* Commission on Natural Resources. National Academy Press, Washington, DC. 263 pp.

National Research Council, 1983. *Acid Deposition: Atmospheric Processes in Eastern North America. A Review of Current Scientific Standing.* National Academy Press, Washington, DC. 375 pp.

Office of Technology Assessment. 1984. *Acid Rain and Transported Air Pollutants: Implications for Public Policy.* Congress of the United States, Washington, DC 323 pp.

Phillips, S.O., J.M. Skelly and H.E. Burkhart, 1977. "Growth Fluctuations of Loblolly Pine due to Periodical Air Pollution Levels: Interaction of Rainfall and Age," *Phytopathology,* 67(6).

Skelly, J.M. 1980 "Photochemical Oxidant Impact on Mediterranean and Temperate Forest Ecosystems: Real and Potential Effects," pp. 22-27. In: *International Symposium on Effects of Air Pollutants on Mediterranean and Temperate Forest Ecosystems.* US Department Agricultural General Technical Report PSW-43.

Smith, W.H. 1981. *Air Pollution and Forests. Interactions Between Air Contaminants and Forest Ecosystems.* New York: Springer-Verlag.

Stone, L.L. and J.M. Skelly. 1974. *Visibility in the Southwest: An Exploration of the Historical Data Base.* Technology Service Corporation, Santa Monica, California.

Ulrich, B. and J. Pankrath. 1983. *Effects of Accumulation of Air Pollutants in Forest Ecosystems.* Proceedings of a Workshop held at Gottingen, West Germany, May 16-18, 1982. D. Reidel Publishing Co., Dordrecht, Holland. 389 pp.

U.S. Department of Agriculture Forest Service. 1978. "Forest Statistics of the United States. 1977." Review Draft. Stock No. 001-001-00437-5.

U.S. Environmental Protection Agency. 1979. *Protecting Visibility: An EPA Report to Congress.* EPA-450/5-79-008. Washington, DC.

U.S. Environmental Protection Agency. 1984. *The Acidic Deposition Phenomenon and Its Effects: Critical Assessment Review Papers. Volume II Biological Effects.* EPA 600/8-83-016AF Washington, DC.

Usher, R.W. and W.T. Williams. 1982. "Air Toxicity to Eastern White Pines in Indiana," *Plant Disease*, 66:199-204.

West, D.C., S.B. McLaughlin and H.H. Shugart. 1980. "Simulated Forest Response to Chronic Air Pollution Stress," *Journal of Environmental Quality,* 9(1):43-49.

Wittwer, S.H. 1979. "Future Trends in Agriculture—Technology and Management," pp. 64-107. In: *Long-Range Environmental Outlook.* National Research Council, Commission on Natural Resources. Washington, DC.

Wolff, G.T. and P.J. Lioy. 1980. "Development of an Ozone River Associated with Synoptic Scale Episodes in the Eastern United States," *Environment, Science, and Technology,* 14:1257-1260.

Wolff, G.T., P.J. Lioy and G.D. Wight. 1980. "Transport of Ozone Associated with an Air Mass," *Journal Environmental Science and Health,* A15(2):183-189.

14

The Nature and Environmental Impacts of the Industrialization of Agriculture

Michael J. Troughton

Professor, Department of Geography
University of Western Ontario, London

Nature and Significance of Agricultural Industrialization

The objective in this paper is to try to characterize the nature and importance of the industrialization of agriculture. It is a broad-brush approach, deliberately intended to place industrialization in an extensive spatial and temporal framework, including its widespread environmental and socio-economic impacts. This presents a major challenge, but the incentive lies in the belief that the industrialization of agriculture is a contemporary process of fundamental significance.

Simply defined, the industrialization of agriculture refers to the process, currently active in most economically developed countries, whereby agriculture (farming) is being transformed from an activity generally carried out on a small scale and at a low level of capital intensity, to one in which the major proportion of production comes from a reduced number of large scale and/or highly capitalized units. Although such a definition suggests a rather straightforward operational shift, even those observers who emphasize its operational nature see industrialization as not just change, but *the* change affecting agriculture throughout the developed world. There is general recognition that, while the central fact is a change in the nature of production at the farm level, the process has a broader impact on both the total food system and the overall rural environment.

Evaluation of impact leads to sharply contrasting viewpoints: for many within agribusiness or agricultural science, industrialization represents a logical and benign extension of the application of technology—progress which, despite its social impacts, cannot and should not be interrupted. At the other end of the spectrum are those who argue that its nature both reflects and is contributing to a breakdown of human society, in ecological and even moral terms, and that industrialization represents the antithesis of human cultural development.

In attempting a more neutral stance, one is nevertheless impressed by a number of factors which point to the significance of the process. For example, although so much recent attention has been devoted to the agricultural development of Third World economies, the rate of change attendant upon industrialization is much greater in developed countries, and is contributing to a widening gap between the systems. Furthermore, agricultural industrialization involves dynamic interaction between the key forces in modern society—technology, economic theory, and political ideology—taking place simultaneously in national and international contexts. We are concerned with a process which challenges policy and environmental management nationally (e.g., in Canada and in each province). In human terms, agricultural industrialization is causing widespread transformation—possibly the final disintegration—of agrarian societies in developed countries. While each of these factors may be judged good or bad, each has both practical and philosophical implications that go beyond a farm-operation level of significance.

Model Frameworks of Agricultural Industrialization

Three broad descriptive models are presented which attempt (1) to describe agricultural industrialization in terms of historical stages-of-development, (2) to identify its inherent characteristics in terms of process and response, and (3) to suggest a preliminary classification of agricultural industrial types.

Three Revolutions

The first model postulates the existence of and seeks to describe the inherent characteristics of three revolutionary stages in agricultural development: (1) the beginnings of agriculture in the Neolithic and its spread over much of the earth by the eighteenth century; (2) the change from subsistence to market orientations, taking-off in 18th century England to become dominant in areas of north-western European settlement; and (3) industrialization affecting both capitalist and socialist developed economies in the post World War II period.

The term "revolution" means a radical change of circumstances. The impact of the "First Agricultural Revolution" is generally acknowledged, to the extent that between 8000 BC and 1750 AD agriculture replaced hunting and gathering in most parts of the world; human population expanded, based on rural settlement and an agrarian way of life. The norm became subsistence agriculture, which, although exhibiting extreme spatial variation, was everywhere characterized by labour intensive methods, a low level of technology, and an emphasis on communal tenure.

Despite being characterized by a high degree of diversity and ecological stability, traditional agriculture failed to meet the requirements of the increasingly merchantilistic society which developed in Western Europe from around 1650 AD. A "Second Agricultural Revolution" took place which was closely linked to the Industrial Revolution. The change from subsistence to market orientation took place in societies in which the rapid growth of urban and industrial populations was supported by agricultural surpluses, of both food and labour. Nevertheless, the two revolutions each had distinct beginnings and continued to develop parallel to one another.

Independent innovations in the farm sector facilitated increased production and encouraged the change from communal-peasant to individual-commercial farm operations. These included the introduction of new crops (roots, legumes) and crop rotation systems, better livestock, and land improvements including drainage and manuring. Although landowners in many countries sought to commercialize agricultural production, modernization was most successful where improved technology and market economics were based on the individual family farm unit.

Commercial agriculture developed side-by-side with urban-industrial society, notably in Western Europe and North America, but strong operational and ideological differences were maintained between agriculture and industry. The latter, after an initial, dispersed "cottage" stage, became a predominantly large-scale, factory operation using large inputs of labour, fossil fuel energy and machines, at specific locations. Agriculture, despite a market orientation, actually proliferated through the establishment of greater numbers of relatively small, family units. Dispersion and "cottage scale" represented major distinctions in the nature of the form between agriculture and manufacturing and the individual family farm became the integral economic and political unit in the structure of new agrarian societies.

By the 20th century, manufacturing adopted the integrated assembly line and achieved new levels of concentration and specialization, whereas, agriculture, despite a gradual adoption of mechanization, attained its greatest efficiencies through small-scale, mixed operations (e.g., Danish agriculture). Although industrial activity was applied to the articulation of agricultural output (e.g., the system of rail movement, elevator storage and milling of Prairie grain), most agricultural processing remained local and small-scale prior to World War II. As significant as the operational differences between farm and factory, was the growth and prevalence of the belief in the separate nature and values of the urban-industrial and rural-agrarian sectors of capitalist society. The political emancipation involved with agricultural transformation in Europe and pioneering in North America fostered a strong attachment to both the concept and reality of a class of individual freehold farmers and an associated rural society serving the farm community and sharing its values.

To identify a "Third Agricultural Revolution," based on industrialization of agricultural production, is to claim a further radical change of direction, including changes in the model of capitalist commercial agriculture just described. Industrialization of agriculture, therefore, involves a combination of technological, economic, and political changes that differ in kind rather than degree, from what has previously characterized agricultural production.

To some extent increased capacity in the technological application of energy, machines and chemicals seems the most obvious change. But applications represent only the means to achieve key economic improvements. At the farm level, the emphasis is on lower unit costs of production, to the extent that productivity and financial performance become both the rationale and the measure of survival. Of greater significance, however, is the concept of the farm not as a separate unit, but rather as part of an integrated food production system, which also includes input-supply and output-processing and distribution sectors. In addition, it is in this assembly-line or factory concept of production, the application of a manufacturing model to agriculture, that the key to the convergence between capitalist (corporate) and socialist (collective) forms of organization is also found.

Although it is arguable that the technological application of industry to agriculture has reached its highest level of sophistication in North America, which remains the centre of technological innovation, leadership in economic and political applications lie elsewhere. Although the industrialization of agriculture is very much a phenomenon of the post World War II era, its beginnings may be logically traced to pre-war USSR. In 1928, collectivization of Soviet agriculture began, a process which was subsequently adopted throughout Eastern Europe. In many cases, collectivization substituted communal tenure under state control for regimes which had not been fully transformed into commercial agriculture (e.g., USSR, Hungary, Romania). Most important, collective agriculture imposed a system which is oriented towards the integration of production based on the factory scale at each level of supply, production and processing, and is consistent in terms of both its economic and political ideology. In contrast, the basically similar corporate industrial model of capitalist societies has to be rationalized with family-farm based agriculture in both economic and political terms. Nevertheless, when applied, both collective and corporate models constitute a radical new direction, with an organizational set-up which rejects both peasant and family-farm operations and ways-of-life, in favour of a total emphasis on production efficiency.

Process-Response Model

The characteristics advanced to support agricultural industrialization as the latest revolutionary stage of development may be more precisely identified in a model of the specific process.

The basic premise expressed in the model is that agriculture may be viewed as an input-output, utilitarian assembly-line sequence, in which secondary inputs from agricultural-supply industries are applied at the production level to meet the food demands of urban-industrial societies. Agricultural industrialization is the amplification of this sequence by a set of processes which are the combined outcome of an agro-industrial technology and an ideology of economic efficiency and rationalization common to both capitalist and socialist systems.

It may be argued that the post-war period has been marked by a stress on fundamental divisions between developed countries, based on opposing ideologies, and including the discussion of agriculture in terms of the sharp distinctions between state-planned, communal collective and private enterprise and individual freehold types. However, an examination of the technological and economic directions, reveals a remarkably similar set of elements and criteria adopted, with the result a common convergence towards agricultural industrialization.

The last 25 years have witnessed the most concentrated effort ever to apply technology to agriculture. While there has been some extension of developments long a part of commercial agriculture, for example, versatile machinery, fertilizers, flexible on-farm energy and the results of crop and animal science, the range and sophistication of these items has increased immeasurably. There have also been entirely new inputs, for example chemicals, including pesticides and drugs, and particularly the development of large scale livestock operations and the application of automated systems to these "factory farms" and to many other specific operations. In respect of technological stage-of-development much of agriculture has actually gone beyond that labelled industrial and has entered the stage of automation. The common nature of agro-industrial technology can be easily verified by the fact of the manufacture of a similar range of machines and chemicals, etc., in all developed countries, and by the widespread adoption of both specific items and even total production systems. It is paradoxical, that although most of the key technological advances have been Western in origin, many have found their most obvious application and unequivocal acceptance by collective farm managers, operating at the factory scale, geared to integrated production and with no worries as to the impact on the small-scale farm.

But agro-technological developments in the West are not taking place in a vacuum. Those engaged in development and promotion see the widespread use of science and technology as part of an ideology of economic efficiency and rationalization applied to agriculture. Other elements of this viewpoint are that efficiency is to be realized through economies of scale and that success is measured in terms of higher land and labour productivity. These ideological goals are also common; the same rationale and the direction in which it leads are espoused equally by Western businessmen, agricultural scientists, bureaucrats and many "successful" farmers, *and* by socialist technocrats, agricultural planners and collective farm managers. If the former have to defend it against concerns over Jeffersonian ideals, the latter find it relatively easy to justify in support of a large scale, integrated state-operated system.

In applied terms, the common inputs of agro-technology and economic efficiency combine to transform agriculture through four common processes. These are:

1. Increased size of the production unit; seen in widespread efforts to attain physical economies of scale, usually involving a marked reduction in the numbers of farm units (even of collective farms).
2. Intensification of capital inputs; evidenced by greatly increased investments per farm and per farm worker in the application of fossil fuel, mechanical and chemical energy, as well as in land and buildings, and aimed at the substitution of capital for human labour.
3. Specialization in production; larger, uniform stands of crops and an especial emphasis on large-scale livestock operations.
4. Integration of farm production with other parts of the total food system. While the other processes (1, 2 and 3, above) emphasize changes taking place at the farm level, integration seeks to strengthen the assembly-line linkages between input-supply, production and pro-

cessing. The chief mechanism is vertical integration applied either via the capitalist corporation or cooperative, or the socialist agro-industrial complex.

Criteria for Classification

Each of the processes contributing to agricultural industrialization may be expected to provide tangible measures of its extent, and thus criteria for evaluation. While the process-response model postulates a unified process, one may also envisage that, in practice, industrialization will exhibit somewhat different characteristics between countries or regions.

Initial measurements, according to some obvious criteria, are presented in Table 1. While selective, the measures substantiate overall tendencies towards economies of scale and increases in capital intensity. On the other hand here are some interesting variations between groups of countries. While the decline in farm numbers is universal, the pattern with respect to collective agriculture (i.e., USSR and Eastern Europe) indicates the already much reduced base. On the other hand, major increases in mean farm size in systems already dominated by large units is outstanding, and reflects the continued consolidation within all socialist systems into the new agro-industrial complexes. In contrast, while some capitalist countries have undergone sizeable reductions in farm numbers based on substantial farm-size increases (i.e., Australia, Canada, and U.S.A.), others, notably in Western Europe, exhibit only modest average size increases. The latter countries, however, have also experienced large reductions in farm labour and high levels of capital input. A large number of other, more discrete criteria could be examined, particularly specific elements of capital input and specialization. However, on the basis of initial measures and examination of official statements of the directions being followed and planned for individual systems, a simple classification of types is offered below.

While it is emphasized that industrialization is the dominant process underlying change in agriculture in all developed economies, it is suggested that the differential nature of such factors as the ownership of supply, production and processing facilities; the prevailing form of tenure; and the decision mechanisms governing integration and control of supply and demand, combine to produce at least three broad types of industrialized agriculture:

1. The "pure" socialist model is the most consistent, especially in terms of scale and overall integration, with the state controlling the whole "assembly line," including the total supply and demand situation.
2. The "pure" capitalist type, in contrast, is largely in private hands, albeit with some government intervention and implicit support for economic rationalization. Corporate style integration, however, is still only piecemeal and divisions exist between supply, production and processing levels; particularly between predominant individual farm production and oligopolistic and conglomerate control of supply and processing.

Table 1
Selected Measures of Change
in Agricultural Systems of Developed Countries

Country	Time Period	DECREASE IN NO. OF FARMS		INCREASE IN AVERAGE FARM SIZE		DECREASE IN AGRICULTURAL EMPLOYMENT	
		Loss '000	*%* *Loss*	*Gain* ha.	*%* *Inc.*	*Loss* '000	*%* *Loss*
Australia	1960-80	73	29	67	41	n.a.	–
Austria	1960-80	94	23	3	32	880	73
Belgium/Luxem.	1959-80	86	47	7	67	161	58
Canada	1951-80	305	49	105	93	248	49
Denmark	1960-82	84	43	10	64	192	52
Finland	1959-81	163	43	5	67	473	66
France	1955-80	999	47	13	85	3348	65
Germany (West)	1960-82	854	53	9	105	2205	61
Ireland	1961-82	132	37	8	58	197	50
Italy	1961-80	2088	49	4	95	3642	55
Japan	1960-80	1395	23	n.a.	–	6480	54
Netherlands	1950-80	82	39	5	45	287	54
New Zealand	1960-80	6	8	n.a.	–	n.a.	–
Norway	1959-80	79	40	n.a.	–	88	35
Spain	1962-80	1068	36	n.a.	–	2439	53
Sweden	1960-82	153	57	18	135	283	55
Switzerland	1955-80	106	51	10	105	137	50
United Kingdom	1960-80	227	48	34	85	162	23
U.S.A.	1960-80	1360	34	67	61	2307	40
Bulgaria	1960-81	1	70	15899	261	1478	62
Czechoslovakia	1960-81	11 *	84	3047	542	509	35
G.D.R.	1961-82	13 *	75	1087	303	517	37
Hungary	1960-82	1	46	1840 * 2041 **	138 248	790	42
Poland	1960-82	C.4 * C.500 p	35 15	272 * n.a.	96 –	1189	18
Romania	1960-80	1	16	579	19	3020	50
U.S.S.R.	1959-82	+ 14 * 28 **	+ 217 52	4141	23	n.a.	–

Sources: O.E.C.D.: 1973-75; World Atlas of Agriculture, 1966; Stateman's Yearbook: Europa Yearbook: Selected national studies.

* = state, ** = collective, p = private

3. Cooperative, represents a third, intermediate type. The name reflects the fact that in certain countries the traditional involvement of farmer-based cooperative organizations at several levels of agricultural organization has persisted. Although these countries are actively pursuing a reduction in numbers of individual farms and farm workers, and programs of capitalization, specialization and integration, the cooperative mechanism, rather than the state or corporation is utilized to develop and apply a policy of rationalization of the production system and its output.

Impacts of and Responses to Industrialization of Agriculture

As evidenced in Table 1, agricultural industrialization produces some very direct results in terms of change in farm operation. Each of the common processes—increased scale, capital intensity and specialization, and the means of integration—gives rise to measurable characteristics. In particular, these provide the basis for internal economic evaluation of the process, with success measured in strictly economic terms, particularly increases in productivity. One major criticism is that "success" measured in terms of fewer farms and farmers, producing more per farm and utilizing greater amounts of energy, ignores the cost in both human and ecological terms.

The industrialization process also results in a wide range of impacts on physical and human systems. To a large extent these are regarded as externalities to the economic performance of agriculture, but they are tangible impacts and may become the responsibility of society outside the agricultural sector to deal with. In contrast to the sweeping scale at which industrialization has been described (and according to which it is often justified) many of the environmental and socio-economic impacts tend to look small and to pose predominantly local management problems. On the other hand, they tend to be universal in occurrence and incremental in nature. In addition, they are symptomatic of at least the possibility of more fundamental problems attendant on industrialization and what some critics have diagnosed as a malignant state of affairs.

Environmental Impacts

At least from the time of transition from a subsistence to a market orientation, there have been alterations in the traditional agricultural land-man relationships: the interruption of local cycling of materials, the introduction of new techniques capable of greater environmental impact, and a gradual divorce of man from his intimate ecological relationship and direct energy input. Industrialization, however, has vastly increased the pace and scale of each such change.

Environmental impacts may be distinguished as to their ecological or landscape amenity effects, but both are directly related to changes in scale, intensity and specialization. Direct ecological impacts have been documented and can be seen on both the cultivated and remaining "natural" ecosystem components of the farm landscape. Remnants of the natural ecosystem (woodlots, hedgerows, etc.) are falling victim to widespread farm and field enlargement to meet the needs of an increased scale of mechanization. Use of heavy machines, chemically supported cash cropping of grains, oilseeds, etc., contribute to an increased potential for damage to soil structure and fertility and to its actual loss through water and wind erosion. In turn, run-off, including excess fertilizers and pesticides, contributes to increased pollution of streams and groundwater, eutrophication and damage to other natural ecosystems. The quantities of organic wastes generated by large-scale specialist livestock operations can lead to similar pollution problems.

Other more fundamental problems that have been raised in ecological terms include the switch from agriculture based on organic renewable energy to high-level reliance on non-renewable fossil fuels. Another problem is the increasing uniformity of the biological base, which may not only leave agriculture susceptible to pest and disease outbreaks of epidemic proportions, but is a denial of the basic strength of an ecosystem that derives from its diversity. A final ecological concern is that of the essential nutritional quality of crops produced under chemical cultivation, and of livestock products from animals raised under the stress of "factory farming" methods.

Many traditional, and even recently formed, agricultural landscapes contribute to what is regarded as rural landscape amenity. Visual and aesthetic value may include farm and field layout, buildings of traditional style and materials and even the presence of livestock out of doors. The effects of industrialization, including farm and field amalgamation, mono-cultivation, housed livestock and the construction of utilitarian farm buildings, have a tendency to contribute to loss of amenity, including a significant transformation of the rural milieu. In addition, there are problems of air (odour) and water pollution seen from an amenity point of view and of the increased propensity of mechanical-chemical farming to produce landscapes unsuitable for alternative countryside uses, including both outdoor recreation and nature conservation.

While amenity is perhaps a less crucial environmental element, it illustrates the fact that agriculture is also an intrinsic cultural element. Potential loss to the system in terms of ecological and cultural linkages is expressed in the following quotation:

> . . . *agriculture cannot survive long at the expense of the natural systems that support it and that provide it with models. A culture cannot survive long at the expense of either its agricultural or its natural sources.* (Berry, 1977, p. 47.)

To date there has been relatively little questioning of industrialization in such fundamental terms, but environmental pressures resulting from its processes are being recognized in all developed countries as resource management problems. To some extent the problems are greatest in relation to scale of farm operation, thus collectivization is creating a major impact on the landscape in terms of its huge fields, concentrations of housed livestock and placement of industrial structures in the open countryside.

Socio-economic Impacts

Agriculture is, above all, a human system, and socio-economic impacts are of major significance. They too have increased in scale as a result of industrialization. Some distinctions may be made between impacts on individuals in the farm population, those affecting the function of rural communities, and broader impacts on the viability of society both rural and in general.

Industrialization generally means a drastic change in the way-of-life of the farm population. The success of industrialization is commonly measured in terms of the decreased numbers of farms required and actual reductions in farm population. To survive in a capitalist setting the individual farmer has to be essentially competitive and adopt a purely business approach. Not only may this literally pit him against other farmers (even his neighbours) but it carries increased pressure of technical and financial responsibility. Many people have been made redundant and have been forced to abandon farming, contributing to widespread off-farm migration; many others have taken up off-farm employment and operate only on a part-time basis, not least because of the competitive pressures of cost-price relationships.

Fewer numbers and increasing specialization tend to isolate the farmer socially, even within rural society, and to accentuate the stress attendant on individual management responsibility. This may be somewhat less so in cooperatively based societies, but there too enormous losses of farm personnel have occurred. Integration into a contrasting or similar situation may lead to problems of loss of individual identity. The latter shows indications of being a particular problem in socialist agriculture (and on large corporate farms) where the majority of persons work only within a narrow speciality, and where even the variegated nature of traditional peasant tasks has been reduced.

Farmer, farm family and farm worker impacts contribute collectively to changes in rural communities. Rural settlement functions change in response to the overall reorganization of agricultural supply, production and processing. Increased scale and integration have resulted in major reductions in the size and number of rural settlements in capitalist countries, with attendant concern over structural problems of declining and aged populations and of the maintenance of basic social and economic services, including employment, retailing, education, health and transportation. Collective farm organizations, especially those based on larger village settlements, may provide a better base on which to preserve rural community, but here also there is evidence of the problems of finding alternative employment, and cleavages between farm and non-farm (commuter) segments of the population.

Another major impact is that of increased regional differentiation, especially the problem of areas made marginal by changes in agriculture. By its nature, industrial agriculture emphasizes physical and other locational advantages, especially the facility whereby land may be farmed extensively and with machines; as Berry has put it: "All land has been divided into two parts; that which permits use of large equipment, and that which does not". (Berry, 1977,

p. 33.) The latter falls out of agriculture. Consequently, a widespread by-product of industrialization is the increased relative disadvantage experienced by areas poorly endowed, of low productive capacity and isolated in terms of the requirements of agricultural industrialization. In each developed country, economically viable agriculture is becoming concentrated in a smaller area and marginal areas are enlarged, exacerbating problems of social and economic hardship and of regional disparity.

Political Responses

The impacts of agricultural industrialization have each resulted in some type of political response, albeit of a piecemeal nature. Specific environmental concerns have led to investigation, policy formulation, legislation and regulation in such areas as the application of agricultural chemicals, agricultural waste disposal and even the process of altering the vegetational and built elements in the landscape. Environmental concern and management practice relating to both physical and human amenity can be evidenced: in some cases there are conflicts between those promoting agricultural and those non-agricultural land uses, but usually a separation is made.

At a broader scale there have been many responses to the changing socio-economic situation. In socialist countries planning for rural areas is seen as part of an overall planning function and includes attempts to increase rural employment, income and opportunity, and to upgrade rural services. In some capitalist countries a similar comprehensive approach is sought, especially in marginal areas, including attempts to rationalize farming through subsidies, land banking or retirement schemes and to maintain rural community structure through provision of health, education and transportation facilities.

Contrasting viewpoints may be taken in regard to the formulation of an overall political response. If one is encouraging agricultural industrialization explicitly or implicitly, then the political response is made in conformity to its goals, with an additional mixture of regulations and controls which try to minimize what can be seen as the inevitable but essentially local or temporary side-effects. These may involve control of certain conditions such as soil erosion and agricultural wastes, or encouragement of the necessary adjustments in marginal areas, including programs to phase out agricultural activity. The loss of distinctive rural environments may be regretted and there may even be attempts at some relic form of preservation, but the net solution, whether overtly aimed at or not will probably be a specialized rural landscape with agriculture protected from other, potentially conflicting uses, and an equally sharp distinction between farm and non-farm populations.

Such an approach may not be yet seen in such stark terms but it seems to reflect a dominant direction and almost certainly includes the demise of distinctive agrarian societies (and landscapes) in developed countries. Are there alternatives? Maybe, but only if one turns one's back on modern agriculture; or identifies it as a thoroughly undesirable stage-of-development, and by noting its faults, suggests what is, in effect, an alternative philosophy and base for resource management. As an indication of how polarized such an alternative might be, the views of one of the most articulate of contemporary critics of industrialization, Wendell Berry, are noted.

For Berry, industrialized agriculture is the latest and most inhumane, exploitive stage in the use of the North American environment, and is contributing to the rapid demise of its only stable rural base, the yeoman/family farm. The agent of industrialization is the corporate institution, whose essentially exploitive nature is based on the short term goal of efficiency measured in terms of profit; this contrasts with the long term attachment of the farmer to the land as a renewable source of life. The general emphasis, epitomized by corporate farming, on specialization versus diversity, on machines rather than men, and on non-renewable versus renewable energy, means that corporate farms are destructive elements in both ecological and human cultural terms, and contrast to farm households and rural communities which are constructive and careful of the land. For Berry (1977, p.10),

> *The cost of this corporate totalitarianism in energy, land and social disruption will be enormous. It will lead to the exhaustion of farmland and farm culture. Husbandry will become an extractive industry; because maintenance will entirely give way to production, the fertility of the soil will become a limited unrenewable source.*

The Canadian entomologist Hill has identified similar undesirable characteristics of the so-called "energy approach"—including vertical integration that through its specialization and simplification creates instability and manipulates food distribution for profit and political influence, and short term economic policies that encourage use of finite resources and damage to both the natural environment and human health (Hill and Ramsey, 1976). Hill is more explicit than Berry in terms of outlining an alternative "eco-agricultural" policy. This would stress permanent production strategies emphasizing nutritional needs and based on local, decentralized production and supply systems, with the primary objective to maintain environmental quality and conservation of the basic resources.

The latter viewpoint is of obvious relevance to resource management, which sees itself as conservationist in orientation and sensitive to the total system framework. However, as Berry notes, in biting terms, institutionalization and specialization in society generally have become so pervasive, that the technology and ideology of industrialized agriculture are not only accepted by agribusiness and corporate farm executives but have made dependents of agricultural economists, scientists and the majority of academics and bureaucrats who might otherwise be the ones to critically examine their nature and implications. Furthermore, as its tenets are equally accepted on both sides of the international ideological boundaries, it seems unlikely that, short of a revolution or system collapse, the process of agricultural industrialization will cease. The non-farm majority, reduced to spectators, will just have to hope that the dire warnings are exaggerated and that the symptoms we do feel able to tackle are not those of a malignant disease.

Postscript

This paper has been argued at a general level. As such it has not dwelt on the wealth of information which describes both the existence and characteristics of industrialization in many areas and the specifics of environmental and social impacts. It is worth making explicit the contention that industrialization is becoming the dominant process affecting Canadian agriculture and that a great deal of empirical investigation is in order, especially for key areas such as Southern Ontario, Southern Quebec and the Prairies.

References

Berry, Wendell. 1977. *The Unsettling of America: Culture and Agriculture.* Sierra Club Books.

Hill, S.B. and J.A. Ramsey. 1976. "Limitations of the Energy Approach in Defining Priorities in Agriculture." Paper presented at the Energy and Agriculture Conference, Washington University, St. Louis, Mo.

15
Love Canal and Environmental Crisis

Lois Marie Gibbs

President, Love Canal Homeowners'/Citizens
Clearinghouse for Hazardous Wastes, Arlington, Virginia

Introduction

This paper on the Love Canal environmental disaster includes a brief history of the Love Canal disaster, why I became involved and committed to working on hazardous waste problems and solutions, the activities of the Love Canal Homeowners Association, and the health and environmental problems that existed in the Love Canal neighbourhood.

I am President and founder of the Love Canal Homeowners Association (LCHA), an organization of over 900 families that live or have lived in the Love Canal neighbourhood in Niagara Falls, New York. These families are lower middle-class citizens, most having only a high school education, with the majority of the residents employed in the chemical industry.

I, like my neighbours, moved into Love Canal totally unaware that a dump existed two blocks from my home. When we moved into Love Canal nine years ago, I had a healthy infant son named Michael. After living in our home for a short period of time, Michael became very ill. At first he developed many common childhood diseases. Then, during the first year of school, he developed new uncommon diseases such as epilepsy, a blood problem, asthma, a liver problem, and a urinary tract disease which required two operations to correct. (My daughter Melissa, born three years later, developed a rare blood disorder when she was four years old.)

At first I thought that I was just unlucky and had a sickly child. Then I read in our local newspaper about the Love Canal chemical dump which was two blocks from my home and just a matter of a few feet from the school which my son was attending. One newspaper article also listed many of the chemicals which were buried in the dump and some of the symptoms and diseases which can result from exposure to these chemicals. This is when I realized that I was not an unlucky mother, but that it was the Love Canal that was the cause of Michael's illnesses. I also believed, at that time, that only the canal property and the school were contaminated. I did not believe that the entire community of ten city blocks was contaminated.

After reading these news articles, I immediately went to our local Board of Education and asked them to transfer Michael to another public school. I even provided the Board, upon their request, with statements from two physicians who recommended that Michael be transferred to another school away from Love Canal because of his medical conditions. The Board refused to transfer Michael. Their reason was that the physicians' statements refer to the school as being unsafe and, if it was not safe for Michael to attend the school, then it would be unsafe for all 407 children who attended. The Board then told me they were not about to close the whole school because of one hysterical mother with a sickly child.

After this experience with the Board of Education, I quickly realized that no one was going to listen to one individual and that I needed to find other people in my neighbourhood who were willing to help fight the Board and close the school to protect our children. So I began a door-to-door campaign to educate my neighbours about the problem and gain their support.

During my door-to-door visits, I discovered that it was not just the school and the school children that were sick. Almost every house I went to had a horror story to tell. There were children with birth defects or who were crippled with bone disease; there were men and women with cancers and other diseases. This is when I decided to organize the Love Canal Homeowners Association.

About the same time, the New York State Department of Health (DOH) began to investigate the problems at Love Canal. My neighbours had noticed DOH taking air, water, and soil samples, drawing blood, and circulating health questionnaires. They were very receptive and interested in what I had to say when I approached them for support. The residents were concerned, frightened and confused about the health risks of living in the Love Canal neighbourhood. They quickly joined our group, which was formed during the summer of 1978.

The History of the Love Canal

In 1892, William T. Love proposed connecting the upper and lower sections of the Niagara River by digging a canal six to seven miles long so that he could harness the water of the upper Niagara River into a navigable channel. This would create a man-made waterfall with a 280-foot drop into the lower Niagara River, thus providing cheap power. However, the country fell into an economic depression and financial backing for the project slipped away. Love then abandoned the project, leaving behind a partially dug section of the canal. In 1920, the land was sold at public auction; it was a municipal and chemical disposal site until 1953. The principal company dumping wastes in the canal was Hooker Chemical Corporation, a subsidiary of Occidental Petroleum. The City of Niagara and the United States Army used the site as well, with the City dumping garbage and the Army possibly dumping parts of the Manhattan Project and other chemical warfare material.

In 1953, after filling the canal and covering it with dirt, Hooker sold the land to the Board of Education for one dollar. The deed contained a stipulation which said that if anyone incurred physical harm or death because of their buried wastes, Hooker would not be responsible. Hooker claims they properly warned the City and the Board—we wonder!

Soon after the land changed owners, home building began adjacent to the 16-acre rectangle which was once the canal. The neighbourhood consisted of approximately 800 private single-family homes and 240 low-income apart-

Figure 1
The Love Canal and the Surrounding Neighbourhood

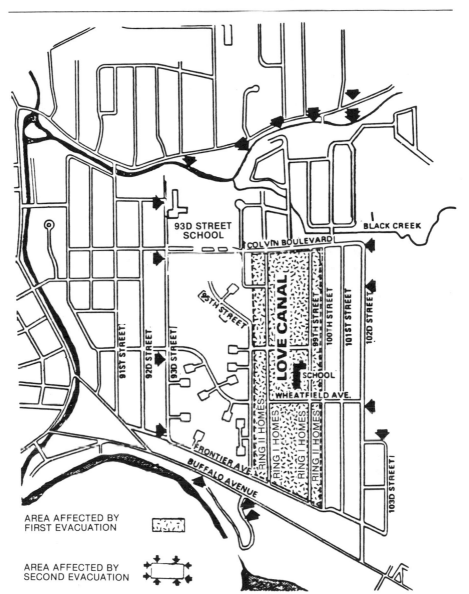

The majority of people who purchased homes in the neighbourhood were unaware of the existence of the landfill. The canal looked very innocent, like any field anywhere. The grass was overgrown with pieces of wood and rubble thrown onto the surface. It certainly did not appear to be a chemical dump with 20 000 tons of toxic wastes buried beneath it. Since the dump appeared to be nothing more than a field, we never thought about it or realized that we had a problem.

ments to the west of the canal. The canal and the surrounding neighbourhood are shown in Figure 1. The Niagara River, which is where our drinking water comes from, is located south of the canal. The Niagara River and a creek located to the north of the landfill form natural boundaries of the area affected by the migrating chemicals.

The 99th Street Elementary School, located near the center of Love Canal, looked very innocent, but the surface soil where our children had played for years was found to be contaminated with toxic wastes. The school, which had 407 students, opened a year after Hooker stopped dumping their wastes.

By 1977, if you walked on the canal and looked a little more closely, you could see signs of surfacing chemicals. Commonly, holes the same diameter as a 55-gallon drum developed; the holes contained thick, black oily substances. The barrels, buried 20 years ago near the surface, rusted away and collapsed; the chemicals then rose to the surface with the topsoil sinking into the vacated space. This black substance gave off a very strong odor which made your eyes water and took your breath away. We watched the progression of one of these holes for several days and found that after a rain this black oily substance reacted with the rainwater and turned into a milky white-coloured substance.

The DOH began investigating the Love Canal problem in June, 1978; they studied the 239 families and their homes that immediately encircled the canal (indicated on Figure 1 as Ring 1 and Ring 2 homes). They completed their study in August, 1978. After reviewing the results of their investigation, the State ordered the evacuation of pregnant women and children under the age of two on August 2, 1978. They also ordered the closure of the 99th Street School. They recommended that families not eat vegetables from their gardens and that residents spend a limited amount of time in their basements (where air samples had been taken). The DOH issued these orders after finding an increased number of reproductive problems among Canal women and high levels of chemical contamination in the homes, soil, and air. A few days after the evacuation order, the State agreed to purchase all 239 homes at fair market value in order to enable families to buy other homes away from Love Canal. The State also began a remedial clean-up program at Love Canal.

Remedial Construction

A cross-sectional diagram of the Love Canal is shown in Figure 2. The "U-shaped" area in the centre is where the wastes were deposited. Because of the relatively low permeability of the soil surrounding the deposited area, the water table would rise and fall according to the amount of precipitation. The canal was a short distance from the Niagara River, which also played a major role in the canal's water level. Furthermore, the soils that were used to backfill the canal were more permeable than the surrounding soils and would readily absorb and collect rain and melting snow. The rise and fall of the water table was the major reason for the migration of wastes into the community. To analogize, the canal is similar to a bathtub: when the liquid in the canal rose, the canal would overflow. This overflow would then travel through the topsoil. There was also an old streambed that crossed the canal; underground

Figure 2
Love Canal Remedial Construction Plan

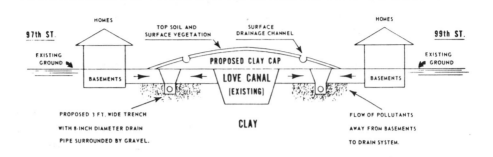

Figure 3
Love Canal Remedial Construction Plan

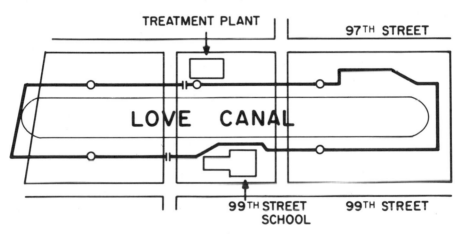

sand layers carried this overflow into the basements of adjacent homes and throughout the community.

The clean-up plan consisted of a containment system which was designed to "contain" the wastes in the canal so that they would no longer migrate out into the surrounding soils. (See Figure 3.) The containment system was designed as a barrier drain which encircled the canal using a graded trench system intended to intercept migrating wastes, emptying into one of several holding tanks. The depth of the trenches varied from 16-25 feet, with the holding tanks located at the deepest portion of the system. After the trench system was completed in one section of the canal, the State found that very little leachate was being collected, as a result of the water pressure being too low to push the chemicals toward the system. This problem was overcome by placing a series of 22 "lateral" trenches perpendicular to the trench system, which provided a pathway for the chemicals to readily reach the trench system.

The wastes in the trench system were carried through the trench to holding tanks from which they were pumped into an on-site treatment plant. This treatment plant used a series of filtration steps (most importantly, activated charcoal) to filter out the chemicals; then the "clean" water was flushed down the sanitary sewer system. Of course, there are wastes such as mercury and other heavy metals which cannot be filtered out through this system and could find their way into the Niagara River.

After the barrier drain was completed, a clay cap was placed over the canal as a cover to ensure that rainwater did not enter the canal and raise the water table, as well as to keep chemicals from vaporizing into the air.

This system cost the State millions of dollars, yet a monitoring system was never installed around the canal to determine if the system is working as planned. Therefore, no one really knows if the Love Canal is still migrating into the surrounding neighbourhood or the Niagara River!

The "Unaffected" Community

Once the State had evacuated 239 families and begun the remedial construction, it suddenly realized the tremendous costs potentially involved; it arbitrarily defined the affected area and erected a 10-foot fence around the evacuated area. This decision was arbitrary because at the time nobody knew how far the chemicals had gone or how many people were affected. At the same time, the State began to make public statements that there was no evidence of abnormal health problems outside the fenced area. Consequently, the families in the outer community became very angry with this arbitrary determination and soon looked at the fence as though it fenced them in. We knew there were health problems outside the first 239 homes because of the health survey that we had conducted and that I will describe below. We also knew that a fence would not keep chemicals from migrating underground. So we quickly began to express our anger and our concerns.

We began to protest, something we would never have believed we would ever do! The protestors included mothers and fathers with their babies and old people who were ready for retirement. We marched into the streets on Mother's Day, carried symbolic coffins to the State capital, held prayer vigils, and burnt the authorities in effigy to express our anger. We also picketed at the canal every day for weeks in the dead of winter—hoping that someone would hear us, that someone would help us. Our children were sick. Our homes were worthless. We were innocent and helpless.

Due to the pressure we created and because we refused to quit, the government authorities could no longer ignore us and they were forced to address our concerns. They began to give us concessions, including an extensive safety plan, a scientist-consultant of our choosing whose salary was paid by the State, and a $200 000 Human Services Fund which was set up to pay some of the residents' medical expenses. BUT we did *not* want concessions! We wanted and needed to be evacuated as the first 239 families were, with the State purchasing our homes.

The Love Canal families became even more frightened during the next spring. They noticed that some of the vegetation in their yards was beginning to die. Many of our hedges had turned brown from the top down, but then, in the spring, began to grow again from the bottom up. Since many toxic chemicals were found in the topsoil of the canal, we believed that the cleanup activities had generated contaminated dust. This was especially alarming since the same form of dioxin that created the health problems in Seveso, Italy had been found in the topsoil. We felt that this dust had killed our vegetation and we could not help but wonder what it was doing to our children!

The scientists who were investigating Love Canal dismissed the vegetation problem saying it was "winter kill." They continued to say there were no abnormal health effects among the residents living outside the fence. Consequently, our group decided to conduct its own health survey to prove that there was a major health problem in the outer community. We found a dedicated and wonderful volunteer scientist to help us and we began to interview the families. Our health study was conducted with the assistance of Dr. Beverly Paigen who at the time was a cancer research scientist at Roswell Memorial Institute in Buffalo, New York. We carried out the study by interviewing each family. Figure 4 shows the homes of the residents who were interviewed and where their homes were located. More than 75% of the homes were included in our study. We did not include the 239 families who lived closest to the canal because they were already evacuated. Therefore, the health effects discussed here are an underestimate of the total health damages because the highest exposed population has not been included. We completed this study by February, 1979.

Once we had collected the health data, we plotted the diseases on a map. We noticed a clustering of diseases in certain areas of the neighbourhood. The elder residents of the community suggested that the clusters seemed to follow the path of old streambeds that had crossed the Love Canal many years ago but which had since been filled when homes were built. So we looked at old aerial photographs and geological survey maps and asked the residents for any available old photographs. The residents came up with several photographs showing how the old streambeds intersected Love Canal. We also found out that these streams could flow in opposite directions. For example, when the Niagara River was high during the spring, the streams would flow to the north; at other times in the year, they would flow to the south. One photograph showed a streambed which appeared to be 10-feet deep and more than 20-feet wide. When the area was developed, the streams were filled with building rubble through which water flows easily. Even though there is no surface evidence of these old streams, they provided an easy pathway for liquid contaminated with toxic chemicals to migrate out of the canal.

The different health problems found in this study are shown in Figure 5. The homes and streets on these maps have been removed so that no family can be identified. The "wiggly" lines are the underground streambeds and the "closed" shapes are the ponded or wet areas. Each miscarriage that occurred at Love Canal is represented by a black dot. As can be seen, the families located in the ponded area had multiple miscarriages. Also, the majority of these

Figure 4
Study Area

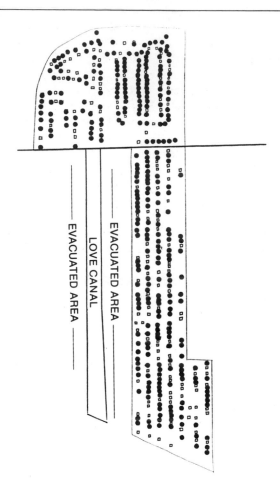

EVACUATED AREA

LOVE CANAL

EVACUATED AREA

EVACUATED AREA

Each home that participated in the survey is covered with a black circle.

Chart courtesy of Dr. Beverly Paigen

Figure 5
Miscarriages and Crib Deaths

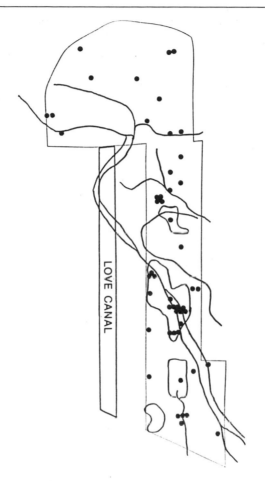

	Number of Pregnancies	Number of Miscarriages	%
Before moving to Love Canal	714	61	8.5%
After moving to wet area of Love Canal	155	39	25.2%
Relative risk	0.03		

chi square 35; probability that difference is due to chance is much less than 0.0005

Chart courtesy of Dr. Beverly Paigen

miscarriages occurred on or near a "wet" area. The observed miscarriages were compared to the number of miscarriages that occurred in the same women *before* they moved to the Love Canal; the miscarriage rate after moving to the area was significantly higher.

We later conducted another study, of pregnancies that occurred between January, 1979 and February, 1980, the construction period. We found that out of 22 pregnancies occurring among Love Canal women, only four normal babies were born. The rest of the pregnancies ended in miscarriage, stillbirth or a child with a birth defect.

We also investigated the number of birth defects found in the Love Canal neighbourhood. (See Figure 6.) When comparing the number of birth defects

Figure 6
Birth Defects

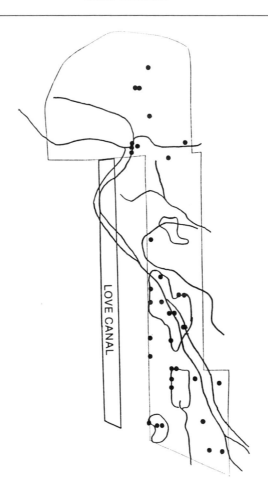

Chart courtesy of Dr. Beverly Paigen

in homes along the streambeds—or in "wet" areas—with homes not on these streambeds, we found almost three times as many birth defects. The DOH found the same results. (See Table 1.) Interestingly, there are *no* birth defects in homes found on the streambed that does *not* cross the canal. We also looked at this information in a different way and found that during the five-year period from 1974 to 1978, 56% of the children in the Love Canal neighbourhood were born with birth defects. (See Table 2.) These include three ears, double rows of teeth, and mental retardation.

There was also an increase in the incidence of nervous breakdowns in the Love Canal population. The black dots shown on Figure 7 each represent either a nervous breakdown, a suicide attempt, or an admission to a mental hospital. No one was included in this map that reported only a "nervous condition." Many of the chemicals found at Love Canal are *known* to affect the central nervous system.

Many of the chemicals in Love Canal are also known to affect the kidneys and the urinary system. In Figure 8, the occurrence of urinary disease reported in the community is shown. We found that a great number of our children had urinary tract disorders. Once again, more disease was found on the streambeds that intercept the canal when compared to the streambed that does not cross the canal.

Table 1
Birth Defects in Children Born in Love Canal Area

	Wet areas	%	Dry areas	%
No. of children born	120		176	
No. with birth defects (New York State Health Dept. data)	15	12.5%	9	5.1 %
No. with birth defects (Residents' data)	24	20.0%	12	6.85%

Relative risk (residents' data) 2.9

chi square 12; probability that difference is due to chance is less than 0.001

Table 2
Birth Defects in Children Born During Last 5 Years in Wet Areas

Children born	16
Number with birth defects	9
Percentage	56%

Figure 7
Nervous Breakdowns

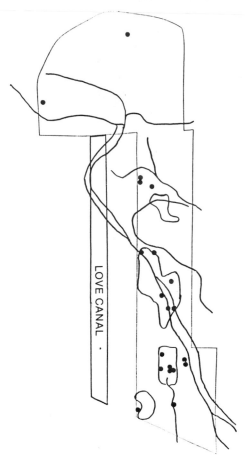

	Number of Adults	Number of Nervous Breakdowns	%
Living in wet areas	149	13	8.7%
Living in dry areas —south section	226	5	2.2%
Living in dry areas —north section	286	2	0.7%

Relative risk wet areas to all dry areas: 6.9

chi square wet/dry south 8

Probability that difference is due to chance is less than 0.005

Chart courtesy of Dr. Beverly Paigen

Figure 8
Urinary Disease in Love Canal Area

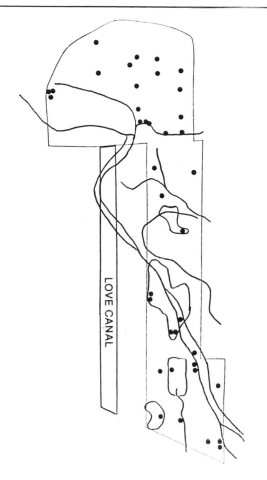

	Number of People	Number with Disease	%
Living in wet areas	314	22	7.0%
Living in dry areas	826	21	2.5%

Relative risk 2.8

chi square 13

Probability that difference is due to chance is less than 0.0005

Chart courtesy of Dr. Beverly Paigen

Figure 9 shows a map of all the diseases combined. I would like to emphasize that these data represent an underestimate of the health damages at Love Canal, since we did not include the 239 families who received the highest exposures. A more detailed discussion of this survey can be found in testimony prepared by Dr. Beverly Paigen and presented before a House Investigating Committee.

Figure 9
Combined Health Disorders

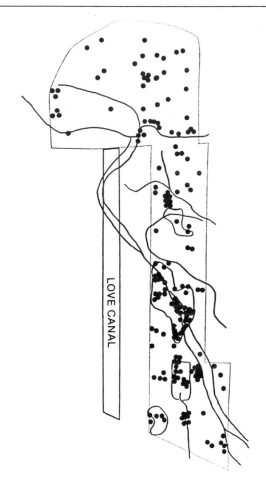

Miscarriages, still births, crib deaths, nervous breakdowns, hyperactivity, epilepsy, and urinary disease in the Love Canal area.

Chart courtesy of Dr. Beverly Paigen

We presented these findings to the health authorities. They quickly dismissed our study calling it "useless housewife data," saying that our illnesses were all in our heads, the birth defects were genetic, and the urinary diseases were the result of sexual activities (in my five-year old son?). So we went back to the streets and explained our problems to the public in order to gain the public support we needed. Thousands of people soon began to write letters and send telegrams to the State Governor, to legislators, and to the President of our country. We created so much pressure and public outcry that the health authorities were forced to investigate our claims.

In February, 1979, after the DOH looked at the reproductive problems in the outer community, they confirmed our findings and issued a second evacuation order for pregnant women and children under the age of two. This evacuation was a step in the right direction—but it was not enough! It was not until October, 1980 that a total evacuation was ordered by President Carter.

Politics, Not Science, Dictates

President Carter's decision was, in part, due to the public pressure he received just prior to the presidential election. Our efforts helped focus this pressure on the President. For example, once the presidential campaigns began, we targeted our protests at the candidates. We made the Love Canal issues and problems a campaign issue. We protested at the political conventions and gave hundreds of interviews to the news media, always including the politicians' names, asking for their position on hazardous waste issues and on Love Canal. This ultimately resulted in a visit to Niagara Falls by President Carter.

President Carter did not want to spend 15 million dollars at Love Canal. Everything—from the health studies to evacuation—was done for political reasons. None of the decisions that were made were based on scientific evidence. I truly believe that if it was not for our large, strong citizen organization, we would still be living at Love Canal with the health authorities saying there was no health problem.

In summary, why did government not move quickly to evacuate our families? There were many reasons, two of the more important of which were: (1) the costs—together the State and Federal Governments spent over 60 million dollars at Love Canal, and we are only one of thousands of dump sites across the country; and (2) because the "scientific" understanding of the human health effects of exposure to low-level chemicals is not sufficient to readily allow cause-and-effect relationships to be determined. Consequently, there is nothing to support any policy decisions that government officials would make. For these same reasons, the Love Canal community has now been declared "habitable"—not to be confused with "safe." The 239 homes closest to the canal have now been demolished and the remaining homes will be sold to new families. One of the homes that will be reinhabited is mine, still contaminated, still unsafe. There have been no cleanup measures taken in or around my home—despite the fact that it was found to have several toxic chemicals in it.

In the case of Love Canal, history will most likely repeat itself. The deeds for the new owners contain a clause stating that if the owners become sick, harmed, or die due to the Love Canal wastes, the City will not be responsible. This clause is similar to the "Hooker Clause" in the earlier land transfer in 1953. This time it will take a little longer before we will see the effects in a new population because some cleanup has taken place, resulting in a lowering of the air contaminants. Eventually, the pain and crying will be the same. Helpless people with "blind faith" in government will again be victimized!

In conclusion, I would like to add that we did not know that we were being exposed to poisonous chemicals, nor were we aware that chemical wastes were being dumped in our rivers, soil, and air. Love Canal awoke my community to the unpleasant and unfortunate realization of how toxic wastes affect our lives and destroy our environment, our fish and our wildlife. We always believed that the Government would automatically protect us. We were wrong—in some cases, dead wrong!

Since Love Canal, I have founded the Citizens Clearinghouse for Hazardous Wastes (CCHW) which provides direct assistance to citizens faced with environmental problems. I started CCHW because I was contacted by hundreds of people seeking help with their hazardous waste problems. As Director, I have traveled extensively across the country working with citizens. I quickly found that, although Love Canal is the most famous, it is not the only major environmental problem. I have seen beautiful lakes being destroyed, no longer safe for swimming, fishing, or drinking water. I have seen areas of our precious land destroyed. I have seen communities with air pollution problems told that it is unsafe to consume food grown in their own backyards. Every time we allow chemicals to be poured into our soils, air or seas, we are destroying our environment. We may not see the destruction immediately, but it is inevitable.

We learned two things at Love Canal: once exposed to even small levels of chemicals, there is an effect on the human body; and government will protect you from this only when you force them to do so. If you think you are safe, think again. Do not let your land be destroyed by chemicals so that it, like the Love Canal, can never be used again!

References

Gibbs, L.M. 1982. *Love Canal: My Story*. Buffalo: State University of New York Press.

Lester, S.U. 1984. "The Problems of Cleaning Up Uncontrolled Hazardous Waste Sites," American Association for the Advancement of Science, Symposia Series 88.

Paigen, B. 1979. "Health Hazards at Love Canal," testimony presented to the House Subcommittee on Oversight and Investigations, March 21.

16
Environmental Impact of Industrialization in a Third World Country

Nart Tuntawiroon

Dean, Faculty of Environmental and Resource Studies
Mahidol University, Bangkok, Thailand

Introduction

The environmental impact of industrialization has received much attention. This paper will attempt to cite some specific cases of what has actually happened in Thailand, an example of a Third World country where a number of problems are "imported" from other countries. Because some of the causes of these problems come from outside the country, they cannot be solved without international cooperation. Japanese involvement is highlighted in the hope of clearing up misunderstanding through a frank academic discussion. Then a better image of Japan can be presented to the Thai public, in order to create a friendly atmosphere conducive to future cooperation. Efforts are also made to point out the ineffectiveness of the present Thai Environmental Impact Assessment (EIA) mechanisms in dealing with rising pressure from vested interests. A multi-million dollar dam construction project partially funded by the Japanese is used as an illustration.

Environmental awareness in Thailand became very acute among students, academicians, and concerned citizens in the early 1970s. The deterioration in the state of the environment became apparent through such phenomena as traffic congestion, deforestation, soil erosion, air and water pollution, etc. Several scientific studies of pollution levels resulted in evidence that there were indeed real causes for concern. One issue that came to light was the import of pollution from industrialized countries, a factor which may be viewed within the context of the North-South confrontation and the struggle to establish a new international economic order. Usually the theme for debate is the exploitation of natural resources of the South for the benefit of the North. In other words, the South is considered to be the *source* from which natural resources can be extracted by the North. In the case of the export of pollution, however, the argument is reversed. Such environmental resources as air, water, and soil belonging to the South are exploited *in situ* by the North. In other words, the South is considered as the *sink* into which pollutants are injected by the North. The degree to which the validity of this accusation can be proven is, of course, open to debate.

Japanese Involvement in Thai Developments

For various reasons, Japan became the main target of this growing environmental awareness. Factors included the *Anti-Japanese Goods Campaign* organized by the students in 1972, and the dominant role of the Japanese among foreign trades and industries operating in Thailand. The accusation that Japan deliberately exported pollution to Southeast Asian countries, including Thailand, was based on the following assumed motives:

1. *shortage of land* to be used as factory sites in Japan;
2. *high cost of labour* in Japan;
3. *abundance of cheap natural resources* in Southeast Asia to feed the factories;
4. *incentives given by Southeast Asian Governments* eager to industrialize their countries at whatever cost; they offer Japanese industries such inducements as tax exemptions, cheap electricity and water, etc., and are also willing to shoulder the investment cost of infrastructure, such as roads, railways, ports, etc.—all these incentives in fact amount to forcing their own people to subsidize Japanese industries and consumers; and
5. *pressure from Japanese people* who demand high standards of environmental quality at home, thus making it more costly to operate factories in Japan; it is, therefore, more attractive to set up factories with low pollution control standards in Southeast Asia where obsolete machinery which could not meet standards at home can still be exported with profit instead of being scrapped.

In fairness, it must be emphasized that the accusing fingers were not pointed at the Japanese people as a whole, but only at some Japanese industries and businessmen. There were, in fact, remarkable signs of sympathy and cooperation between Thai and Japanese people in fighting this practice of pollution export. In 1973, for example, environmentalists in Japan organized a march against Asahi Company's caustic soda plant in Bangkok which discharged mercury into the environment. In 1974, the Japanese organized another march, while Thai environmentalists simultaneously organized an exhibition on pollution export at Thammasart University in Bangkok.

Thai environmentalists were also dismayed with their own people in both business and official circles who, being obsessed with their own individual gain—financial or otherwise, went out of their way to protect the polluters. A case in point is the Thai Asahi Company. The company was accused of being a typical example of an irresponsible industry willing to sacrifice public well-being in order to maximize its own profit. The following story illustrates the point. The Ministry of Health reported that the mercury discharged from Thai Asahi's plant was 2.718 parts per million (ppm), whereas the Ministry of Industry reported only 0.003 ppm. When the public expressed amazement at the large discrepancy, it was revealed that this was due to the different procedures for collecting water samples of the two ministries. Whereas the Ministry of Health's officials went to collect the samples by boat at night without warning, the Ministry of Industry's officials announced the exact time of their arrival well in advance and arrived punctually at the front gate of the factory. Hence the large discrepancy.

Thai environmentalists were jubilant when celebrating their successful lobbying, which helped to pass the Enhancement and Conservation of National Environment Quality Act on February 12, 1975. Their excitement became shock when it was announced that among the members of the newly-formed National Environment Board (NEB) would be one of Thai Asahi's expert employees. The Government at that time was widely criticized for this tactic of using a thief to catch a thief. However, this incident brought home to the public the point that the power wielded by business and industry was quite formidable and could penetrate through very high levels in the Government. So came the sad realization that their hard-won environmental law and EIA mechanisms would at best be only a paper-tiger.

Environmental Impact Assessment

Unfortunately, the aforementioned despondency has been only too justified. During the seven years of its existence, the NEB has hardly made its presence felt, not achieving anything worthy of note. It has concentrated on farming out research and monitoring activities to foreign consultants and institutions, a practice that could hardly be expected to earn respect and credibility for itself. On major issues such as the pros and cons of a nuclear power plant or a soda ash plant (the re-emergence of Asahi Company), it took a noticeably low-profile and left the major work to be tackled by concerned environmentalists.

What, then, has gone wrong? Obviously, the main problem is the magnitude of the projects involved. The larger the scale of a project, the more powerful the prime mover behind it. It is difficult to expect typical civil servants to come out openly against such power for fear of reprisal. They would prefer to take refuge in their research on wildlife and plankton, or else to play safe with such non-controversial matters as garbage collection or tree planting. Issues concerning large-scale projects such as nuclear power plants or dam construction can only be tackled effectively by an organized, knowledgeable public, and that is exactly what is wrong with the present Thai EIA mechanisms. Thailand copied its EIA procedure from the United States without fully realizing the limitations of its own institutional arrangements. In the United States, after an EIA report has been prepared, it is circulated to all interested parties including the public for comments and criticisms. Even after the Government has decided to go ahead with a project, dissatisfied parties can bring the case to a lawcourt in an attempt to stop the project. In other words, not only the executive, but also the judiciary branch is brought in to play its role in the EIA mechanism. There is no such provision for public hearing and court procedures in Thai EIA legislation. EIA has thus become a mere cosmetic. It is the usual practice for the proponent agency to shop for the cheapest and most obliging consultants and hire them to prepare thick, colourful, and usually meaningless volumes of an EIA report, ending up with the message that, in spite of some minor problems here and there, all would be well with the project should it be given approval. If a report were not to end on such a note, it would be too bad for the consultants; they would have to close down their shop as there would be no more clients for them in the future.

The proponent agency then shows the EIA report to NEB and funding agencies (such as the World Bank) to seek approval for the project. Apart from such agencies, it will try to restrict the circulation of the report as much as possible as it knows too well the many weaknesses probably contained therein. Public participation is quite out of the question. The very fact that EIA reports in Thailand are still written in the English language is a good indicator that they are not intended to be understood by the common people whose lives would be affected by the projects; they are produced solely for the benefit of the so-called foreign experts. After the project has been approved, the EIA report will be tucked away somewhere never to be looked at again no matter what happens. Nobody really cares whether the content of the report can actually be substantiated—and most of the time it cannot! No lesson is ever learned from past mistakes, which is why the mistakes continue to be repeated. When something really bad happens to the project after completion, one cannot find a trace of those responsible for writing the EIA report; sometimes even the report itself disappears.

A Case Study: The Kwae Yai Dam

A very good case study is the Kwae Yai Dam Project. (The Japanese were also involved in the construction of this dam, since part of the funding included a loan from Japan; in addition, Japanese manufacturers, notably Mitsubishi, supplied the majority of the equipment.) The Electricity Generating Authority of Thailand (EGAT) wanted to build this dam on the Kwae Yai, a tributary of the Mae Klong River in Western Thailand. It contracted the Asian Institute of Technology (AIT) to write an EIA report for the purpose of submitting it to funding agencies. When environmentalists learned of this in 1973, they asked to see the report in order to make comments. Surprisingly, they were told by AIT that the report was a secret document not to be shown to anybody but EGAT. After a large public uproar, the EGAT general manager agreed to release the report and meet the environmentalists at the first and last public hearing on EIA ever held in Thailand. It was a very interesting meeting, well-attended with very active public participation. The participants in the meeting agreed that the AIT report was so shoddily prepared that it should not have been called an EIA report at all. To save face, EGAT and AIT promised that they would prepare another report called "Part II"! Very few people have seen that report; EGAT constantly pushed forward the project, ignoring the environmentalists' warning of ecological backlash until the matter finally faded from public attention.

Now, eight years later, several problems have surfaced. Construction of the dam was completed in 1978 and the reservoir has been accumulating water since then to build up its water level for electricity generation; however, successive periods of drought, coupled with perhaps a high percentage of leakage due to the nature of the reservoir which is mainly limestone, made the build-up time much longer than expected. Meanwhile, the holding back of fresh water caused saline water intrusion into the estuary of the Mae Klong River, wiping out some farmland in Samut Songkram, once the richest province in the kingdom. The people who wrote the EIA report had by this time all gone home abroad!

From the very beginning, environmentalists expressed doubts about the real benefits of this dam considering its large investment cost and the area to be flooded. They pointed out to EGAT that the dam would be situated in the vicinity of a fault. This could be dangerous since there were reports indicating that an earthquake generated by sheer weight of water in the reservoir might cause a slip in the fault. Furthermore, the terrain of the reservoir is mainly composed of limestone which is soluble in water, and usually full of holes, caves, and tunnels. The implication is that this dam would at worst be in danger of cracking, and at best would only create a leaky reservoir (which could not be relieved by grouting at the dam site) that would not be worth its cost.

EGAT, however, always quoted the opinion of the Japanese experts who, it was alleged, assured them that all was well. As a result, the public tended to suspect that the Japanese did not really care whether the dam was dangerous or useless and that all they were interested in was selling the equipment.

Finally, while we are still struggling with the problems generated by the Kwae Yai Dam, construction of a new dam—the Kao Lam Dam—is already well under way on the Kwae Noi River (another tributary of the same Mae Klong River). No one has seen the EIA report for this project—nor would people trust it—if such a report has actually been written. There does not appear to be any good reason for the rush to compound problems which have not yet been solved. However, this time it is not a Japanese but rather an Australian team who will be responsible for the outcome. We can only keep our fingers crossed and wait to see what will happen 5-10 years from now.

Part 5:
The Role of Non-Governmental Organizations

This Part deals with the efforts of various types of non-governmental organizations (NGOs) in promoting environmental education to broader segments of the population. These NGOs have a wide range of styles, concerns, and approaches. Both the United Nations Environment Program (Brown) and Great Lakes Tomorrow (Timms) are illustrations of large-scale attempts to bring together concerned environmental groups on particular topics through education and government action. Similarly, the European Community Environmental Education Network (Trant) is an example of an international network of environmental educators. On the other hand, Greenpeace (Mason) is an organization with a small number of active members (backed by the financial support of many contributing members) who are dedicated to using non-violent direct action to arouse media and public concern over very specific environmental causes. Ecuador's Fundación Natura (Kakabadse) is an example of an innovative program in the developing world.

17

The United Nations Environment Program: The Second Decade

Noel Brown

Director, Environment Program
United Nations, New York

After The Stockholm Declaration: The First Decade

Initiatives such as the Man-Environment Impact Conference encourage us at the United Nations to believe that the revolution and thought necessary for safeguarding the environment and enhancing the quality of life have indeed started—and we are also encouraged that educators are beginning to accept their own role in helping to develop the understanding and ethical values, skills and attitudes that are necessary to enable us to play more productive parts in the challenges of environmental protection.

It is now over 10 years since the Stockholm Conference on the Environment and the founding of the United Nations Environment Program. Stockholm could be said to have been a challenge to educators to develop the necessary knowledge for interpretation of the complex phenomena that shape the environment and the skills required in devising and applying effective solutions to environmental problems. It could also be said to challenge educators everywhere to design systems of learning that would provide individuals and communities with a means of interpreting the interdependence and interaction between the various elements in space and time so as to deepen our awareness of our changing relationship to the biosphere.

For the second decade after Stockholm, this challenge would seem more urgent than ever. Let me illustrate what I mean. In May, 1982, the United Nations commemorated the 10th anniversary of the Stockholm Conference with a session of special character in Nairobi, Kenya. The session was attended by more than a hundred governments and was convened to review and assess the achievements of the last decade, as well as major environmental trends, potential problems, and priorities for action by the United Nations system during the decade ahead. The documentation was impressive, as was the information on which this assessment was to be based. Among other things, it was revealed that during the past 10 years we have gained considerable insights into how the Earth works, as well as new perceptions about the intricate and important interactions between the components and processes which support life on this planet. It was also revealed that, while in the last 10 years no environmental miracles have been wrought and while the world has yet to turn the environment corner, so to speak, the world community seems to have started in earnest its long march toward environmental quality and planetary security.

Environment is not only part of a working global vocabulary, but a new global value which most states share. This value is premised on the declaration of Stockholm, which recognized man as both a creature and molder of his environment. These states have established mechanisms for its expression and implementation at the national level. Moreover, most of these states have developed a variety of procedures for assessment of environmental effects on a number of development activities. Others have highly developed regulations and standards for the protection of air and water quality and the management and disposal of wastes, as well as land-use programs with varying degrees of effectiveness.

At the international level, machinery is being carefully assembled for the defence and enhancement of environmental values through the monitoring and assessment of changes in environmental phenomena and the development of reliable data bases from which sound policies can be made. UNEP's own Earth Watch Program is one such effort. When fully operational, Earth Watch will improve our capacity to evaluate the full consequences of decisions which affect both the physical and social environments before such decisions are made and to improve techniques for allocating real costs for activities to those who benefit from them and assigning real values to traditionally free goods such as air and water.

Within the United Nations system itself, environment is increasingly becoming an integral part of the programming process, as organizations and specialized agencies of the United Nations embark on system-wide programming. This effort holds the prospect of providing greater coherence and order within the United Nations system, thereby expanding its capacity for effective action. In this connection, the soon-to-be-released, system-wide, medium term plan which goes under the code name, SWMTEP, for the period of 1984-89 could very well become one of the most innovative arrangements yet devised by the United Nations.

The progress in value building is most encouraging to UNEP. For example, in the area of development financing, environment is increasingly becoming an operation of principle and a standard part of the code of conduct of development financing agencies. Following a UNEP initiative and the leadership of the United Nations Development Program and the World Bank in 1980, nine development financing institutions have subscribed to a declaration of principles regarding the incorporation of environmental standards in their investment programs. When it is considered that collectively these institutions commit more than $20 billion a year to development activities, there can be no doubt as to their potential in shaping or mishaping the development process and with it the environment. This process, moreover, is vital to any attempt to bridge the gap between development and environment; the power of development financing institutions might yet help guide the transition to a most sustainable society in a livable world.

Efforts are also being made to incorporate a similar set of principles in the programs of bilateral aid agencies. Agencies such as the US-AID, CIDA

(Canada), and SIDA (Sweden) have shown remarkable interest in and sensitivity to this concept. The United Nations hopes that in time commercial banks will likewise see the value of environmentally sound investment in both their national and international programs. After all, they too influence the development process and their investments do have environmental implications. At the same time, however, we recognize some difficulties facing these commercial banks; after all, they feel the prospects of competitive disadvantage since there are as yet no universal standards of conduct in this regard. Perhaps this is an area where the United Nations Environment Program might accelerate the standard setting process.

In this connection, environmental values have also been reflected in the new international development strategy for the Third Development Decade, reiterated recently in a decision of the United Nations General Assembly. It reaffirms that the new international economic order must reflect serious regard for environmental constraints, particularly in connection with the management and use of the world's resources, disposal of its wastes, and a growth process that would not be inimical to the stability of the biosphere. The General Assembly also requested the assistance of the United Nations Environment Program in giving operational content to this principle. This challenge is seriously handicapped by our own current financial constraints.

Finally, environmental values have been the basis of systematic evolution of a body of environmental law and the development of an emerging environmental diplomacy. For example, many countries are developing multinational or bilateral agreements to protect wildlife or to deal with toxic substances.

The Declaration of Nairobi: The Second Decade

In Nairobi in May, 1982, the governments involved issued a second declaration, known as the Declaration of Nairobi, which forcefully reflects what during the last decade has become a truism—that the environment cannot be nationalized. That is, the solution to many environmental problems cannot be solely a matter of sovereign prerogatives or left to the vagaries of national politics. As a result, bold new initiatives and strategies of cooperation for environmental control and protection must be evolved.

Thus, while acknowledging the impressive levels of achievement in the area of value building and information development, it was also acknowledged that governments had not shown sufficient vigor and determination in tackling some very fundamental problems. As a result, the state of the environment in 1982, particularly in the developing countries, was still deteriorating and would continue to do so unless there were new and vigorous commitments to act. To this end, the Declaration of Nairobi urged governments to discharge their historic responsibility and address environmental challenges with a renewed sense of urgency. It also urged renewed emphasis for the second decade on a number of issues, including: deforestation; soil and water deterioration; desertification; diseases associated with adverse environmental conditions; changes in the atmosphere, such as ozone, carbon dioxide, and acid rain; pollution of the seas and inland waters; the extinction of animal and plant species; and careless use and disposal of hazardous wastes. I would like to examine briefly some of these issues which form the basis of action for the United Nations Environment Program at this time.

The Issues

1. Atmospheric Resources

With respect to the protection and the management of atmospheric resources, we have to get away from the mistaken notion that air is a free good. The atmosphere is a resource which has to be managed like any other resource; today there is an acute sense of urgency to do so. It is one of the global "commons"; as such it challenges us with a new global responsibility. Despite its importance to our collective survival in setting the biological and chemical conditions of life on the planet, surprisingly very little is known about the atmosphere. In other parts of the world, the problem is becoming equally acute. Such countries as Greece and Italy are beginning to appreciate the fact that the cultural heritage of classical civilizations may erode because of acid rain. The Greeks maintain that they may have to put some of their monuments under glass. The Romans are worried because the marble surfaces are beginning to show a texture of a soggy plaster as a result of pollution caused by automobiles. These are the implications of the breakdown of air quality as a result of human activity. The impacts are now beginning to be felt visibly and require urgent action.

Another atmospheric problem is the buildup of CO_2. Scientists believe that by the year 2035 the CO_2 level in the atmosphere is likely to double. If this does occur, a warming trend would follow, which in turn would change the climatic balance as well as world-wide agricultural practices, not to mention melting the polar caps and raising the sea level by a metre or more. These are processes which cannot be reversed.

2. Biological Productivity

Second, there is a need to protect the biological basis of productivity of soils, water, forest, grasslands, and water systems. Scientists warn that approximately one-third of the world's arable land will be destroyed in the next 20 years; that is, approximately 20 million hectares of productive land are degraded annually—reduced to a state of complete uselessness. In other words, the soil capital of the world is being diminished at an alarming rate. This problem is not confined to developing countries as might be expected, but represents a serious global phenomenon. In developed countries, for example, approximately 3000 sq. km of prime farmland disappear every year to buildings and highways. In light of the urbanization revolution that is underway throughout the world, one can appreciate why this particular problem is so acute and why the need for land-use strategies is becoming an urgent challenge to many governments in developed as well as developing countries. For example, in the United States, the loss of cropland to non-agricultural uses is estimated at some 1.2 million hectares a year. This has very significant implications, not only for the United States, but for the world's food system and more importantly for the problems of global food security. Scientists are now beginning to wonder whether this process can be reversed.

In addition, the forest resources of the planet must be protected from overexploitation and neglect. There is a danger that humans may have destroyed the forest's capacity to serve essential ecological functions. One of the priorities of my own program is trying to determine the essential ecological minima for the forests to perform their ecological functions—maintaining the moisture balance, the temperature in the atmosphere, the carbon and oxygen cycles, etc. What would be the minimum requirement in terms of forestry vegetation for these functions to be performed? I can assure you that we do not know. My program is in the process now of trying to sense some baselines in terms of the forests that will be required to perform these functions.

What we do know is that we are destroying the forests at an alarming rate: 40% of the world's tropical rainforests and deciduous forests have disappeared already; the remainder are being felled at the rate of 110 000 sq. km a year—or 20 hectares a minute. The effects of this destruction cannot but be detrimental to a number of other processes and life forms within the planet. For example, we are beginning to appreciate the relationship between soil and the forest cover. Perhaps the most dramatic case of this relationship is to be found in the Bay of Bengal, where an island of some 50 000 sq. km was recently reported as having been formed as a result of soils washed away from the Himalayas and the nearby watershed. Can the Governments of this region be made to protect the forests so that this kind of accretion will not take place in the future?

3. Genetic Diversity

A third item concerns the problem of genetic diversity—what we might call nature's biological insurance program. The issue for too long has been confined to narrow scientific circles or the higher echelons of conservationists. One of the world's 5-10 million species becomes extinct each day. By the end of the decade, the extinction rate will approximate one an hour: a million species may have vanished by the year 2000. It is not just the conservationists who worry about the disappearance of obscure species from distant plains or jungles. Cancer specialists know that two of their most important drugs come from a flower of the tropical rain forest, the rosy periwinkle. Seed growers have to develop new strains of wheat every five years or so, as the old ones become susceptible to disease. We must come to understand the importance of preserving the diversity of gene pools. The ancestral gene pools for staple American crops lie abroad; without foreign genes, farmers would supply little more than cranberries, pecans, and sunflower seeds. The world's gene pools have already made a vital contribution to the pharmaceutical and agricultural industries, yet only 1% of the species have been examined for their commercial value. The growing rate of extinction must be stopped or slowed by preserving habitats and ensuring that the public is much more enlightened about the value of genetic diversity to a collective and future well-being.

It is important to understand and appreciate that the genetic material on the planet plays a very important and vital role to our collective survival and that we may be destroying it at a rate that cannot be sustained. I am not sure how many people appreciate the fact that, by destroying genetic material, we are shrinking the base of our food production. When we prepared the World Conservation Strategy, we concluded that the narrowing of the genetic base poses a clear and present danger to global food security. For example, only four varieties of wheat produce 75% of the crops grown on the Canadian prairies and more than half the prairie wheat comes from lands devoted to a single variety. Seventy-two percent of United States potato production depends on only four varieties. Just two varieties supply the United States pea production. Most of Brazil's coffee production descends from a single plant. The United States soybean industry is entirely derived from six plants from Asia. At present the world depends on less than 20 crops for 90% of its food production. This is a rather precarious and thin base. The more it shrinks, the greater are the hazards to present and future generations.

4. The Chemical Revolution

The next issue is the expanding chemical revolution. The synthesizing of chemical compounds has brought untold blessings and benefits to our lives. Without these chemicals, we could not enjoy the health, the foods, the clothing, the shelter that we have today. With them, however, we have some new risks that will have to be addressed very seriously.

In agriculture, one of the technologies that made for expanding food production during the last 30-40 years was the introduction of biocides and pesticides. The pesticide revolution certainly changed the face of agriculture and brought incredible benefits to many people around the world. Famines have been reduced and global food stability has been enhanced. Nonetheless, we now have to reckon with the price of these benefits as resistence to pesticides has become a critical problem within the world community. For example, many people applauded the fact that malaria had been virtually exterminated, but new immune strains of mosquito are now developing and malaria may be on the rise again.

Scientists are beginning to observe with a great degree of alarm, double, triple and multiple resistence to pesticides. In time, most of the pesticides that we have produced may become unworkable against most of the pests. The spectre of a pest-resistant world is not some figment of scientific imagination, but something that we must grapple with as a very serious question.

In Canada, recent reports characterize the Great Lakes as a virtual cesspool containing some 400 known chemicals. But what is more ominous is that no one knows what happens when 400 chemicals are blended together. We know enough about each chemical to be able to manage it, but what happens when there is a brew—a virtual witches' brew? We do not know.

A similar issue is the disposal of toxic and hazardous material—the by-products and the end-products of industrialization and urbanization. As the world shrinks in terms of dump sites, as the standards in the industrialized countries become more stringent, there will be the temptation to look for sites overseas. The midnight dumper may take his cargo to unsuspecting countries or to corrupt countries by negotiating deals for the disposal of toxic and hazardous products. This will expand the danger to areas that may not be in a position to cope with them.

5. The Oceans

A final concern is that of the world's oceans. The Law of the Sea Conference successfully concluded recently a convention to protect seven-tenths of the Earth's surface by bringing order to the oceans, including safeguards for environmental protection of ocean exploitation and exploration. Scientists do not fear too much for the open oceans because they are very resilient; rather scientists are very concerned with the coastal regions—those narrow bands of water, wetlands, and estuaries that form an interesting harmony with the sea. Hectare for hectare, the coastal areas are among the most productive places on Earth; they are often called the "ocean nurseries." They provide food and shelter for an incredible amount of life forms; they are utilized by an estimated two-thirds of the world's fisheries, including some, such as shrimp, which are the most lucrative in the fisheries trades. Unfortunately, this harmony seems to be in jeopardy as human pressures on coastal ecosystems are beginning to assume dangerous proportions. Wetlands, flood plains, sea-grass beds, and even coral reefs are being destroyed the world over. Offshore sources of energy; the construction of dams, blocking passage of migratory fish and destroying their habitats; dredging to create and deepen harbours—these are among the most visible and perhaps the most obvious evidence of human impact.

Not so visible but equally dangerous are the problems of pollution caused by agriculture runoff. Much of land-based abuses end up in the oceans and in the coastal areas. Scientists state that 80% of all land-based activity and land-based pollution ends up in the oceans. In my own region, the Caribbean, we are told that, if present trends continue, the Caribbean could be the sea most damaged by pesticides of any body of water in the world. This too, then, presents clear and present dangers—challenges that we need to face.

Conclusion

I have sketched a rather bleak profile of the core agenda of the United Nations Environment Program and the challenge that it poses to educators to help us realize whence we have come and where we are going. Only in this way can we begin to perceive the intricate interrelationships that exist between us and our life support system, and to understand the fact that as a result of changes in our numbers, our wealth, waste, speed, learning, and mobility, we have created a virtual technosphere which places us on a collision course with the biosphere. In order to survive in our new situation, we may have to reinvent the modalities of our adaptation. The human species has shown remarkable capacity to adapt to changing environments.

The challenge that we face today is whether we can survive the man-made future, because the future—if there is a future—is likely to be largely man-made. Educators who are concerned with trying to apply the mind to issues and challenges must become involved with this urgent task and challenge.

There are those of us who, despite the bleakness of the statistics, remain somewhat optimistic. We have faith in the human genius; more importantly, we are convinced that despite the challenges facing us, we need not be defeated in advance, nor become victims of a passivity borne of pessimism. There are grounds of optimism since the really important problems of our time are not merely technical, but originate in our thoughts, in our minds, in our uncertainty and even in our poor judgment concerning how we manage the first truly technological civilization.

René Dubois, in one of his last public utterances, advanced the possibilities of the triumph of the human spirit when he stated that the deteriorating condition in our cities and the adversarial relationship with nature, are determined more by technological imperatives than by our choice of desirable human goals. He went on to encourage us to rediscover our innate celebrations of life and to overcome the belief that things are going to get worse and that we cannot change them. This is what he said that impressed me: "that we can be optimistic because the logical future need not be the future that obtains, that quite often the volitional future—the future of choice—has equal validity and provides an equal challenge."

I hope that what we can do is to expand our capacity for choice and provide ourselves with the ability to choose wisely. I would like to think that, in trying to develop these strategies for choices and the capacity for choices, education is extremely important. Again it was René Dubois who cautioned us that after all *homo sapiens* can create humanized environments that are stable, profitable, pleasureable, and favourable to the health of the Earth and the growth of our civilization. And why not? After all, this planet was not designed with us in mind, but we have it in our power to make it an agreeable home. You can help us to understand these facts and to design the strategies that are necessary for the care and maintenance of a planet of which we and successive generations can be proud.

18
Public Involvement in Great Lakes Decision Making

Arthur M. Timms

Executive Director, Canadian Cerebral Palsy Association, Toronto

Introduction

Great Lakes Tomorrow (GLT) is a unique binational organization devoted to improving citizen participation in Great Lakes decisions. The 36 million American and Canadian "Great Lakes citizens" who live and work in the Great Lakes basin share the lakes and can work together in helping to safeguard their future through Great Lakes Tomorrow—today! GLT provides the effective, common voice of Canadian and American Great Lakes citizens together, that is needed if the best planning and management decisions affecting the lakes are to be made in the years ahead.

GLT, the only organization of its kind, has a unique set of goals:

- to secure from the governments of Canada and the United States a commitment to rehabilitate and restore degraded areas of the Great Lakes and to maintain that state;
- to promote a shared Great Lakes perspective and binational concern for the consequences of decisions affecting the lakes;
- to build a comprehensive future oriented planning capability; to mobilize binational cooperation of Great Lakes problems; and
- open up the decision-making process to greater public inspection and participation.

GLT believes that the Great Lakes system must be preserved and that citizens have a right and responsibility to get involved in what happens to them. GLT is a non-profit, charitable organization with a Board of Directors from both nations. The board and members together decide on GLT policy annually.

We all rely on the Great Lakes for our drinking water, municipal sewage treatment, industrial and power-plant cooling water, recreational boating, swimming and fishing, commercial fishing, transportation of raw and manufactured goods, and agricultural products. The Great Lakes region is the industrial heart of North America.

The Great Lakes are an economic necessity to the industries and communities on their shores, a storehouse of natural resources, a source of recreation and personal wonder. Like any resource, the lakes can sustain only limited exploitation. Because of the many uses and demands upon the lakes and their surrounding watersheds, changes occur which affect the water quality or quantity and ultimately the lives and livelihoods of those who depend upon them. There is danger that we can err in our decisions and actions because we do not fully understand the complexity of this unique freshwater resource—the largest in the world.

But the lakes are in trouble. Pollution has caused water quality to deteriorate, in turn harming human health and that of fish, birds and plants. Agriculture, diversions, dredging, energy generation, shoreline erosion, urban run-off, and winter navigation are all issues that, if not properly managed, can make the health of the Great Lakes even more critical.

Decisions will be made. Millions of public and private dollars will be spent over the next 10 years on water quality and fisheries management, on transportation, energy and industrial development, on control of toxic materials and shoreline erosion. Safe drinking water and edible fish are a concern of everyone. Our two countries have said they must allocate a minimum of 10 million dollars annually just to monitor the success of pollution control and identify new problems. Divergent views need to be brought into the decision process. Resolution of these critical issues should include the concentrated effort of knowledgeable citizens. All of us have a stake in the outcome.

GLT's Program

By means of a program of public education, information gathering, research, and action, GLT plays a vital role in Great Lakes management and control. Working with the institutions of government and others such as the International Joint Commission which already have a mandate to look after the Great Lakes, GLT can offer assistance and a "grass-roots" viewpoint about the care of the health of the Great Lakes. Through information gathering public workshops and the expression of analytical comment in testimony, briefs and letters, GLT monitors the state of the Great Lakes and the performance of those who are charged with managing them.

The program has the following objectives:

– to create an informed binational constituency for the Great Lakes;
– to build public understanding of existing management structure and process and encourage better decision making through citizen access and participation;
– to organize a continuing network of citizens, scientists, educational institutions and agencies to share and use information and data to better manage the lakes;
– to develop system-oriented strategies to improve the management of the lakes; and
– to encourage continuing use of the Decisions Course (described below) and to maintain citizen interest and information levels.

GLT's action program includes the following:

- championing routine environmental impact assessment of projects in the basin,
- urging an ecosystem approach to managing the lakes,
- pressing for tough water and air quality policies,
- undertaking public workshops and dissemination of information,
- supporting a rehabilitated fishery,
- advocating a systems approach to energy and transportation develop- ment in the region,
- cooperating with Great Lakes institutions and monitoring their perfor- mance, and
- interacting with others working toward solutions to environmental problems in the region.

Course on Managing the Great Lakes

Decisions for the Great Lakes, a project coordinated by GLT, is a program to improve decisions for the protection and wise use of the binational resource of the Great Lakes through informed citizen participation. A course on manag- ing the Great Lakes as a system, *Decisions* is funded by grants from: United States Environmental Protection Agency, Region V; Environment Canada and Environment Ontario representing the Review Board of the Canada-Ontario Agreement Respecting Great Lakes Water Quality; Canadian National Sports- men's Fund; Joyce Foundation; Charles H. Ivey Foundation; Gund Found- ation; and Max Bell Foundation. This program is offered without charge with the understanding that participants will commit themselves to improving Great Lakes Basin policy and resource management decisions.

The course consists of 40 hours of classtime over a 10-week period; it began in 1982 at seven Lake Erie locations and was followed by nine Lake Ontario courses in 1985. The course is a seminar-discussion format with most classes meeting from 6:00 to 10:00 p.m. Optional Saturday field trips may be offered. Participants are limited to 30 at each location. A certificate of completion is awarded. Faculty members from area universities and staff of public interest groups, environmental education centres, research laboratories, industries and government contribute to the program. Some were involved in the preparation of a resource manual, *Decisions for the Great Lakes;* others lead various ses- sions in the course. Over a five-year period, *Decisions for the Great Lakes* will be offered at 24 locations around the international Great Lakes. Lakes Superior and Huron courses have not yet been scheduled.

The courses are of interest to a variety of people: local, state, provincial or federal officials; persons active in a community, service, or environmental group; executives in industry; regional planners; members of a technical or citizen advisory panel; labour leaders; agribusiness managers; teachers; scien- tists; sportsmen; or concerned citizens.

The course covers the following topics:

1. The Natural Setting of the Great Lakes Basin: its origin, geology, climate, drainage and circulation and their effects; ecological concepts and principles and their constraints on what we do to the lakes.
2. Water Quality in the Great Lakes: biology, chemistry, pollution control and lake rehabilitation objectives.
3. People in the Great Lakes Basin: the economic and social development that made the basin what it is; current uses and conflicts; human health issues.
4. Governing the Great Lakes: what you should know about Canadian and American approaches and institutions for managing Great Lakes resources; differences and what can be done.
5. International Institutions, Treaties and Agreements: what are they, how they affect the resources in the basin, and public access to international decision making.
6. Resource Management: principles and problems in the day-to-day management of the Great Lakes; the need for new problem solving approaches to the sustained use of the resource; barriers to innovation and the public role.
7. Major Issues Facing Great Lakes Decision Makers: why toxic substances, hazardous wastes, lake diversions, navigation proposals, dredging, and shoreline erosion are important.
8. More Great Lakes Issues: can we keep our lakes fishable and swimmable in the face of atmospheric pollution and pollution from land mismanagement? How should fisheries, wetlands, and public recreational access relate to development?
9. Public Participation: a binational perspective on how, where, and when to participate, and why the citizen is an invaluable resource in planning and decision-making; barriers to participation and ways to overcome them.
10. The Great Lakes Basin-Decisions for the Future: key issues and strategies for conflict resolution and creative binational resource management; the Great Lakes as a continental and global resource.

The Conservation Council of Ontario

The Conservation Council of Ontario is Great Lakes Tomorrow's secretariat in Canada. The Council was founded in 1952 by Dr. F.H. Kortright "to promote the welfare of all persons by encouraging the conservation, restoration and best use of soil and water and the life sustained thereby." Support for such an objective is even more necessary in Ontario today. Economic development and population growth have brought problems of natural resource use to the forefront in this, Canada's most urban and industrialized province.

For an all-too-visible example, look to the land. Too much of it is being covered with concrete or spoiled by waste as we pursue a "higher standard of living." And each time we allow the land or any one of our other natural resources to suffer in this economic/environment trade-off, we are irreversibly mortgaging the future. Not just our own future—but also our children's.

The Conservation Council of Ontario is the senior coordinating group for 32 member organizations, each concerned about specific conservation and environmental problems. In its membership the Council has enrolled those major provincial associations that have an active concern for the quality of the environment, and outstanding individuals having fundamental knowledge and experience in phases of conservation. Total membership of its constituent organizations exceeds one million persons. The services of these people are freely given and unselfishly dedicated to the advancement and application of conservation principles. The forum for debate provided by the Council's monthly meetings is unique in the province, and without question the organization's most important reason for being. Out of this invaluable interchange of information, ideas and opinions there emerges a single, powerful voice—a combined, unified effort.

The Council keeps environmental concerns continuously before the public as well as the Government by providing community leaders, teachers and other decision-makers with seminars and scores of authoritative publications, including its own monthly *Ontario Conservation News*. The Council is reviewing the Central Ontario Lakeshore Urban Complex Planning Proposals, activity on the Niagara Escarpment, and development in Northern Ontario, and is developing action strategies for many other problem areas.

The Council has the following objectives:

- to promote the welfare of all persons by encouraging the conservation, restoration and best use of natural resources of soil and water and the life sustained thereby;
- to promote the cooperation of organizations engaged in various phases of conservation and related human betterment;
- to promote the coordination of the activities of conservation organizations;
  to provide the opportunity for representatives of environmental and conservation organizations to meet on common ground for the planning and development of conservation programs, at both provincial and regional levels;
- to institute and encourage research in all phases of conservation and to stimulate public education, particularly that of the younger generation, in the conservation of natural resources; and
- to cooperate with other organizations and governmental agencies having the conservation, restoration and development of natural resources as their objectives.

All signs point to the fact that the nation's economic growth, the creation of job opportunities and, indeed, the maintenance of our standard of living will all depend more and more on how effectively we deal with the many resource problems facing us in this latter part of the 20th century. The Conservation

Council of Ontario—a non-profit, non-political public service body—feels there is an increasing need for a credible "third voice" in addition to that of government and industry to provide guidance in planning to meet those problems now.

19

The European Community Environmental Education Network

Anton Trant

Director, Curriculum Development Unit
Trinity College, University of Dublin, Dublin, Ireland

The European Community Action Program

The European Community has an action program for the environment. First adopted in 1973 and later extended in 1976, it is concerned with practical and important issues, such as the reduction of pollution, the rational use of space and natural resources, measures to protect and improve the environment, and cooperation with non-member countries and international organizations. Through its interest in promotion of public awareness of environmental problems and education, the Community in 1977 established a network of pilot schools for the exchange of information and experience in environmental education.

The Network was sponsored by the Environment and Consumer Protection Service of the Commission of the European Communities (1976). Before establishing the Network, a feasibility study was undertaken of current trends in environmental education and of models of good practice in the schools of the member states of the European Community. Finally, after several discussions among officials from the Commission and from the Ministries of Education of the member states, it was agreed at a meeting in Brussels in February, 1977 that the Network could begin.

The principal aims of the Network were: to enhance the quality of environmental education in the pilot schools through mutual cooperation and learning from each other's experience; and to collect, test and disseminate environmental education materials. The first aim implied that the pilot schools had already acquired some worthwhile experience in the area of environmental education and that they were willing to share this experience with other schools in the Network. The second aim implied that the exchange of ideas and experience among schools would be accompanied by an exchange and development of learning materials. The development of these materials, which included audio-visual and printed matter, was envisaged as a dynamic process involving the active participation of all members of the Network.

In the development of the Network, it was envisaged that the term "environmental education" would be interpreted broadly as taking into account urban as well as rural situations, and involving disciplines of both the social and natural sciences.

The Structure of the Network

The pilot schools were selected by the national ministries for education, using the following criteria: the schools catered to pupils aged 9-11 years (later extended upwards in some countries to 14 years, and downwards in others to four years); and the teachers in the schools were committed to the promotion of environmental education and were willing to experiment with new teaching and learning approaches in cooperation with schools from other countries. Eleven schools and two environmental education centres, representing the nine member states of the Community, were nominated by their respective ministries between February and June in 1977. During the following four years, the number of pilot schools was increased to a total of 29.

The responsibility of coordinating the activities of the Network was entrusted by the Commission to the Curriculum Development Unit (CDU), Dublin. The Unit was established in 1972 by the City of Dublin Vocational Education Committee (CDVEC) and is managed jointly by the CDVEC, Trinity College, Dublin, and the Irish Department for Education. The coordinating team stayed in touch with all members of the Network and facilitated the inter-communication necessary for the dynamic development of the project. The activities of the team included visiting the pilot schools regularly; organizing meetings, exchange visits and seminars; and producing learning materials, newsletters and reports. An advisory committee, composed of officials from the Commission of the European Communities, representatives from the member states (national experts) and members of the coordinating team, was responsible for overseeing the progress of the Network and advising on all policy matters. The national experts also played a vital role in their own countries in supporting the activities of the pilot schools.

The Joint Study Program

At the first general seminar, held for teachers of the Network in Dublin, 1977, one of the recommendations adopted was that the schools would undertake a joint study program and that the results would be compared at a general seminar at the end of each school year. This joint study program was operated by the schools over four years and was a major activity of the Network.

1. The Local Area

During the first year of the program (1977/78), each school undertook a study of some aspect of its local area. Some schools chose to explore their local area on topographical lines; for example, a rural school looked at the quarries and caves of the surrounding countryside, while the pupils of an urban school studied the layout of their city. Two schools studied the livelihood of the inhabitants of their local areas, in one case, tourism and in the other, fishing. A number of schools took broad themes such as food, shelter, the weather, earth, air, water, and related these themes to their own situation. Finally, three schools chose to study topical issues: the use of a public park, the construction of a dam, and a plague of insects on a local river. The results of the first year's work were displayed at the Network's second general seminar held in Hertfordshire, United Kingdom, in July, 1978. Based on the presentations of the various projects, a general report was compiled.

2. The Wider Environment

During the second year of the Network's existence (1978-79), the joint study program was extended from the local area to the wider environment, and the topics covered by the pilot schools could be broadly classified under six headings:

- use and abuse of the natural environment,
- human pressures on the natural environment,
- human relationships in modern society,
- the effect of urbanization,
- environmental action, and
- contrasts in the environment.

A common format for reporting on the work done was adopted by all the pilot schools. This format comprised: (1) project theme; (2) objectives; (3) subject areas involved; (4) number and ages of the pupils; (5) duration of the project and the number of hours per week spent on it; (6) a step-by-step description of the course of the project; (7) the teacher's review of the project in relation to the original objectives. Presentations based on the second year's work were made by the teachers at the Network's third general seminar held in Rovereto, Italy in July, 1979. A record of this work was afterwards published (CDU, 1980a).

3. European Environmental Issues

During 1979-80, the joint study program was devoted to European environmental issues. The Network was divided into three working groups and each group selected one of the environmental issues referred to in *The European Community's Environmental Policy*, a brochure published by the Commission of the European Communities (1976). Mid-year seminars were arranged for each of the three groups, in order to provide the groups with a forum for comparing and compiling their work, with a view to establishing a format for their final products. All three groups met together at a general seminar in Luxembourg at the end of the year. During this general seminar, the groups made presentations of their year's work and also drew up plans for the following year.

The first group (Group A) was French/English and represented schools from Belgium, Federal Republic of Germany, France, Ireland, and Luxembourg. The members of this group based their year's work on the theme "Man-made Environment: Cultural Heritage." By the end of the year, the group had produced a booklet based on an experiment carried out in one of the schools represented in the group. The booklet was entitled *Restoration of a*

Playground: Report of an Experiment carried out at the École Communale de Han-sur-Lesse (CDU, 1980b). The subject matter of the booklet was important only insofar as it illustrated a particular approach to environmental education which could be applied to other situations in urban or rural settings. In order to highlight this, the group concentrated on an analysis of the objectives set, rather than on a chronological account of events and activities.

The second group (Group B) was Italian/English speaking and consisted of schools from Ireland, Italy, and the United Kingdom. The members of the group chose the issue "Recreation and the Environment" and by the end of the year had produced a teacher's manual, based on the following objectives:

- to make the children aware of how much free time is available to them,
- to examine the ways in which children, adults and old people use their free time,
- to make the children aware of recreational possibilities in their own environment and to assess their adequacy, and
- to discover suitable interests in the environment by introducing the children to a wide range of activities (cultural, aesthetic, social and physical) (CDU, 1981b).

The third group (Group C) was German/English speaking and consisted of schools from Denmark, Federal Republic of Germany, Luxembourg, the Netherlands, and the United Kingdom. The members of the group chose the theme "Energy Production and Conservation" and by the end of the year had produced a teacher's manual in English in the form of a loose-leaf folder, with the following two-fold purpose:

- to be a source of ideas, methods and procedures for other teachers working on the energy theme, not in a prescriptive or definitive way, but as a pedagogical aid; and
- to increase teachers' and pupils' awareness of the energy crisis and to develop positive and constructive attitudes towards the use, misuse and conservation of energy.

One of the interesting features of the loose-leaf folder on energy was that it spanned the age groups from four to 14 years, suggesting ways in which a primary teacher who had no formal scientific training could deal with the kind of topics contained in the energy theme (CDU, 1982).

Teaching Methodologies and Environmental Education

It was decided at the Luxembourg general seminar, July, 1980, to retain the group structure established the previous year. The joint study program had now widened into "Teaching Methodologies and Environmental Education."

The members of Group A chose a variety of themes for the school year 1980-81: "The Use of the Environmental Centre at Han-sur-Lesse," "Study of a Pond in an Amenity Area," "Improvement of the School Grounds," "The Development and Use of a Cultural Centre by Pupils," "Creation of a Nature Trail," and "Study of a Valley." Each school in the group worked on its own theme according to a common approach established by the group: "observe, understand and act." A report on the group's work, including an analysis of objectives and methods, was presented at a mid-year seminar in February, 1981, and a group product based on this approach was prepared by the end of the school year (CDU, 1981a).

Group B selected a group theme, "Man's Impact on the Environment," with each school working on particular sub-themes: "Urbanization," "Pollution and Conservation," and "Transport." The group product, which was intended for teachers' use, dealt with various aspects of the main theme, such as change, adaptation, use and abuse of the environment, conservation and the interrelationships between man and his environment. By the end of the school year, it was published as *Man's Impact on the Environment.*

Group C chose the theme "Water" and the member schools selected sub-themes focused on a particular case study based on an environmental concept. Examples of the concepts and case studies selected were "Use and Abuse of Water," with a case study on Food and Food Production in the Sea; "Protection of a Unique Water Landscape," with a case study on the Wetlands of West Jutland; and "Pollution in Running Water," with a case study on the Middle Rhine. The final product was a teacher's manual on "Water" (CDU, 1981d).

Evaluation

An evaluation seminar, held in Luxembourg, May 21-22, 1979, was attended by representatives of the Commission of the European Communities, representatives from the nine member states of the Community, and members of the coordinating team. The two principal aims of the seminar were: (1) to evaluate the progress of the Network to date, and (2) to make plans for future development. The analysis indicated that the operation and progress of the Network to date had been satisfactory. However, it was also felt that the time had come for a greater concentration on the dissemination of information on the Network and on the production and dissemination of environmental education materials produced by the Network schools. During 1980-81, it was felt that a more formal analysis of the projects should be carried out. Therefore, the coordinating team prepared a synthesis of all the Network's projects in the four years of its existence (CDU, 1981e). This document contained a number of conclusions very similar to the guidelines issued by the UNESCO Conference at Tbilisi in 1977 (UNESCO, 1978). The following are some of the major conclusions:

Aims of Environmental Education

The aims of environmental education involved the development of knowledge, skills, attitudes and values. As such, they fell within the aims of general education, but added a specific environmental dimension. This environmental dimension—the interrelation among people, culture and the biophysical surroundings—suggested three aspects which could form part of any comprehensive program in environmental education: (1) learning about the environment, i.e., knowledge, concept and skill objectives; (2) learning for the environment, i.e., attitudinal and value objectives; and (3) decision-making and action based on the acquisition of these earlier objectives.

Reasons for Undertaking Environmental Education Projects

Environmental education projects were undertaken because of their local nature; or because they were of a topical or controversial nature. The local area of the school was the main focus for the environmental education projects. This created an immediacy and relevance for the children. In some schools, the local area, or some aspect of it, was the entire subject of the project; in other schools, it served as an immediate example in a study of a wider topic or global issue.

Disciplines Underlying Environmental Education

Environmental education involved both the social and natural sciences and, as such, was normally interdisciplinary. Some school programs included studies which were unidisciplinary or multidisciplinary. However, the main emphasis throughout the Network was on the interdisciplinary nature of environmental education. The major disciplines in the environmental education projects were science (especially biology), history, and geography. There was a tendency for science-based projects to be used with older children and for geography- and history-based projects to be used with younger children. Vernacular language, mathematics, arts, crafts, drama, and music all contributed to the projects in all cases. Fieldwork was regarded as an essential component in environmental education.

Methodologies

The methodologies used depended on the aims and themes of the various projects. However, it was possible to distinguish four different types: (1) historical/geographical; (2) investigation/experimental; (3) survey; and (4) problem-solving. All the projects had a variety of activities, took place in and out of school, and involved various groupings of pupils. All the activities, however, could be summarized in three stages: observation, understanding, and action. The most common ways of presenting the results of the projects were through school exhibitions, pupil workbooks and the completion of a practical task.

In-Service Seminars for Teachers

Four in-service seminars for Network teachers took place, each with a different purpose:

1. École Normale Mixte de Foix in France, March/April, 1978: to introduce teachers to the practice in France of taking classes into the out-of-doors—"les classes de nature."

2. Institut für die Pädagogik der Naturwissenschaften (IPN), Kiel, Federal Republic of Germany, November, 1978: to inform Network teachers about recent developments in environmental education and to provide them with the opportunity of seeing materials and documents which could be of use to them in their own work.
3. Centre Permanent d'Initiation à l'Environnement des Hautes-Pyrénées, Argelès-Gazost, France, April, 1979: to provide Network teachers with the opportunity of exploring and developing teaching methods and pupil activities for field trips in both natural and man-made environments.
4. Teachers' Resource Centre, Aberdeen, Scotland, April/May, 1979: to produce environmental education materials on the theme "Urbanization" which would be of use to teachers from the various countries in the Network. These materials were afterwards published in book form under the title *Our Changing Locality* (Grampian Regional Education Committee, 1980).

Continuity of the Network

During the final general seminar of the Network at Sèvres, Paris, in July, 1981, the three working groups made final presentations of their group products. On the eve of the seminar, the Network Advisory Committee met and made two important decisions. First, it was agreed that the Network would have a supplementary year to consolidate the various initiatives at national, regional or local levels, and to establish a regular pattern of communication at the European level. Second, it was also agreed that the Network idea should not be allowed to die and, to this end, a secondary phase should be developed catering to pupils from an older age group. Furthermore, both phases of the Network, primary and secondary, were to be linked together through the activities of the coordinating team.

Conclusion

The idea of the Network is both simple and dynamic. Schools from different European countries and traditions came into contact and interacted with each other. The result was predictable: a greater awareness of the possibilities of environmental education in the European cultural tradition. It was in this context that insights were shared and experiences exchanged by practitioners in the field.

Within the last decade, various guidelines for environmental education have been drawn up at both international and national levels. These have been helpful up to a certain point, but it must be realized that they present a major challenge: how to translate a set of aspirations about improving the environment into practical school realities. We must be able to describe the different sets of conditions which make successful teaching about the environment possible. We must set about discovering what works best and why. We must be able to devise pilot projects if we are to get a clear idea of content and methodology. In a word, we need case studies of environmental education in action.

The European Community Environmental Education Network is such a case study. It provides a context for comparative work in environmental education for pupils aged 9-14 years in schools from the member states of the European Community over a period of five years. It does this at different levels: (1) as an example of how programs in environmental education can be developed which are best suited to the character of individual schools and to the area which they serve; (2) as an example of how a project in environmental education can act as a unifying force, operating across the boundaries of different national cultures and traditions; and (3) as an example of how a comparatively small group of pilot schools may exert an influence both within and beyond the European Community.

References

Commission of the European Communities. 1976. *Continuation and Implementation of a European Community Policy and Action Programme on the Environment (Bulletin of the European Communities, Supplement 6/76).* Luxembourg: Office for Official Publications of the European Communities.

Commission of the European Communities. 1976. *The European Community's Environmental Policy.* Luxembourg.

Curriculum Development Unit. 1980a. *Profiles of School Projects 1978/79. Profils de Projets Scolaires 1978/79.* Dublin.

Curriculum Development Unit. 1980b. *Restoration of a Playground: Report of an Experiment Carried Out at the École Communale de Han-sur-Lesse, Belgium.* Dublin.

Curriculum Development Unit. 1981a. *Environmental Actions: An Approach to Teaching Through Objectives. Actions sur l'Environnement: Une Approche de la Pédagogie par Objectifs.* Dublin.

Curriculum Development Unit. 1981b. *Recreation and the Environment. Tempo Libero e Ambiente.* Dublin: O'Brien Educational, rev. ed.

Curriculum Development Unit. 1981c. *Man's Impact on the Environment: A Teacher's Environmental Education Handbook. Incontro/Scontro Uomo Ambiente: Un Manuale per Inseqnanti.* Dublin.

Curriculum Development Unit. 1981d. *Water: A Presentation of Case Studies and Teaching Methods.* Dublin.

Curriculum Development Unit. 1981e. *A Synthesis of Environmental Education Programmes Carried Out in the European Community Environmental Education Network.* Dublin.

Curriculum Development Unit. 1982. *Energy: A Teacher's Manual.* Dublin.

Grampian Regional Education Committee, in conjunction with Curriculum Development Unit. 1980. *Our Changing Locality: A Presentation for Teachers.* Dublin: O'Brien Educational.

UNESCO. 1978. *Intergovernmental Conference on Environmental Education, Tbilisi (USSR) 14-26 October 1977: Final Report.* Paris.

20
The Greenpeace Foundation: Communication Through Non-Violent Direct Action

Maury Mason
Education Director, Greenpeace Foundation of Canada, Vancouver

Introduction

Civil disobedience is the action of defying an unjust law in order to bring about the enactment of a just one. When the laws of the land are in direct violation of the laws of nature, it is the mandate of our organization—the Greenpeace Foundation—to confront them. Occasionally in a campaign, laws may be broken and we may be regarded by some as anarchists. According to Henry David Thoreau, civil disobedience is often confused with either anarchy or disregard for the law. However, we are not anarchists, for anarchy is disregard for all laws. We want changes to be made to environmentally-damaging statutes and to have new laws implemented that place importance on natural systems and ecology.

Greenpeace appeals to those who view us as people who are actually doing something about environmental problems. An organization like ours is an important counterbalance to polluters who view the environment as a disposable commodity; we are as hard-nosed and uncompromising as they are. It is this confrontational stance that people with a more passive nature find offensive. Our public relations image sometimes suffers because of this; however, our goal is not to make friends, but to effect change. Our policy is founded on a philosophy based on a subjective value judgment: environmental balance is critical and should be protected from destruction.

Greenpeace has grown from a group of 30 Vancouver idealists in 1971 to a large organization. We have two Canadian offices with more than 60 000 members; seven United States offices with a membership of 550 000; and 15 European, African, Australian, and New Zealand branches with a total membership of over two million people. We are growing at a rate of approximately 200 000 supporters per year.

Application of Philosophy

In 1971, the United States government planned a series of underground nuclear tests hundreds of times the magnitude of the blast that destroyed Hiroshima. We had grave concerns, not only about the buildup of nuclear weapons and the danger of release of radioactivity into the atmosphere, but also about the chosen site: Amchitka Island was along a known fault line which had recently been responsible for several major earthquakes along the west coast of Alaska.

We began writing letters and attending meetings in an effort to voice our opposition to the powers that were in control. Our letters went unanswered and our objections fell on deaf ears: the tests were going ahead as planned. After exhausting every formal channel, we needed a new avenue of persuasion. It was time to bear witness. A Quaker principle states that, if you know something is wrong, you have an obligation to stand beside it—to witness it—and tell as many people as possible.

Included in our group were journalists who knew how effective mass media could be in getting the message across to millions of people in a short time. In order to get your message delivered in the media, however, you must provide a newsworthy event to act as the vehicle for your message. At strategy meetings, it was decided that we would send a boat to the test site and, as a last resort, put ourselves inside the test zone. For protection, we brought along the focused public attention of millions of people. The combination of adventure, dedication, and—above all—danger made it a very appealing news item.

Press releases were issued daily. Photos and film were sent back to newspapers and television as our tiny boat visited each community along the coast; voice actualities were transmitted for radio broadcasts. The public response was overwhelming: thousands of people assembled at Canadian-American border crossings and United States consulates; tens of thousands of letters poured into the government offices of both countries.

On November 6, 1971, an atomic blast of five megatons rocked the island, creating a crater one kilometre wide. While the immediate campaign had failed, one year later the tests were cancelled; eventually, the island was turned into a bird sanctuary. This is typical of many Greenpeace campaigns: where the immediate action may fail, the ultimate battle is won over a period of years. This is why we believe that, for example, our current campaigns against seal hunting in eastern Canada and trophy hunting in western Canada will be ultimately successful.

The Save the Whales Campaign

Out of Amchitka developed a philosophy of non-violent direct action focused on an anti-war, anti-nuclear sentiment. What we needed was something to counteract the depressing thoughts of nuclear holocaust—something which ultimately stood for life in the future. We had our Peace; now we needed our Green. This feeling led directly to the Save the Whales campaign.

We began with the facts about whales. Unknown, intelligent beings were being slaughtered, some to the brink of extinction, but the general public was just beginning to be aware of their plight. We needed a sound strategy, the first step in putting policy into action. The strategy was again to bear witness at the scene of the slaughter, but this time to go a step further, putting ourselves in the path of the harpoon and acting as human shields to protect the whales.

The strategy was a good one, but the tactical considerations were overwhelming. A list of logistical problems emerged. We needed money, fuel, food, boats, motors, and supplies. We needed a competent crew willing to work for no pay. We needed to find the whalers. Then, we had to launch our inflatables, start the engines, and intercept the killer boats, all in front of the media cameras.

Our actions were split into two interconnected parts: information feedback and mass communication through the electronic media. Information feedback determined the action of the crew and organizers of the campaign. For example, we discovered from research just before we set out that we would not be able to find the whalers for several months because of their unpredictable travels. So, a reevaluation of the strategy had to occur. We had to find a way of keeping up public interest during that time. We did so by sailing along the west coast of Vancouver Island and sighting pods of whales in the area. Our media directors on land were standing by to record any communication from the ship and to feed it to the radio broadcast network. Interest in the story was maintained by daily progress reports to the media. Movie cameramen as well as still photographers recorded the events for distribution to television and newspapers. And, it worked. Just as our last media tactics expired, we found the whalers and a confrontation occurred. After the confrontation, press conferences were held in San Francisco with all major media attending. The story went worldwide; within days, it had reached approximately 850 million people. Scores of whale-saving organizations sprang up while those already in existence swelled with support.

In less than 10 years, public attitudes towards whales changed from seeing these creatures as large masses of blubber to seeing them as beautiful, intelligent creatures in urgent need of protection. Letter-writing campaigns were initiated to heads of governments about their voting role at the International Whaling Commission (IWC). Petitions were signed by millions.

While conventional education methods such as lectures and scientific documentation were effective in informing people about whales, the Greenpeace voyages captured the imagination of a massive public, with the image of people in inflatable boats putting their lives on the line for what they believed in. From these voyages came one of the most successful environmental films to date, "Voyages to Save the Whales," which captured numerous international awards, including the American Film Festival award and the Genie, Canada's equivalent to an Academy Award for best documentary under 60 minutes in length.

Methods Other Than Direct Action

Direct action is the peak of the pyramid; underneath are several support bases. *The legal aspects of our work* enabled us to bring to court and halt a radioactive dumping operation by the Dutch in the Atlantic Ocean. Our *political efforts* have included attempts to stop atmospheric testing by the French at Mururoa Atoll in the South Pacific. Through use of the *media*, we made millions of people aware of increased super tanker traffic along the west coast at British Columbia and Washington State. Public pressure forced restrictions on the size of tankers allowed to ply west coast waters. *Local organization* brought about the end of a plan to spray Vancouver with insecticides to control Gypsy moths, a problem which later was discovered not to exist. *Research* enabled us to expose and bring about an end to pirate whaling operations in Taiwan. *Fund-raising* to finance our operations comes from special events and a membership which donates frequently to continue our non-violent direct-action philosophy. We receive neither government nor large corporate financial support.

Criticisms of Greenpeace

Greenpeace has been accused of manipulating the media. We respond simply:

1. The media is one of the few weapons we have; our opposition has many more.
2. Most journalists find we are much more honest than our opposition.

Some people view Greenpeace's tactics as radical, over-zealous, and publicity-seeking. Those who do are only seeing *us* and not *past* us to the reason for our protest.

It has been stated that our direct-action campaigns are the first steps towards environmental terrorism. Nothing could be further from the truth. While we understand the frustrations of some individuals, we do not condone the use of force. We adhere *strictly* to our policy of non-violence. Terrorism victimizes the innocent and public sympathy shifts to its victims. In our campaigns, we put ourselves in the position of being the victims, with any act of aggression falling on us. Our volunteers are aware of this and accept the risks.

Results of Greenpeace Campaigns

Every environmental campaign that Greenpeace has conducted has begun with attempts to change government or industrial policy by conventional means. After exhausting those attempts, we take the issue to the public and let them decide. Results from public opinion polls have shown that there has been widespread support for our positions. For example, with respect to Canada's support of the whaling industry, the result of a 1980 Gallup poll showed that 86% of the respondents were not in favour of the Government's stand on this issue. The following year, instead of listening to the wishes of its constituents to vote for a ban on commercial whaling, Canada merely decided not to take part in the IWC.

We have little hope of altering laws by ourselves. But, with our ability to create widespread public awareness and to mobilize masses of people to demonstrate physically, verbally or through letters, our lawyers can bring to court the will of the people, and our lobbyists can receive prompt attention from government agencies and private industry, who do not wish to have their environmentally-unsound policies made public. Our growing membership attests to the fact that many people feel that we are an expanding and effective voice against environmentally damaging government and industrial practices.

21
Recovering Forgotten Efforts: Ecuador's Fundación Natura

Yolanda Kakabadse

Executive Director, Fundación Natura
Quito, Ecuador

The Existing Situation of Environmental Education in Ecuador

Global environmental education is a relatively new idea in Ecuador. Its implementation began only a few years ago and it is still too early to assess its initial educational results. In spite of existing evidence concerning the country's environmental problems, leaders and decision makers have not incorporated sound policies into their priorities for development plans in Ecuador. This attitude has led to a lack of coherent and systematic actions necessary to cope with the environmental problems of this country. Nevertheless, during the past two years a sequence of events has induced a positive and receptive change in the attitude of leading groups and the general public towards environmental issues through educational activities. Some of these activities will be described in this paper.

In this field, Ecuador shares a similar position to most developing countries, and, indeed, to some developed ones:

- development patterns are not autonomous and original;
- there is no deep knowledge of environmental problems;
- there is no actual information on the availability or limitation of Ecuador's natural resources;
- there are not enough legal and technical rules and regulations to lessen or prevent adverse environmental impacts resulting from development projects and plans;
- legal and institutional mechanisms are insufficient to deal with environmental problems in any coordinated and well-focused manner;
- economic resources are scarce, and thus the commitment of financial, human and institutional resources to environmental issues is a "luxury" —a low priority;
- there is no public awareness on the part of national leaders which would require any form of commitment to facing these problems; and
- the general public as a whole has never taken an active role in forcing decision makers to address environmental issues adequately, due principally to lack of knowledge and an inadequate perception of Ecuador's natural resources.

Given these conditions, the influence of environmental education has been of limited political, technical, and social significance. Several of the causes and elements which in some way explain the condition of natural resources in the country are valid topics for environmental education.

Owing to the lack of information available in Ecuador, it is difficult to be precise in describing the results of previous efforts that have been directed towards environmental education. As a whole, nevertheless, there exists a substantial conceptual weakness in this field, which has had a negative effect in relation to:

- educational programs that focus on nature and the environment,
- institutional efforts dedicated to studying environmental issues,
- technical-pedagogical approaches to environmental education,
- motivation in designing and implementing programs, and
- financial and budget priorities that give adequate attention to environmental issues.

Environmental education, which would have led to the comprehension of the interrelationships that exist among environmental and other problems, has not been integrated into the educational structures of the country. Instead, environmental concerns, on the few occasions that they have actually been incorporated into programs, have been treated as isolated phenomena. The lack of attention to this area in educational programs (formal and non-formal) has been offset only by isolated efforts from several institutions. Their efforts have only begun to touch the consciences of a few local groups and have had no significant influence on the national conscience.

Even though actual educational programs theoretically recognize the need to consider this as part of other social, economic, and political concerns, appropriate environmental education activities have not as yet been implemented. A recent review of formal educational programs has led to the conclusion that the overall concept of environmental education is very weak. This is evident in the formulation of plans, activities, curricula, and teaching-learning patterns used at the moment. These must be changed if the objectives of environmental education are to be achieved—the goal being a public awareness among all social levels in the country of development processes and their impact on the environment.

Several problems are evident. First, there seems to be little continuity between the objectives proposed for primary and secondary school levels. Second, the content of educational programs scarcely touches eco-development problems and their implications—a matter which is of considerable concern within Latin America. Instead, too much attention is given to scientific studies, turning the subject into a heavy, unilateral, and unattractive discipline for the student. Third, the teaching methods applied to transmit ideas of conservation and sustainable development are inadequate in view of the importance of having students face the environment and nature with an attitude of admiration, respect, and love. Primary and secondary teachers who feel this educational void have unfortunately not been trained to fill it; that is basically the reason why educational programs have not been efficiently implemented, leaving substantial gaps in formal education. Because environmental education in some form has been included in educational programs only since 1981, not one teacher has been specifically trained for this purpose. Small training seminars have been held that have awakened interest in more than a few teachers; however, due to the lack of additional support from the Government in continuing to develop and incorporate this interest, these teachers have become easily frustrated. Fourth, there is a lack of specially designed materials to aid teachers and students. Generally, the material is imported and is based on situations in other countries, which are not always applicable to Ecuador. Time constraints and costs are also too high for the majority of local teachers to develop educational components on their own.

In relation to informal education, environmental subjects have not been addressed in any significant way. In the areas of adult education and literacy programs, no specifications have been set. Priorities are usually related to survival of the human being as an individual; most of these learning situations are totally opposed to conservation principles in those regions where there is an evident lack of resources and where economic, cultural, and social conditions are very poor.

Within the formal educational system of Ecuador, there is little attention dedicated to the environment. Unfortunately, as is apparent in other developing countries, Ecuador has no tradition of interest and concern in this field; this has contributed to negative effects on the environment. Few institutions dedicate efforts to this area and their actions are directed to isolated and temporary information-education campaigns. Such limited efforts have contributed to the view that environmental education is of little importance and can be ignored under most circumstances.

Of the existing Ecuadorian institutions, only two take responsibility for the implementation of environmental education activities: the Ministries of Health and Agriculture. The former has been working on public awareness activities related to the problems of drinking water, sewage systems, and water and air pollution. Unfortunately little thought was given to the importance of changing individual and institutional attitudes and behaviour towards the environment, as part of the solution to these problems. Information usually tends to exaggerate the beneficial effect of the Government's actions, with little emphasis on creating learning conditions which promote (1) use of natural resources, and (2) the importance of their protection for sustainable development and preservation for future generations.

The Ministry of Agriculture has developed a somewhat more systematic and coherent environmental education action plan, even though its activities are quite limited. Some of this can be seen through the Forestry, Soil and Water Programs that have started to work on a "warning" campaign about deforestation and erosion as significant elements of Ecuador's environmental problems. Recently, the Ministry has dedicated more attention to environmental education on these activities. Nevertheless, until now, only the Soil Program has been solidly supported by the Ministry. A public awareness program directed towards erosion problems has been held in abeyance pending the commitment of additional funds from the Government. So far no effective response has emerged.

In the private sector, several specialized institutions have taken part in different ways in the analysis of environmental problems. The most significant of these institutions has been the Fundación Natura. This organization has focused on the role of the private interest in the solution of environmental problems in Ecuador and has become the strongest and largest effort to incorporate environmental education into Ecuador's formal and non-formal programs. Some of these actions are reviewed below.

Educational Activities of the Fundación Natura

The Fundación Natura, founded in 1980, has been working on an environmental education program called EDUNAT I, the first program of its kind in Ecuador. Its main objective has been to identify the most important environmental problems of the country and to inform leaders and decision makers, in order to assist and promote the search for immediate and adequate answers to the problems. The program has helped to reveal the importance and significance of environmental education. It has facilitated a climate for rethinking the past efforts with respect to the implementation of environmental education in the country and giving it the global perspective required to analyze national problems. In no way does it pretend to be a substitute for governmental responsibilities.

It has tried to do two things: (1) to motivate public institutions to respond to environmental education; and (2) to address the general public with the intention of generating learning processes focused on natural resources and the environment within the context of eco-development in order to encourage action among local and national as well as private and public institutions.

In the short-term, the educational program carried out by the Fundación Natura has greatly influenced the public's attitudes towards environmental problems and the need to start solving them now. Its fundamental objective during the first stage (of approximately two years) has been to create an acceptable level of public environmental awareness. Simultaneously, it has been informing the leaders and decision makers about the origins of present environmental conditions in the world and in Ecuador and their direct or indirect causes, with a view to immediate action.

While working with the general public, we have taken special care not to oversaturate people with factual or emotional information. The general public has been allowed to find its own levels of interest on the subject, to search for adequate patterns of information, and to use them. The basic instrument used for achieving these goals has been communication via the mass media. Some of the programs were produced at low cost or no cost, or were supported by private companies or non-profit institutions, making contributions in order to gain a respectable level of credibility. All messages are aimed at giving the general public a better understanding of the problems that could affect the individual, his or her family or future generations, and of the possibility of solving or preventing them through individual, collective or institutional action.

In brief, no specific actions are being suggested; instead, information is being provided which will allow the general public to assess positive or negative actions taken by governmental and non-governmental entities in relation to the environment. To date, it has worked to create a state of mind among the Ecuadorian public that will favour the implementation in the near future of more definite and substantial environmental education activities.

While focusing on the general public, the Fundación Natura's educational activities have not been oriented toward drastic changes in the attitudes of decision makers, but rather toward creating favourable conditions for decision-making. It has been understood, therefore, that there is an unlimited number of possibilities for decisions to be made now in relation to the environment; these range from national planning, research and training, to modification and implementation of existing legislation.

Future Expectations

The overall results of educational activities, through communication strategies mainly supported by dialogues among decision-makers, have been positive. On the one hand, the general public seems enthusiastic and is looking for additional information on environmental problems; on the other hand, there is evidence that leading groups in the country are responding in a positive way to several environmental concerns, as indicated for example by the creation and modification of new laws. It is hoped that in the near future, through additional educational actions, several other existing laws and regulations will be put into action. Such activities will predictably include both the public sector—the Ministries of Agriculture, Health, and Education—and the private sector — the Fundación Natura.

The Ministry of Agriculture has oriented most of its efforts to two objectives: obtaining more governmental resources for educational purposes and gaining greater institutional recognition of their policies. If these were achieved, the institution as a whole would consider environmental topics within its principal priorities. Some experts foresee that attention will be given to environmental education in the Soil Program since environmentally-sound practices are fundamental in preventing erosion. An educational program is especially needed in this area, since the most seriously eroded land is in the hands of peasants who have received no previous formal education.

The Ministry of Health will concentrate on the problems related to water/food contamination, and drinking water/sewage services as essential elements in achieving basic sanitary levels in rural and marginal urban areas. Such educational activities have been limited to date because the Ministry of Health faces serious financial, technical, and trainee personnel limitations in all the fields related to health education. As occurred in 1981 and 1982, new governmental budget reductions will probably affect environment-related activities.

The Ministry of Education has demonstrated a high interest in environmental topics within its present education reform plans. In the near future, when all the proposed changes have been accepted, the treatment of the environment will take a new turn. From unofficial sources, it is known that the Government is willing to consider environmental topics in this education reform, introducing serious curriculum changes. These changes will include training of teachers, production of adequate material adapted to national requirements, design of text books and manuals on Ecuador's environment, and periodic revisions of these programs in accordance with the changes in the country's natural resources. The future of informal education is, however, as yet unclear. Educational programs for adults will continue to search for new methods to suit their objectives, which will not necessarily agree with the objectives of environmental education.

In general terms, however, all actions concerning the environment have been postponed from the highest to the lowest levels. An example of this is that neither the Constitution nor the National Development Plan have considered environmental policy in an integral way; this is also true in the sectoral and institutional programs that have not considered ecological variables.

In the private sector, only the Fundación Natura has developed programs following the pattern described in this paper. The immediate objectives of the Fundación Natura will be to strengthen environmental education procedures within private and public institutions. This effort must include stimulation of decision makers, contribution to personal training, and development of material and methods suited to environmental education. At the same time, the acute lack of coordination in environmental activities must be considered. The Fundación Natura will work toward greater coordination and will promote scientific research that will contribute to environmental policy making.

The Fundación Natura, with the support of national and international funds, has good prospects for helping Ecuador to continue and improve on past efforts in the field of environmental education. At the same time it can serve as an example to other countries in similar circumstances.

Other titles of interest:

CONTROVERSIES IN TEACHING
William Hare
1985/ paperback

GIVING TEACHING BACK TO TEACHERS
A Critical Introduction to Curriculum Theory
Robin Barrow
1984/ paperback

LANGUAGE AND THOUGHT:
Re-thinking Language Across the Curriculum
Robin Barrow
Third printing 1983/ paperback

ISSUES IN SECONDARY SCHOOLING
R.J. Clark, R.D. Gidney, & G. Milburn (Eds.)
Second printing 1984/ paperback

A SCHOOLMAN'S ODYSSEY
Harold Disbrowe
1984/ paperback

UNDERSTANDING MATERIALS:
Their Role in Curriculum Development
R. Anderson & G. Tomkins (Eds.)
Revised edition 1983/ paperback

PHILOSOPHY OF SCHOOLING
Robin Barrow
Third printing 1984/ paperback

Further details from:

THE ALTHOUSE PRESS
Faculty of Education
The University of Western Ontario
1137 Western Road
LONDON, Ontario, Canada
N6G 1G7